GYMNOSPERMS
STRUCTURE AND EVOLUTION

By

CHARLES JOSEPH CHAMBERLAIN, Ph.D., Sc.D.

WITH 397 FIGURES

DOVER PUBLICATIONS, INC.
NEW YORK

Published in Canada by General Publishing Company, Ltd., 30 Lesmill Road, Don Mills, Toronto, Ontario.

Published in the United Kingdom by Constable and Company, Ltd., 10 Orange Street, London W. C. 2.

This Dover edition, first published in 1966, is an unabridged and unaltered republication of the work originally published by the University of Chicago Press in 1935.

Library of Congress Catalog Card Number: 66-20503

Manufactured in the United States of America
Dover Publications, Inc.
180 Varick Street
New York, N. Y. 10014

TO
MY WIFE AND DAUGHTER

PREFACE

A few centuries ago people believed that the earth was created suddenly, and that plants and animals were created just as they are today; but no one with any scientific training now believes in such an origin of the earth or its inhabitants. The first living things were simple and, in some way or another, originated from non-living matter. Such simple forms gradually developed into more and more complex organisms. No one believes that any organism as complex as a fern, or even as complex as a moss or liverwort, ever developed directly from non-living matter; they came from simpler forms. We may take it as a fact that the plants and animals on the earth today are the lineal descendants of plants and animals which lived hundreds of millions of years ago. Line after line of these ancient forms became extinct; but, here and there, an individual varying in some way from the main line, with some variation which made it able to withstand changing conditions which were fatal to its neighbors, survived and became the progenitor of a new race.

Consequently, if we are to understand the gymnosperms, or any other great group of plants, we should study not only those which exist today, but also those extinct ancestors whose fragmentary records can be read in the rocks. And beyond the available records, we should try to imagine the missing parts of the life-histories, and try to picture to ourselves the still more ancient progenitors.

Since this book is intended to be of service not only to those who would gain some knowledge of the gymnosperms, but also to those who would go farther and do productive research in this great group, a few admonitions may be helpful.

Read, and read widely, that you may know what has already been accomplished; and read critically. But no one can read critically whose knowledge comes entirely, or even principally, from reading. You must have a first-hand knowledge of the material, must study it in the field and in the laboratory. The student who has not had sufficient experience to make a first-class preparation for microscopic study cannot safely interpret slides made by others. He is in the same class with the one who claims he sees it but can't draw it; while the real trouble is not in his hand, but in his head. Studies in the field bring a kind of knowledge which cannot be gained in any other way; and the technical work of making slides and drawings, if properly done, affords a great stimulus to mental development.

A chapter on "Alternation of Generations" has been added because the gymnosperms stand in such a suggestive place in the evolution of the sporophyte and, particularly, in the reduction of the gametophyte.

There is a single alphabetical Bibliography, numbered consecutively. The small numerals throughout the book, both in text and illustrations, refer to this Bibliography.

It is a pleasure to acknowledge helpful advice and criticism, especially from Dr. A. C. Noé and Dr. Fredda D. Reed, who have read the entire manuscript and have definitely improved the paleobotanical features. Dr. John T. Buchholz read and criticized the chapter on "Embryogeny of Conifers." I am indebted to Dr. E. J. Kraus for suggestions in regard to the anatomy of conifers.

Corrections and suggestions will always be welcome.

Charles Joseph Chamberlain

University of Chicago
August 1934

CONTENTS

CONTENTS

CHAPTER I

INTRODUCTION

The gymnosperm line is one of extreme age, reaching back at least two or three hundred millions of years—so far back that its origin is lost in that distant past. But when we get our first glimpse of the group there were already two distinct lines, the Cycadophytes and the Coniferophytes, differing from each other in easily distinguishable characters. Whether these two lines, millions of years back of any records yet discovered, may have had a common origin, we do not know. We simply know that the earliest material which has been found and studied shows the two lines about as sharply separated as their living representatives are today.

That the gymnosperms did not originate as seed plants we believe to be self-evident. The old Greeks believed that Minerva, dressed in full armor, sprang from the head of Jove; but such an explanation of the origin of a group of plants would hardly satisfy a modern biologist. For the more immediate origin of the gymnosperms we look to the Pteridophytes, for we believe that they were the ancestors of the gymnosperms.

Of course, all the material for a study of the early gymnosperms is fossil, a record left in stone. By far the greater part of this record consists of impressions, and most of the impressions are those of leaves and stems, with some roots; but there are some impressions of reproductive structures. A leaf would fall into the sand or clay; then the sand or clay would become solid stone; all organic parts would be dissolved, and only the form would remain.

Some material behaved differently. The most valuable material is in the form of calcareous nodules, called "coal balls," which are found scattered through coal seams like raisins in a cake. Coal balls were probably produced when water, with calcium or silica in solution, invaded a swamp which formed a coal bed. The solution saturated plant tissues and preserved them, just as fixing solutions do today. Then the material solidified so that the plants were imbedded in solid rock. During the swampy conditions leaves, stems, roots, together with sporangia, spores, and seeds, falling into the swamp, where the water contained calcium or silica, became changed into stone. Starting with a piece of stem or leaf and some sticky clay, the mass would pick up other pieces of stem and leaf, and also spores or seeds, just as one sees the process going on today, until balls as large as one's fist, or even larger than one's head, would be formed. The mass, soaked with lime water, would become calcified, preserving the material so perfectly that not only cell walls but often cell contents can be studied about as in living material.

To get such material into condition for microscopic study, the time-honored method, and still probably the best method, although very tedious, is to saw through a coal ball, polish a sawed surface, cement this smooth surface to a piece of glass; then saw as close to the glass as possible, thus leaving a thin section firmly cemented to the slide. This thin section is then ground and polished until it is thin enough to be studied with a microscope. It is then cleaned and dried, some balsam and a thin cover glass are added, and the mount is ready for study.

A later method, much more rapid, and for some purposes almost as good, has come into favor because it is so easy and saves so much time. After sawing through a ball and polishing a surface, the polished surface is immersed in 4 per cent hydrochloric acid for a minute or two; the acid is gently rinsed out with water; the water is removed with 95 per cent and 100 per cent alcohol; the surface is flooded gently with ether alcohol, and then with a rather thick solution of celloidin in ether alcohol. When the ether alcohol evaporates, the celloidin can be peeled off in a thin film, which is placed in equal parts of bergamot oil, cedar oil, and carbolic acid, and then mounted in balsam. Such mounts look much like those prepared by the other slow, laborious process; but all calcareous structures are lost. This method proves that the old theory, that all organic material was changed completely into stone, is incorrect. If it were correct there would be no plant structures in a celloidin peel.

After taking off a peel, the surface from which the peels are being made is polished for half a minute, then cleaned and dried. It is then ready for another peel. One great advantage of the method is that serial peels can be made with comparatively little loss, for it is possible to get five, or even ten, peels to the millimeter. When sections are cut with a saw, they are generally a millimeter in thickness; and the saw, with the polishing for the next section, takes another millimeter. Consequently, serial sections are seldom less than two millimeters apart.

However, it must be remembered that in the peel method all material which is soluble in the acid is etched away, leaving the insoluble material standing erect. The celloidin surrounds the standing material and hardens. When the peel is pulled off the standing material is torn loose from the surface and, being held in place by the hardened celloidin, can be mounted and studied. While the method is very popular, its limitations must be recognized.

Instead of celloidin, many paleobotanists are now using gelatin in making peels.

From impressions, and from sections and peels of petrified material, plants which lived hundreds of millions of years ago have been studied and described until paleobotany has become a major subject of critical importance in any study of evolution or phylogeny. Besides, plant remains have been so thoroughly identified that they serve to identify geological horizons, and are of great

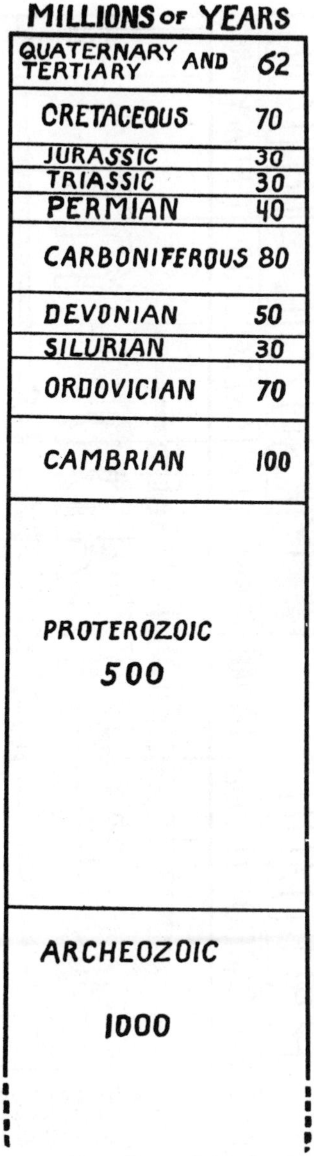

MILLIONS OF YEARS

QUATERNARY AND TERTIARY	62
CRETACEOUS	70
JURASSIC	30
TRIASSIC	30
PERMIAN	40
CARBONIFEROUS	80
DEVONIAN	50
SILURIAN	30
ORDOVICIAN	70
CAMBRIAN	100
PROTEROZOIC	500
ARCHEOZOIC	1000

FIG. I.—Diagram of geological time.—Compiled by Dr. A. C. Noé from various sources.

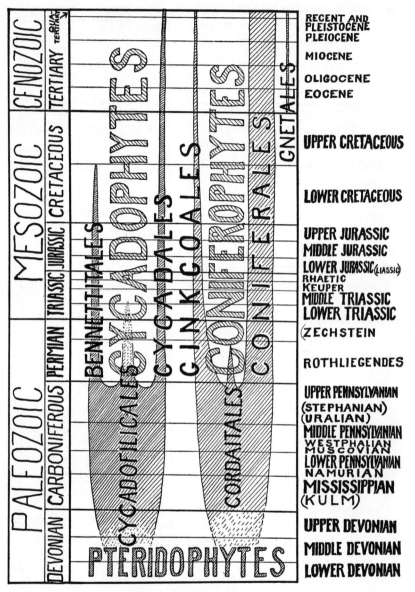

FIG. 2.—Diagram indicating a conjectural position of the various gymnosperm groups in geological time. The horizons were compiled by Dr. A. C. Noé from various sources. The comparative amount of space does not equal the comparative amount of time on account of the lack of space for the illustration.

economic importance on account of their relation to coal, oil, and gas.

How old are fossils? Many people, by various methods, have made estimates, some even guessing at the age of the earth. Geologists may claim that the earth is 10,000 millions of years old, and astronomers make no objection. But, whatever the age of the earth may be, it is certain that, in only a comparatively small portion of that time, has there been any life upon it.

Diagrams are useful, even if they are only estimates (fig. 1). In our study of gymnosperms, we have no material below the Devonian, less than one-fifth of the time since the hardening of the original crust of the earth.

In fact, very little gymnosperm material from the Devonian has been studied. Most of the fossil material has come from the Upper Carboniferous strata, the Coal Measures. One reason why so much material has come from the Upper Carboniferous is that this is the age of coal. It has been called the "Age of Ferns," because the early gymnosperms looked so much like ferns that they were mistaken for them. Comparatively little of the material would have been secured had it not been for the fact that mines have been dug to get the valuable coal, thus uncovering the coal balls and impressions. People would not dig hundreds of feet and spend millions of dollars to get coal balls. They dig the mines to make money, and, as a mere incident, the scientists get the coal balls. WIELAND used to say he wished he could make rich people believe that the Permian and the Mesozoic were really the best places to dig for coal.

A diagram is very definite, often too definite; but it will help to visualize the situation, and it represents a guess at the real relationships of the great gymnosperm groups (fig. 2).

Most of the historical evidence has come from the university zone of the northern hemisphere. When the rest of the world has been studied, our knowledge will be much more complete; but, as far as great groups are concerned, additional discoveries are not likely to affect the outline of life-histories, but merely to move origins farther and farther back.

CHAPTER II

CYCADOPHYTES—CYCADOFILICALES

The two great groups, Cycadophytes and Coniferophytes, are very distinct as far back as any historical evidence has been obtained. The most striking differences are shown in fig. 3.

The Cycadophytes are comparatively small, with unbranched stems and pinnate leaves; while the Coniferophytes are large, profusely branched, and have simple leaves. A glance at sections of the stems shows that the Cycadophytes have a large pith, scanty wood, and thick cortex; while the Coniferophytes have a small pith, abundant wood, and scanty cortex. The entire phylum is phyllosiphonic.

The Cycadophytes include three orders, the Cycadofilicales, the Bennettitales, and the Cycadales, of which only the Cycadales have living representatives, the Cycadofilicales having become extinct in the Triassic, and the Bennettitales in the lower Cretaceous.

In the Cycadofilicales, the sporangia are borne on leaves, more or less modified, but never grouped into a cone.

In the Bennettitales, the female sporophylls have lost all resemblance to leaves and are grouped into a cone. The male sporophylls are leaflike, forming a loose crown; they are never grouped into a cone.

In the Cycadales, both male and female sporophylls are grouped into cones, except the female sporophylls of *Cycas*, which are in a loose crown, like the male sporophylls of the Bennettitales.

Throughout the Cycadophytes, the sporophylls are in simple strobili or cones.

In the Coniferophytes, most of the male sporophylls form simple cones; but the female cones are compound, the sporophylls being borne on shoots coming from the axils of bracts. The shoots may be so reduced that their presence may seem theoretical rather than actual. While these statements are general in their application, the male and female cones of *Dioon*, and the male cone of *Pinus* may be taken as illustrations of typical simple strobili. The female cone of *Pinus* is a typical compound strobilus.

CYCADOFILICALES

The Carboniferous period was once called the "Age of Ferns" on account of the numerous impressions of fernlike leaves; but most of these leaves are now known to belong to seed plants which looked like ferns. Seed ferns would seem to be a good vernacular name for the group, and our British friends simply translate it into Pteridosperms. We object to the name because it sounds and looks as if it were coordinate with gymnosperms and angiosperms. The angiosperms have their seeds enclosed in a chamber, usually called the "ovary"; while, in the gymnosperms, the seeds are naked, not at all enclosed in any chamber. In the Cycadofilicales the seeds are naked, and, consequently, the forms are genuine gymnosperms and cannot be separated from them on the basis of characters as important as those which separate gymnosperms from angiosperms.

WILLIAMSON, SCOTT, and others described stems with characters intermediate between ferns and cycads and, in 1899, POTONIÉ proposed the name "Cycadofilices" to indicate the composite character. In 1903, OLIVER and SCOTT[423] found that the seed, *Lagenostoma*, belonged to the stem, *Lyginodendron*, and thus initiated a series of investigations which has resulted in linking up scattered seeds, stems, and leaves, until most of the plants which gave the Carboniferous the

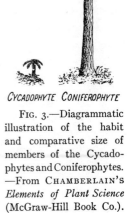

CYCADOPHYTE CONIFEROPHYTE

FIG. 3.—Diagrammatic illustration of the habit and comparative size of members of the Cycadophytes and Coniferophytes. —From CHAMBERLAIN'S *Elements of Plant Science* (McGraw-Hill Book Co.).

name, "Age of Ferns," are now known to be seed plants. This assembling of scattered parts recalls the earlier assembling of scattered stages in the life-history of wheat rust.

In the Cycadofilicales the most complete assembling has been the one started by OLIVER and SCOTT when they found that the seed, *Lagenostoma*, and the stem, *Lyginodendron*, belonged together.

Gradually, it was found that the leaf, *Sphenopteris*, the petiole, *Rachiopteris*, and the root, *Kaloxylon*, also belonged here, and that the sporangia, *Crossotheca*, were the microsporangia of the assemblage. What should the plant be called? *Lyginodendron Lagenostoma Sphenopteris Rachiopteris Kaloxylon Crossotheca?* That is obviously too long and too burdensome and so the whole assemblage is called *Lyginopteris*.

In others, various parts have been found associated and the linking-up process is going on, but in no case has the assembling been so complete as in *Lyginopteris*.

As long as only scattered parts are known, it is convenient to describe them under names which indicate the incompleteness. Such names are called form genera: they should not be regarded as equal in rank to the generic and specific names of living plants.

Names of leaves in this group are likely to end in *-pteris* or *-phyllum*, and so we have *Neuropteris*, *Dictyopteris*, *Sphenopteris*, *Pecopteris*, *Titanophyllum*, *Sphenophyllum*, *Pterophyllum*, and others.

Names of stems are likely to end in *-dendron* (tree), or *-xylon* (wood), e.g., *Cycadoxylon*, *Dadoxylon*, *Dictyoxylon*, *Kaloxylon*, *Megaloxylon*, *Cladoxylon*, *Poroxylon*, *Araucarioxylon*, *Asteroxylon*, *Lyginodendron*, *Schizodendron*, and others.

Names of seeds usually end in *-spermum*, *-carpon*, *-carpus* or *-stoma*, e.g., *Neurospermum*, *Stephanospermum*, *Cycadinocarpus*, *Cardiocarpon*, *Trigonocarpus*, *Lagenostoma*, *Conostoma*, *Physostoma*, and others.

A common ending for stamens or microsporangia is *-theca*, e.g., *Crossotheca*, *Codonotheca*.

Names for cones often end in *-strobilus* or *-strobus*, e.g., *Anthostrobilus*, *Androstrobus*, *Zamiostrobus*, and others.

DISTRIBUTION

In describing either the geological or geographical distribution of any extinct groups, it must be kept in mind that intensive work has been done only in the university zone of the northern hemisphere. In institutions of the southern hemisphere botanical work is still confined, principally, to the taxonomy of living plants, a very natural field, since the first thing, in a new country, should be to find out what is there. Expeditions into the southern hemisphere and into out-of-the-way parts of the northern hemisphere, while valuable, cannot spend the time or cover the ground so thoroughly as it is covered within the paleobotanizing range of a well-financed university. It is practically certain that a much more extensive geographic distribution can be plotted when all the evidence is as complete as it now is for Great Britain; and even the geological distribution may go down a little deeper and extend up a little higher than available material now indicates.

There is no doubt that the Cycadofilicales reached their greatest development in the Upper Carboniferous (Pennsylvanian). Their greatest display in this period gave the name "Age of Ferns." That they go back through the Lower Carboniferous and far down into the Devonian is certain; but just when they first appeared will probably never be determined. In the other direction members can be identified with certainty in the Permian, probably in the Triassic, and there are suggestions of even Lower Jurassic forms; but neither here nor in the Triassic has there been any complete assembling of root, stem, leaf, microsporangia, and seed.

The best evidence for the presence of Cycadofilicales in the Devonian is furnished by *Eospermatopteris*. About 50 years ago a flood in the Catskill region of New York tore away soil and rocks and exposed fossil trees standing where they had grown. In the museum at Albany, New York, there is a reconstruction showing a shore of the Devonian sea, with these trees as the dominant vegetation. They were referred to the genus *Psaronius*, a well-known genus of the later Carboniferous; but a more thorough study showed that there are two kinds of reproductive organs which are better interpreted as microsporangia and seeds. It is to be noted that the seeds are small, only 5 or 6 mm. in length. The trees reached a height of more than 30 feet, a diameter of 3 feet, and had a crown of leaves 6–9 feet long; so that it had the appearance of a stout tree-fern. There are fragments of other forms which may belong here, but the evidence is not so strong.

In the Carboniferous the Cycadofilicales reached their highest development. Associated with the giant lycopods and calamites they formed a prominent part of the vegetation which finally became coal. *Lyginopteris*, *Medullosa*, *Heterangium*, and many others have become well known. It was from this vast assemblage that the Bennettitales and Cycadales were developed.

In the Permian, the Cycadofilicales declined, became very scanty in the Triassic, and, with a few somewhat dubious fragments, disappeared in the Lower Jurassic.

If we could be transported back into the Carboniferous and collect living material in the swamps and forests we could write, with confi-

FIG. 4.—Carboniferous swamp-forest. Reconstruction in the Field Museum at Chicago. This figure shows only a part of the entire reconstruction.

dence, the life-histories of these ancient plants, and could speculate intelligently as to their probable ancestry and also their progeny. As it is, there is enough in the way of impressions to warrant a reconstruction of a Carboniferous swamp forest (fig. 4). This splendid reconstruction, made possible by abundant material, mostly from the vicinity of Chicago, has been done at the Field Museum of Natural History in Chicago. Paleobotanists, paleozoölogists, geologists, sculptors, and painters, working for three years, produced this remarkable restoration, of which about 90 per cent has been made from actual specimens. The illustration probably looks very much as it would if a photograph could have been taken 250 millions of years ago. The big trees are *Lepidodendron* and *Sigillaria*, but the fernlike

FIG. 5.—Carboniferous swamp-forest. Reconstruction in Field Museum, at Chicago, showing the entire reconstruction.

plants, except the true fern, *Psaronius*, belong to the Cycadofilicales. The view in fig. 5, taken from a different angle, shows the entire reconstruction. The key (fig. 6) will be helpful, even to the botanists who are more or less familiar with the flora of the period.

LIFE-HISTORIES

LIFE-HISTORY OF *Lyginopteris*.—The life-history of the best known of all Carboniferous plants will help not only in understanding the Cycadofilicales themselves, but will be useful when we try to speculate about the ancestry and progeny of the group.

The stem.—The stem was long and slender, with large leaves, too scattered to form such a crown as that of the familiar tree ferns, and with rather large roots, some of which were adventitious. The restoration shown in the frontispiece of the second volume of SCOTT'S *Fossil Botany,*[535] and that shown in the Field Museum swamp forest,

agree in making *Lyginopteris* a climbing plant. It is certain that the
stem was so long and slender and bore such large leaves that the
plant could not have stood erect, like the familiar tree-ferns.

The stems, pieces of which are common in European and American
coal balls, range from 2 mm. to 4 cm. in diameter. A transverse section shows a mesarch siphonostele, with a rather large pith, an
abundant development of secondary wood, and a thick cortex dif-

FIG. 6.—A diagram giving the names of most of the features of the reconstruction

CARBONIFEROUS SWAMP FOREST GROUP

Lycopodiales: 1. Lepidodendron clupeatum Lesq.; 2. Lepidodendron obovatum Sternberg; 3. Lepidodendron modulatum Lesq.; 4. Lepidostrobus ovatitolius Lesq.; 5. Sigillaria rugosa Brogniart; 6. Sigillaria
saulli Brogniart; 7. Sigillaria scutellata Brogniart; 8. Sigillaria lacoei Lesquereux; 9. Sigillaria laevigata
Brogniart; 10. Sigillaria trunk; 11. Stigmaria Ficoides Sternberg; 12. Lepidophloios laricinus Sternberg;
13. Selaginellites sp.—*Cycadofilicales:* 14. Neuropteris heterophylla Brog.; 15. Neuropteris decipiens Lesq.
(Medullosa stem, Cyclopteris leaves, Trigonocarpus seeds); 16. Lyginopteris oldhamia Williamson
(Neuropteris hoenighausi leaves 16a, Lagenostoma ovoides seeds 16b).—*Pteridophytes:* 17. Caulopteris
giffordi Lesquereux Psaronius stem; Pecopteris leaves 17a); 18. Megaphyton frondosum Artis (Psaronius
distichus stem); 19. Mariopteris muricata (Schloth) Zeiller; 20. Sphenophyllum emarginatum (Brog.)
König; 21. Calamites Annularia stellata (Schloth) Wood.—*Gymnosperms:* 22. Cordaites borassifolius
(Sternb.) Unger.—*Insects:* 23. Stenodictya lobata Brogniart; 24. Meganeura monyi Brogniart; 25. Gera-
rus donielsi Handlirsch; 26. Archeoblattina beecheri Sellards.—*Vertebrates:* 27. Diplovertebron punctatum
Fritsch; 28. Ceraterpeton galvani Huxley; 29. Eogyrinus attheyi (in background).

ferentiated into two distinct regions. Leaf traces are conspicuous
(figs. 7 and 8).

The leaf traces are distinctly mesarch, with most of the wood centripetal. In the stele, the leaf traces are single, but the protoxylem
soon branches and the trace becomes double, often before leaving
the stele.

The tracheids of the protoxylem have spiral markings; the centrifugal tracheids of the metaxylem are sclariform and the centripetal tracheids have multiseriate bordered pits. All the tracheids of the secondary wood of the stele are pitted.

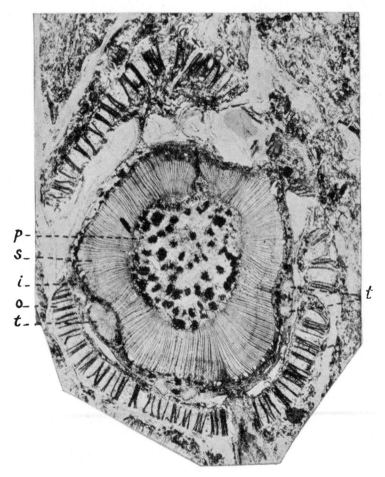

FIG. 7.—*Lyginopteris oldhamia:* *p*, primary wood; *s*, secondary wood; *t*, leaf trace; *i*, inner cortex; *o*, outer cortex. The dark masses in the pith are groups of sclerotic cells. The dark lines in the outer cortex are radially arranged plates of thick-walled cells.— From a photograph by KIDSTON.

In most stems the cambium is poorly preserved, but occasional specimens show it with the young secondary wood and phloem standing out almost as clearly as in a living plant (fig. 9).

The secondary wood is in the form of plates, mostly one or two cells thick, with medullary rays usually one to four cells thick separating them.

The cells of the primary phloem are small, irregularly arranged, and soon become crushed as in living plants. The cells of the secondary phloem are as regularly arranged as those of the secondary wood and, in transverse section, a line of phloem cells is continuous with a line of xylem cells formed from the same cambium. The cells of the

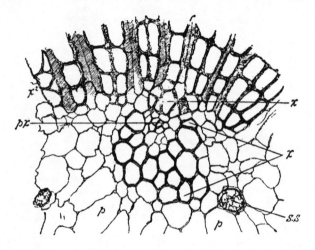

FIG. 8.—*Lyginopteris oldhamia*: x, centripetal primary wood; x^2, centrifugal primary wood; px, protoxylem; p, pith; ss, secretory sac; $\times$100.—After WILLIAMSON and SCOTT.

phloem are alternately larger and smaller, the smaller ones dividing at a right angle to the row of cells so as to make a short transverse row of two or three small cells. These small cells have a tendency to become suberized, a condition which reaches an extreme in Bennettitales and in the living Cycadales.

The pith is large, consisting of parenchymatous cells with scattered groups of thick-walled cells called "sclerotic nests." The cortex is sharply differentiated into two layers, the inner one consisting of large thin-walled cells, and the outer one, with plates of thick-walled cells alternating with plates of thin-walled cells, a structure giving great strength combined with flexibility.

The leaf.—Of all the Gymnosperm leaves which caused the Carboniferous to be called the "Age of Ferns" none are better known than those which belonged to *Lyginopteris*. Before the connection between leaf and stem was discovered the leaf of *Lyginopteris oldhamia* was described as *Sphenopteris hoenighausi* (fig. 10). As in many Cycadofilicales, the rachis forked, and the forks bore strong pinnae, which were again pinnate. Twice- and thrice-pinnate leaves of both

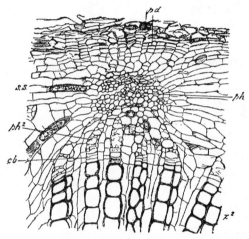

FIG. 9.—*Lyginopteris oldhamia: x²*, secondary wood; *cb*, cambium; *ph*, primary phloem; *ph²*, secondary phloem; *ss*, secretory sac; *pd*, periderm; ×52.—After WILLIAMSON and SCOTT.

Cycadofilicales and ferns, some of them strongly dimorphic, were common in the Carboniferous (fig. 11).

The histological structure is not very different from that of living plants with leaves of this habit. The epidermis is cutinized on the adaxial surface, there is a palisade and a spongy parenchyma, and the stomata are on the under side. The leaves have strong spines which are rounded and glandular at the tip. Similar spines on the stem and leaf stalk suggested to WILLIAMSON that *Rachiopteris aspersa*, *Lyginodendron oldhamium*, and *Sphenopteris hoenighausi* were the leafstalk, stem, and leaf of the same plant, which we now call *Lyginopteris oldhamia*.

The root.—Roots are abundant and splendidly preserved, so that the name, *Kaloxylon*, was well chosen. Some of them, especially those of larger diameter, were adventitious and aerial. Since the roots come off anywhere in the periphery, the stem could not have been prostrate. Its symmetrical character and great length in pro-

FIG. 10.—*Sphenopteris hoenighausi:* photo of a leaf, showing forking of the main rachis; ⅔ natural size.—After POTONIÉ.

portion to its diameter, as well as these radially arranged roots, indicate a climbing habit.

The roots have a radial exarch cylinder with phloem alternating with xylem rays. In the larger roots, secondary wood is developed, the strands alternating with the protoxylem points. The protoxylem consists of spirally marked tracheids. Rootlets develop opposite the protoxylem points. The tips of rootlets are not so well preserved; consequently, it has not yet been determined whether the growth is by a single apical cell, as in the ferns, or by a group of cells; but it is quite possible that there is a single apical cell.

The cortex of the root is sharply differentiated into two regions, an outer layer two or three cells deep, consisting of thin-walled cells

FIG. 11.—*Neuropteris decipiens:* from the reconstruction in the Field Museum at Chicago. The photo was taken while the individual plants were being made. The leaves are strongly dimorphic. Most of the seeds (*Trigonocarpus*) are terminal, but some are lateral.

with scanty contents and no differentiation in the alternating plates of thick-walled and thin-walled cells which characterize the stem; and an inner cortex, about twice as thick, many of the cells of which show dense contents, which may be largely mucilaginous.

The microsporangium.—In 1905 Dr. KIDSTON[318] discovered impressions of *Crossotheca* in connection with leaves of *Sphenopteris hoenighausi,* thus proving that *Crossotheca* is the microsporangium of *Lyginopteris* (fig. 12). Their fertile pinnules are more or less peltate, each bearing six or rarely seven pendant, bilocular microsporangia, the whole structure resembling the microsporophyll and sporangia of *Araucaria*. The microsporangium is about 3 mm. long and half as wide, with microspores 50–70 microns in diameter. Sections of microspores show tissues of cells, but not so definitely as to prove whether they are prothallial or spermatogenous (figs. 13 and 14).

FIG. 12.—*Crossotheca hoenighausi:* leaf with both sterile and fertile pinnae. The sterile leaves were known as *Sphenopteris hoenighausi*, later found to be the leaf of *Lyginopteris*; ×2. From a sketch made from a photograph by KIDSTON.

The microspores, or pollen grains, alighted so close to the female gametophyte, perhaps even in contact with the neck cells of the archegonia, that there could not have been any pollen tubes. The sperms must have been shed much as in *Isoetes*, *Selaginella*, and the water ferns. Consequently, there could have been no prolonged interval between pollination and fertilization, an interval of months in most of the living Gymnosperms. ENGLER'S term, *Siphonogamia*, would not be appropriate for these early seed plants.

Miss MARGARET BENSON[42] (fig. 15) described an interesting section through the nucellus of *Lagenostoma ovoides*, showing pollen grains in the pollen

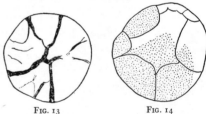

FIG. 13　　　　　FIG. 14

FIG. 13.—*Stephanospermum akenioides:* section of a pollen grain, showing cellular structure.—After OLIVER.[426]

FIG. 14.—*Physostoma elegans:* section of a pollen grain, showing internal structure; the dotted part is the exospore, where it has not been ground away in making the section; ×480. —After OLIVER.[431]

chamber, two of them with the intine protruding from the spore, reminding one of the protrusion of the male gametophyte in *Azolla*. She even showed bodies, described as sperms, in the pollen

chamber. They could not have been numerous, probably not more than four, judging from the comparative size of the microspores. The sperms, as she figures them, are distinctly of the Cycad type, rather than the fern type. Sperms, probably then as now, were such short-lived organisms that their preservation is very surprising.

The seed.—Fifty years ago, in tracing phylogenies, the greatest gap in the plant kingdom was that between ferns and seed plants; but the discovery of seeds upon leaves which had been assumed to be ferns closed the gap so completely that fern-like leaves, without seeds in organic connection, cannot be assigned with confidence to either group. The earliest seeds were, doubtless, very small. The best-known of all Carboniferous seeds is *Lagenostoma*, the seed of *Lyginopteris* (fig. 16). It is small, only 5 or 6 mm. in length; but is already so highly developed that is has progressed a long way in the evolution of the seed. The Mexican god of war, according to tradition, came into the world, like Minerva, full armed,

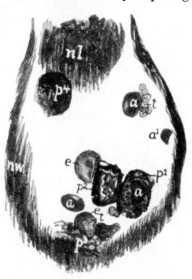

FIG. 15.—*Lyginopteris ovoides:* section of part of nucellus with pollen chamber containing pollen grains and sperms; *nl*, part of central core of nucellus; *nw*, wall of nucellus; p^1, p^2, p^3, and p^4, pollen grains; *a*, sperm; a^1, sperm cut across; *e*, protrusion of endospore; *t*, tissue, probably fungal; ×155.—After MARGARET BENSON.[42]

with a spear in his right hand, a shield in his left, and a crest of green plumes on his head. When that myth originated, the origin of the Cycadofilicales might have been explained in a similar way; but now we feel skeptical in regard to any theory of the origin of the seed which would make it begin with such a highly organized structure as that of *Lyginopteris*.

Surrounding the seed is a cupule, fig. 17, which reminds one of the cupules of living forms like *Corylus*, *Fagus*, *Juglans*, and *Carya;* although it must be remembered that in the living forms the cupule

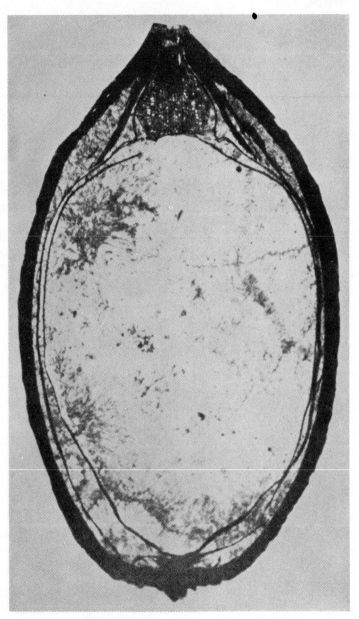

FIG. 16.—*Lyginopteris ovoides:* longitudinal section of a seed (formerly called *Lagenostoma*); ×19.—From a photomicrograph by LAND.

surrounds not a naked seed, but an ovary. A diagram of the seed described as *Lagenostoma lomaxii* (fig. 18) shows the general structure of the seeds of *Lyginopteris*. The nucellus is free only at the tip and, at maturity, has a central core surrounded by a bell-shaped crevice, the pollen chamber. The outer part of the ovule, shown in black in fig. 18 is hardened, like the stony layer of a cycad seed; within the hardened portion is a fleshy layer, with the inner set of bundles. Another set of bundles, more numerous than those of the inner set, supplies the cupule. If the cupule were closely applied to the ovule, as it probably was in the early stage of development, a longitudinal section would look somewhat like that of a cycad seed, with a vascular system on each side of the stony layer. A detail of the top of the ovule, with microspores in the pollen chamber, is shown in fig. 19. An earlier stage, drawn from the same

FIG. 17.—*Lyginopteris lomaxii:* seed surrounded by a glandular cupule.—From a restoration by OLIVER and SCOTT.[431]

section from which the photomicrograph, fig. 16, was made, is shown in fig. 20.

The embryo.—While some of the seeds show traces of the female gametophyte and even enough of the archegonia to show that they are of the elongated type, no embryo of any of the Cycadofilicales has ever been discovered. Where mature seeds, in organic connection with foliage leaves, have been discovered, only impressions have been available. Isolated seeds, which dropped off and got into suitable places for preservation, were probably abortive and never would reach the embryo stage.

OTHER CYCADOFILICALES.—While *Lyginopteris* is the most completely known of any of the Carboniferous plants, there has been a partial assembling in many others; in fact, there has been so much assembling that an unattached fernlike leaf, in the vegetative condition, is more likely to belong to the Cycadofilicales rather than to the true ferns, just as in the angiosperms double fertilization is so prevalent that one now assumes it to occur unless there is good proof to the contrary.

Heterangium.—This stem is well known and is one of a more primitive type than *Lyginopteris*, for it has a protostele resembling that of the living fern, *Gleichenia* (fig. 21). The vascular strands are intermingled with thin-walled tissue. At the center, their tracheids have bordered pits; but at the periphery, there are tracheids with spiral

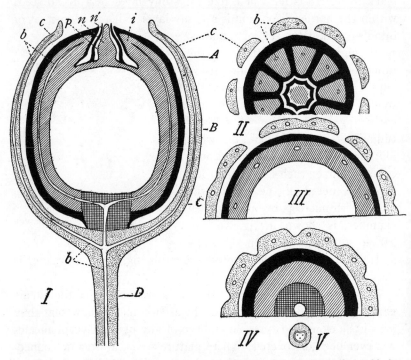

FIG. 18.—*Lyginopteris lomaxii:* I, diagrammatic longitudinal section of a seed in its cupule; II, III, IV, and V, show the structure in transverse section at the levels *A*, *B*, *C*, and *D* of I; *n*, central part of nucellus, and *n'*, sclerotic outer part of nucellus with pollen chamber (*p*) between; *i*, integument with outer stony layer shown in black; *b*, vascular bundles; *c*, cupule.—After OLIVER and SCOTT.[431]

markings, the protoxylem, surrounded by other tracheids, so that the strand is mesarch. The centrifugal tracheids have spiral or sclariform markings; the centripetal tracheids are pitted. The secondary wood of the stele consists of tracheids with multiseriate bordered pits (fig. 22).

The cortex is differentiated into an inner layer of thin-walled cells, and an outer layer with layers of thin-walled and thick-walled cells alternating with each other, as in *Lyginopteris*.

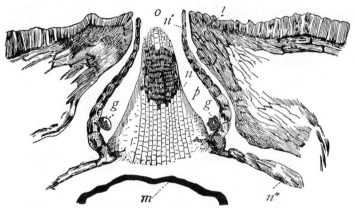

Fig. 19.—*Lyginopteris lomaxii:* longitudinal section of upper part of seed; *o*, micropyle; *i*, integument; *n*, central core of nucellus and *n'*, outer part of nucellus with the pollen chamber (*p*) between; *g*, pollen grains; *n''*, part of nucellus; *m*, thick megaspore membrane; about ×50.—After OLIVER and SCOTT.431

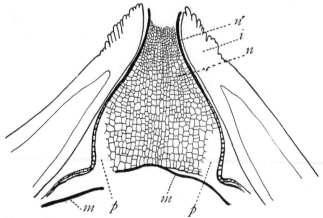

Fig. 20.—*Lyginopteris ovoides:* upper part of the seed shown in fig. 16; *n*, inner part of nucellus; *o*, hard outer part of nucellus; *p*, pollen chamber; *m*, megaspore membrane; ×36. Drawn from a slide in the paleobotanical collection of the University of Chicago. —From COULTER and CHAMBERLAIN's *Morphology of Gymnosperms* (University of Chicago Press).

Spherostoma is probably the seed of *Heterangium*, but no organic connection has yet been discovered. The seed is small, about 3.5 mm.

long, and resembles the seed of a cycad. The leaf, which has been found in organic connection with the stem, is described under the name *Sphenopteris elegans*.

Medullosa.—The stem of *Medullosa* has a polystele, transverse sections usually showing three steles, somewhat as in *Selaginella wildenovii;* but each primary stele is surrounded by its own secondary wood and phloem. The primary xylem is mesarch. Its protoxylem

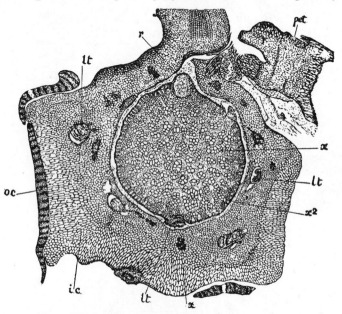

FIG. 21.—*Heterangium grievii:* transverse section of stem; *x*, primary wood; x^2, secondary wood just beginning to develop, just outside the secondary wood, the phloem, mostly broken down; *ic*, inner cortex; *oc*, outer cortex; *lt*, leaf trace; *r*, base of adventitious root; *x* (in the inner cortex), a group of sclerotic cells; *pet*, petiole; about ×5.—After Scott.

consists of spirally marked tracheids surrounded by a few sclariform or reticulate tracheids; but most of the primary wood and all of the secondary wood has multiseriate bordered pits. In the secondary wood the pits are becoming restricted to the radial walls. Sieve plates, resembling those of living gymnosperms, are found on the lateral walls.

Neuropteris.—Beautiful impressions of this fernlike leaf have long been familiar. Immense seeds, seeds more than 6 cm. in length, belong to *Neuropteris decipiens* (fig. 23). The seeds were borne at the ends of the midribs of the leaf and its primary branches, as shown in the Carboniferous Swamp Reconstruction (figs. 4, 5, and 11). Other species of *Neuropteris* have smaller seeds.

Others.—Many others have been described, mostly from impressions, but a goodly number from well-preserved material. One with a leaf resembling that of *Aneimia*, with seeds in organic connection, was found in the Lower Pottsville of Virginia[672] (fig. 24).

Pecopteris pluckenetii[221] bore seeds in about the same position as in the living genus Cycas (fig. 25). The seed *Stephanospermum akenioides* bears considerable resemblance to a cycad seed. *Physostoma* is another well-preserved seed.

With an occasional bit of repetition, this chapter will be concluded with some general remarks, some observations on phylogeny, and an attempt to reconstruct parts of the life-history where material is not yet available.

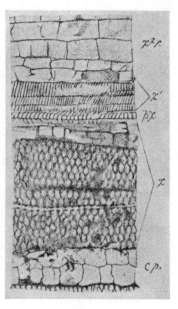

Fig. 22.—*Heterangium grievii:* longitudinal section of stem showing primary wood; *px*, protoxylem; *x*, centripetal metaxylem; *x'*, centrifugal metaxylem; *x²r*, parenchyma of medullary ray; *cp*, conjunctive parenchyma; ×135.—After SCOTT.

GENERAL REMARKS

The investigations upon the Cycadofilicales have brought results which constitute the greatest achievement of paleobotany. During the past forty years the number of investigators, and the importance of their results, have been increasing with great rapidity. As early as 1883 it was suspected that some of the plants regarded as ferns might be seed plants. In 1903 OLIVER and SCOTT found the seed, *Lagenostoma*, on the foliage of *Sphenopteris*, thus proving that the supposed fern was a seed plant. In the same year, GRAND D'EURY found hundreds of seeds on leaves of *Pecopteris pluckenetii;* KIDSTON found the seed, *Trigonocarpus*, on the leaf of *Neuropteris;* and DAVID WHITE found seeds of a Carboniferous form which he called *Aneimites fertilis*.

With such a start the work went on rapidly and seeds were found on so many of the supposed ferns that it began to look as if these primitive seed plants, rather than the ferns, were the dominant fernlike plants of the Carboniferous.

FIG. 23.—*Trigonocarpus:* contained in coal ball found in strip mine of Sunlight Coal Company, near Evansville, in southern Indiana; natural size.

Of course, there were true ferns in the Carboniferous, both homosporous and heterosporous, and they were probably abundant. Not all of the ferns became heterosporous, and not all of the heterosporous ferns advanced to the seed stage. They remained ferns and the ferns of today have come from them by direct descent.

The most intensive work has been done in Great Britain, with WILLIAMSON, KIDSTON, OLIVER, SCOTT, SEWARD, and more recently GORDON and H. H. THOMAS, WALTON, and HARRIS as the most prominent investigators. SCOTT, not being burdened with a teaching position, has made this study his life-work, and in addition to his research papers, has presented the whole subject in his book, *Studies in Fossil Botany*, with comparative morphology as its dominant feature. This book makes it possible for those with less training and less mature judgment to secure valuable results when they find material. He has also done a great service in presenting the subject in a less technical, but still thoroughly scientific way, in his book, *Extinct Plants and Problems of Evolution*.

SEWARD, also, in addition to a long series of research papers, has organized the subject in his book, *Fossil Plants*. Although both authors deal with morphology, taxonomy, and phylogeny, in SEWARD'S book taxonomy is the dominant character. SEWARD, in his *Plant Life*

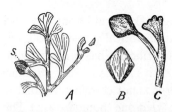

FIG. 24.—*Aneimites fertilis: A*, sterile pinnules and a seed (*s*); *B*, a seed showing wings; *C*, a sterile pinnule and a seed with a long stalk; ×2. —After DAVID WHITE.[672]

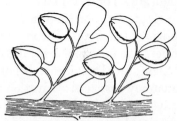

FIG. 25.—*Pecopteris pluckenetii:* fertile pinnae with seeds at the ends of lobes of pinnules; ×3.—After GRAND D'EURY.[221]

through the Ages, has done a great service to the educated public and especially to the botanists who are not specialists in paleobotany.

In Europe the most prominent names are STUR, RENAULT, POTONIÉ, ZEILLER, C. E. BERTRAND and PAUL BERTRAND; more recently GOTHAN, KUBART, KRÄUSEL, and FLORIN. POTONIÉ and ZEILLER, besides their research papers, have written books which are of great service to investigators.

In America, some work had been done with impressions and a few sections had been made of fossil woods; but coal balls, with their well-preserved material, were not known until NOÉ, in 1922, discovered coal balls in various places, and, followed by various students, began a series of investigations which indicate that American material is as abundant and as well preserved as material in Great Britain and in Europe. It is interesting to note that many of the genera, and perhaps even the species, are the same as on the other side of the Atlantic.

What was the origin of the group? From their striking resemblance to ferns it was natural to assume that they were modified ferns, and the English promptly named them "Seed Ferns," or, to say it in Greek, "Pteridosperms." The earlier name, Cycadofilices, based upon the anatomy of the stem, was discarded. While the name "Seed Ferns" is appropriate, the plants are true gymnosperms, as we have said before, and not separated from them by any character of such importance as separates the gymnosperms from the angiosperms. So we simply use the earlier term, modifying the ending to indicate its ordinal rank.

Gradually, our English friends became skeptical about any fern origin of the group. The argument that, historically, the Cycadofilicales have been found as far back as the Filicales has practically no weight; for the evidence is not all in yet. The claim that vascular anatomy is against derivation from ferns is not convincing; for the advance in stelar development is about what one should expect. The dominant sclariform tracheid of the ferns has given way largely to the pitted tracheid. The fact that secondary wood is so prevalent in the Cycadofilicales is not surprising. It is an advance in stelar development, but it does not separate ferns from seed ferns; for even some living Pteridophytes of rather insignificant size, like *Botrychium*, have secondary wood; and the pitting stage has been reached, even by some of the living homosporous Pteridophytes. On the other hand, a seed plant may retain the fern sclariform tracheid, even in the secondary wood, as in *Stangeria*.

We believe that the leaf affords strong evidence of a derivation from ferns. The reproductive structures reached the seed level while the leaves were little or not at all modified. This would make it very natural to mistake the leaves of these early seed plants for those of ferns. Of course, everyone knows that plants entirely unrelated to each other may have very similar forms. *Euphorbia canariensis* looks like a cactus in the organ cactus group, but the superficial resemblance does not make any trouble for the taxonomist. Many of the Euphorbiaceae look like cacti. *Stapelia*, one of the Asclepiadaceae, also looks like a cactus. *Equisetum*, *Ephedra*, and some species of *Casuarina* are strikingly similar in some features, although so widely separated taxonomically. There is not the slightest doubt that these resemblances have been attained independently. None of them have been transmitted from one to another.

But we could not regard the fern–seed-fern resemblances in this way. In the cases just mentioned the resemblances are superficial and not at all misleading; while in the fern and seed-fern leaves the structures, even to margins and venation, are so identical that the leaves cannot be assigned to either group unless they are associated with other structures.

The most decisive evidence of a fern ancestry is the seed itself. What is a seed and how does it differ from a spore? We cannot imagine a seed, phylogenetically, originating as a seed; or even a heterosporous fern originating in the heterosporous condition. It is a fundamental of comparative morphology that homospory preceded heterospory. The Bryophytes never got beyond the homosporous stage, and those ferns and lycopods which are regarded as primitive are homosporous. In the advance from homospory the ferns and even the seed plants show an ontogeny which indicates their phylogeny. In all of the living heterosporous ferns and lycopods, the early development of the sporangium is that of a typical homosporous fern. In *Azolla*, the two kinds of sporangia develop alike, even producing the same number of spores. In the microsporangia, all the spores develop; while in the megasporangia all the spores, but one, abort, giving up their nourishment to the successful spore, which becomes the large megaspore. In the various heterosporous Pteridophytes the differentiation takes place in different ways, but one feature is found in all—the disorganization of some of the spores to feed others, which, with the abundant nutrition, become large.

Just how far must the evolution of the megaspore advance before we call it a seed? To place an absolute limit which would satisfy one's ideas about logic is impossible; but, arbitrarily, we make the retention of the megaspore within the sporangium, so that it is *never* shed, the feature which distinguishes a megaspore from a seed. If the megaspore is shed from the sporangium, it is only a megaspore; if it is permanently retained, the megaspore has reached the dignity of a seed. By this character, all botanists separate the Pteridophytes from the Spermatophytes.

Besides the undoubted seeds of the Cycadofilicales and the Cordaitales, seed-like structures are well known in the Carboniferous. After the spores become differentiated into microspores and megaspores, there was doubtless much difference in the stage of development reached before the shedding of the megaspore, just as in living forms. In *Isoetes*, the megaspore is shed at the uninucleate stage; while in *Selaginella* it germinates and the female gametophyte may reach the archegonium stage before shedding occurs. By keeping strobili of *Selaginella apus* on moist filter paper in a Petri dish, so as to avoid complete dehiscence, development may be forced still farther, so that fertilization occurs, the embryo is formed and even breaks through the wall of the sporangium. It thus satisfies the definition of a seed. In other strobili, on the same plant, the sporangia, allowed to develop naturally, shed their megaspores. The same plant is thus, by accepted definition, a Pteridophyte and a Spermatophyte.

We believe that the seed habit was attained by the Cycadofilicales in the same way. It is a natural tendency in evolution. At first, there would be little difference in the two kinds of spores. As the megaspore became larger, it began to germinate inside the sporangium, and as the development of the female gametophyte proceeded farther and farther, the megaspore was shed later and later, until it finally became permanently retained within the sporangium, and the seed condition was achieved. After the retention of the megaspore became permanent, the thick protective coats, no longer necessary, became thinner and thinner. They were still prominent in the Cycadofilicales, thinner and thinner as the evolution of the gymnosperms progressed and finally, in the angiosperms, became unrecognizable as spore coats.

As the early seed plants emerged from the heterosporous fern condition, we should expect the seeds to be small, with several in a sporangium; but, as evolution progressed, the number would be reduced, until only one remained, and the size would increase. There would naturally be increased complexity of the sporangium as it became a more permanent structure, taking over the protective functions which had been performed by the thick spore coats of a megaspore adapted to shedding. The further development of the seed need not be discussed here, since we are considering only the origin of the seed, not its later history.

The microsporangium and its microspores, taken by themselves, do not prove, with much certainty, whether they belong to the ferns or seed plants. They are conservative, and their line, even as we see it in living seed plants, has not differed so greatly from the heterosporous fern condition, or even from the earlier homosporous condition. Living heterosporous Pteridophytes shed their microspores in the uninucleate stage or, later, after a tissue has formed inside the spore. Even in a living homosporous fern, *Onoclea*, there may be several cell divisions within the spore, and the prothallia may undergo considerable development before they escape from the sporangium. The sporangium with small spores must be associated with other structures before it can be known definitely whether it is the sporangium of a fern or seed plant.

The close resemblance between the sporangia of ferns and those known to be the microsporangia of the Cycadofilicales is a strong evidence of genetic relationship.

It is doubtful whether any two genera of the living heterosporous Pteridophytes are closely related to each other with the possible exception of *Marsilia* and *Pilularia;* but they are all heterosporous and their heterospory has been achieved in the same way—by the disorganization of megaspores which have been absorbed by the growing megaspores. We should be slow to believe that *Azolla* has been derived from *Salvinia* by direct descent, or that *Salvinia* has come from *Azolla;* it is easier to believe that similar conditions and a general tendency in evolution have produced heterospory independently in the two genera. Heterospory seems to be the goal toward which a general tendency of evolution is urging all the vascular plants.

The Cycadofilicales resemble ferns so closely that they were mistaken for ferns until their seeds were discovered. Could it be possible that transmigrants, coming upon the land at different periods, could have developed into these two groups independently? Since the two groups are associated geographically and edaphically, the conditions which they had to meet must have been somewhat similar. The demands of protection, absorption, conduction, and assimilation would probably have resulted, in both cases, in the production of roots, stems, and leaves; but we doubt whether these organs, developed independently, would be so similar that the two groups would be mistaken for each other. It is easier to believe that the Cycadofilicales have come from the Filicales by direct descent. We believe it to be a fundamental of development that homospory must precede heterospory, and that the heterosporous Pteridophyte condition must precede the seed condition. This tendency toward heterospory is so strong that this condition has been achieved independently in various lines of vascular plants.

The seed is the final stage in the development of heterospory. From what has preceded, it is plain that there might be cases in which it would be difficult or even impossible to draw a line between an heterosporous Pteridophyte and a seed plant. If the retention of the megaspore makes the sporangium, with its contained megaspore, a seed; while a sporangium which sheds its megaspore, even at an advanced stage of development, has not yet reached the seed condition, a single individual might be partly fern and partly seed plant. As we have already noted, such a condition actually occurs in *Selaginella*, and may have been rather frequent as the early seed plants were evolving from the heterosporous Pteridophytes. The two groups, at the transition stage, would be separated by artificial definitions rather than by facts.

During the period while the advanced megasporangium was developing into the true seed stage, it would not be surprising to find the leaf remaining at the fern level. In very recent times, apples have developed so that numerous varieties, of very different aspect, have arisen, while the leaves remained about the same.

In vascular anatomy, the Cycadofilicales are more advanced than the ferns with which they were associated. To cite a single feature, circular pits are very characteristic of the xylem of the higher seed plants, while a sclariform marking is equally characteristic of ferns. The known Cycadofilicales have quite generally progressed beyond the sclariform stage, but we should expect to find it in their seedlings; for even the living cycads pass through the sclariform stage and *Stangeria* does not pass beyond it, except in certain tissues. This genus also retains a very fernlike leaf. The case of *Stangeria* is particularly instructive because it was long mistaken for a fern, so that a very advanced seed condition may be attained, while the leaf and vascular anatomy remain at the fern level. So the stelar structures may advance while the leaf and general topography remain more or less stationary.

We cannot agree that the heterosporous ferns may be as old as the homosporous; or that the seed plants may be as old as the ferns. When all the geological evidence is in, it must confirm the sequence: homospory, heterospory, seed. Heterospory in the Carboniferous, and earlier, was attained in the same way as it is today. A section of *Bothrodendron* from the Upper Carboniferous of Illinois, described by REED,[461] shows four megaspores and a plasmodium-like mass which can hardly be anything else than the broken down remains of wall cells, tapetal cells, and abortive spores (fig. 26). The resemblance to a sporangium of *Selaginella* at this stage, where the origin of the mass is definitely known, is striking. In all the living genera of heterosporous Pteridophytes the homosporous ancestry is unmistakable.

While the ancestors of Cycadofilicales were in the heterosporous condition, but were not yet up to the seed stage, they were Pteridophytes, and this would be true, whether they were coming from some known Pteridophyte by direct descent, or were coming by parallel development from some Pteridophyte ancestry not yet discovered.

When structures like the leaves are so similar in ferns and seed plants that the two groups cannot be distinguished by their leaves, it seems more probable that the sporangia, and also the vascular system, of the higher groups have advanced from the heterosporous fern condition to the seed condition, while the leaves have remained stationary. It is logically possible that leaves so identical as to be indistinguishable may have developed in ferns and seed-ferns from entirely unrelated ancestors; but it seems more likely that the similarity is due to genetical relationship. A Latin poet, in giving advice to young play writers, once advised them not to bring a god upon the stage unless the situation demanded it. In the case of ferns and seed-ferns, it would seem that genetical relationship, functioning as it is known to function in living plants, where the relationship is fairly well known, is a sufficient factor to account for the observed structures without putting upon parallel development the strain of producing, in two great groups of plants, leaves so identical that they cannot be distinguished.

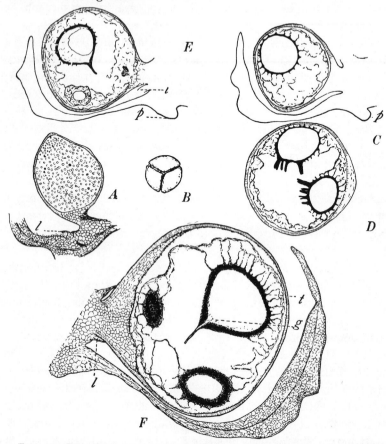

FIG. 26.—*Bothrodendron*. *A*, microsporangium, showing portion of sporophyll, course of vascular strand, ligule, and tetrads of spores; ×10. *B*, tetrad of microspores; ×230. *C*, diagram of megasporangium showing sporophyll with lobe or projection of lower side, and one of the four megaspores; ×9. *D*, diagram of megasporangium showing two megaspores; ×9. *E*, diagram of megasporangium: *l*, ligule; *p*, lobe on sporophyll; ×9. *F*, megasporangium with three of the four megaspores: *v*, vascular strand; *l*, ligule; *t*, tapetal plasmodium; *g*, female gametophyte; somewhat diagrammatic; ×16. —After DR. FREDDA D. REED.[461]

We believe that the evidence is sufficient to prove, as well as anything is proved in the way of genetic relationships, that the Cycadofilicales have come, in the natural course of evolution, from the heterosporous pteridophytes. The homosporous ferns, in the natural course of evolution, gave rise to the heterosporous ferns, which, in turn gave rise to the Cycadofilicales.

SPECULATIVE RECONSTRUCTION

The splendid Carboniferous swamp-forest reconstruction in the Field Museum makes us wonder what we might find if we could go back to those ancient times, collect living material, and get complete life-histories of all the forms. Many, even at that far away time, would be so advanced that we should speculate as to what their Devonian and even Silurian ancestry might be. In the swamp-forest reconstruction, there was so much material available that the view is probably much the same as greeted the eyes of *Archeoblattina* and *Diplovertebron*. In a reconstruction of finer details of gross structure, and especially in the microscopic anatomy, not so much material is available, except in the harder woody parts which are very well preserved. Spore coats and impressions of seeds are preserved in great abundance, but our knowledge of the internal structure of spores and the gametophytes is very fragmentary.

For the reconstruction, we have not followed any living form in detail, although certain features of *Azolla* and *Trichomanes* have had some influence. It does not seem necessary to reconstruct any homosporous type or even the earliest beginnings of heterospory, since the development of the sporangia of all the living heterosporous genera is well known, and all of them show very clearly their homosporous ancestry. So let us take a sorus terminating a leaf, as the seed, *Trigonocarpus*, terminates the leaf of *Neuropteris;* and then, without reference to any particular forms, extinct or living, let us trace the evolutionary course through the heterosporous condition to the seed stage.

In fig. 27 the oldest sporangium is at the top of the sorus. We shall assume that this sporangium continues its development while the sporangia below it disorganize, giving up their material to the terminal sporangium. The early stages of development up to the spore-mother-cell stage, and even through the two reduction divisions, are still those of a homosporous type. Then some of the spores disorganize, and give up their food supply to their more successful neighbors. Let us assume that all disorganize except one tetrad of spores and that, even of this tetrad, three spores develop only slightly before they, too, break down (fig. 28). The growing megaspore then absorbs the disintigrating megaspores, the tapetum, and finally all of the wall cells of the sporangium, except the outer, epidermal layer. Even the lower sporangia of the sorus disorganize, and the megaspore in the terminal sporangium germinates. In the early stages in the phylogeny of heterospory, the megaspores must have been small and there might not have been any free nuclear stage in the development; but, as the megaspores became larger, a free nuclear stage would appear, just as it is likely to appear anywhere, when the mass of protoplasm is large in proportion to the nuclear figure; and then cell walls would be formed (fig. 29). In the earlier stages, in phylogeny, the female gametophyte would probably break out, extend beyond the spore coats, and become green, just as it sometimes does in living heterosporous Pteridophytes (fig. 30).

Later, as the megaspore became larger, the gametophyte would be retained within the spore, exposed for the sperms only at the triradiate crack. Fertilization might occur at this stage and the embryo might begin to develop; but if, even at such a late stage, the megaspore, with its embryo, should be shed, the plant would still be a heterosporous Pteridophyte (fig. 31).

As the megaspore became larger and larger, it would reach a more advanced stage before shedding, until, finally, it would not be shed at all, and the true seed stage would be achieved (fig. 32).

With the permanent retention of the megaspore, the thick spore coat, so necessary while the megaspore was in the discharged condition, would not only be unnecessary, but would be disadvantageous. Consequently, they became thinner and thinner, while the sporangium wall, especially at the top, became thicker and the protective and nutritive functions were gradually transferred from the megaspore itself to the sporangium (figs. 32 and 33).

The formation of a pollen chamber is practically universal in gymnosperms. It is formed by the disorganization of cells in the region above the eggs, the product of the disorganization being the sparkling pollination drop which catches the pollen. The drying of

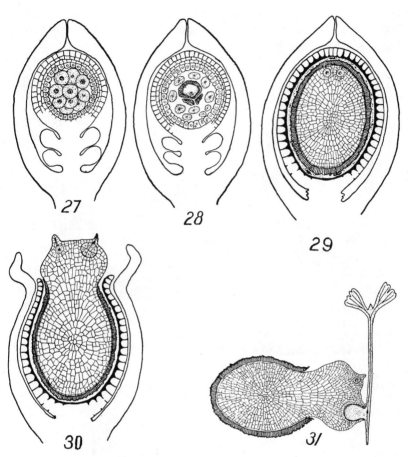

FIGS. 27–31.—Hypothetical development of a heterosporous carboniferous fern ancestor of the Cycadofilicales. Fig. 27, a megasporangium with spore mother-cells, at this stage indistinguishable from a homosporous sporangium. Below are aborting sporangia and the sorus is surrounded by an envelope which might be called an integument. Fig. 28, one mother-cell has divided. Fig. 29, one megaspore has germinated and has produced two eggs, and has developed a heavy spore coat. Fig. 30, the female gametophyte is protruding and has an embryo. The sporangium wall has been ruptured. Fig. 31, the megaspore, with its embryo, has been shed from the sporangium and is germinating outside the sporangium. Therefore it has not quite reached the seed stage.

the drop not only brings the pollen into the pollen chamber, but seals the chamber, so that the male gametophyte is protected during its further development.

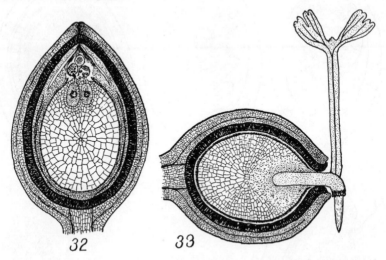

FIGS. 32, 33.—Hypothetical sections of megasporangia of a member of the Cycado-filicales after it has passed beyond the heterosporous fern stage and become a seed plant. Fig. 32, a megasporangium at the time of fertilization. Three pollen grains in the pollen chamber. No pollen tubes. The megaspore coat is thinner than in the heteros-porous fern stage. Fig. 33, the seedling is developing while the megaspore is permanent-ly retained within the megasporangium. The seed stage has been reached.

FIG. 34.—Hypothetical development of the male gametophyte in a member of the Cycadofilicales, showing, in order, a microspore; a prothallial cell and a fertile cell; both vegetative and fertile portions developing; differentiation into spermatogenous cells and wall cells; mature sperms; sperms escaping.

In early stages, in phylogeny, the male gametophyte, by the breaking down of a few cells at the top of the sporangium, came into contact with the female gametophyte, and there was no formation of a pollen tube. When the sperms were shed, they were in as close

contact with the eggs as in a living cycad after the development of
its pollen tube. After fertilization, the degree of development of the
embryo or the presence or absence of a resting period are not concerned in the definition of a seed.

In the development of the male gametophyte there was probably
not much difference between the heterosporous fern and the early
seed plant. In the homosporous fern, the development was probably
about like that of the homosporous fern of today, with practically

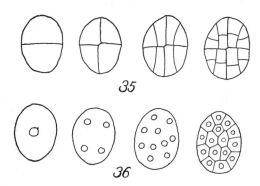

35

36

Figs. 35–36.—Development of an embryo with walls forming from the beginning.
Fig. 36, Development of an embryo with a free nuclear stage preceding wall formation.

all of the gametophyte outside the spore. In the early development
of heterospory, the gametophyte probably protruded considerably
and became green, as it sometimes does in living heterosporous
forms. As heterospory advanced, the gametophyte tissue became
more and more included within the spore, protruding only enough to
crack the spore coat and shed the sperms (fig. 34). The pollen tube,
at first only a haustorial organ, is a comparatively modern development. The Cycadofilicales had not reached this stage.

A guess at the development of the embryo might be hazarded. As
the homosporous fern condition was passing into the heterosporous
fern condition, while the fertilized egg was still quite small, there
may have been no free nuclear period; but as the megaspore and its
eggs became larger, there would be a free nuclear period, followed
by the formation of walls and body regions (figs. 35 and 36).

Why no embryos are found is still a mystery. They are abundant in the Bennettitales, and structures as delicate as these embryos may have been are well preserved.

Although it may seem presumptuous to dispute the claims of the two greatest living paleobotanists, Scott* and Seward, nevertheless, a lifetime study of the comparative morphology of living plants, especially Pteridophytes and Gymnosperms, makes me feel confident that the course of evolution has been from homospory, through heterospory, to the seed. The genetic line must have been homosporous Filicales, heterosporous Filicales, Cycadofilicales.

* D. H. Scott died on January 29, 1934.

CHAPTER III

CYCADOPHYTES—BENNETTITALES

Just as the Carboniferous has been called the "Age of Ferns," the Mesozoic has been called the "Age of Cycads."

In the Carboniferous, the Cycadofilicales reached their highest development and began to decline. While they were still plastic, probably in the Upper Carboniferous, two great lines, which later became prominent, began to differentiate from the plexus, while the ancestral lines became weaker and weaker and, finally, in the Triassic and early Jurassic, became extinct. One of the new lines is called the Bennettitales; the other, the Cycadales. The Bennettitales developed rapidly, reached their greatest display in the Jurassic, and became extinct in the Upper Cretaceous; while the Cycadales, although not so prominent a feature of the vegetation, still flourish in various tropical and subtropical regions.

What caused the Bennettitales to become extinct, while the Cycadales survived, can only be conjectured. Both were probably eaten by the immense herbivorous dinosaurs of the Jurassic and Triassic. Their leaves and trunks, the parts constantly exposed to the weather, were very similar; the flower buds of the Bennettitales would seem to be even better protected than those of the Cycadales and, edaphically, the two groups faced the same conditions. But the covering of the strobili by bud scales may not have been entirely advantageous for, if the seeds were as short-lived as those of the living Cycads, many of them would have died before they were shed from the plant. The seeds of the Cycadales are larger and their thick stony layer may have made them more resistant than the small seeds of the Bennettitales. At any rate, one group died while the other lived.

Many have made contributions to our knowledge of this group; some to its taxonomy, some to morphology, and some to phylogeny; but the name of WIELAND will always be most prominently associated with the Bennettitales, for he has collected more than all others combined, has prepared his own material for microscopic study, developing excellent methods, and has made his own drawings, photographs, and photomicrographs. Three large quarto volumes, with scores of plates and numerous drawings in the text, together with a clear and interesting literary style, present the results of a lifetime of productive research. And besides there are numerous shorter papers.

DISTRIBUTION

At this time, any account of the geographic distribution of the Bennettitales must be regarded as merely a beginning. Whenever WIELAND makes a trip into a Mesozoic region, a new locality for fossil cycads is added to the list. Wherever members of this group have flourished, they are likely to be preserved, because their armored trunks and tough leaves, with heavy cuticle, make sharp impressions even when no internal structure is preserved. In many localities the material is silicified.

American forms were first brought to notice in 1860. Various people picked them up between Baltimore and Washington and kept them as curiosities, calling them fossil bee hives, fossil wasps' nests, etc. Ward[657, 658, 659] first described these specimens; and later about 60 of them were taken to the Woman's College in Baltimore, where they are now on exhibition. Specimens have also been found in North Carolina, Pennsylvania, Kansas, Colorado, Texas, and California; but the most extensive collections have been made in the Upper Jurassic of Wyoming and the Black Hills of South Dakota. To protect the richest part of the Black Hills region, WIELAND took up 360 acres as a claim, and then succeeded in having it made a national preserve. More than 700 trunks from this locality are now in the Yale Museum, where, with many specimens from other localities, they constitute the largest collection in the world. WIELAND has recently discovered a rich locality (not yet described) in Arizona.

Prince Edward Island, in Canada, has silicified Triassic material.

WIELAND,[682] in 1909, visited the Mixteca Alta, near Oaxaca, Mexico, and discovered a region wonderfully rich in fossil cycads. The result of this investigation, published (in Spanish) by the Mexican government, is illustrated with 50 excellent plates made from photographs. The principal genera in this locality are *Ptilophyllum, Ptero-*

phyllum, *Otozamites*, and *Williamsonia*. Many of the species are new. While the impressions of leaves and fruits are abundant and wonderfully clear, there are no silicified specimens to show the internal structure.

In England and Scotland well-preserved specimens have been found in various horizons in the Triassic, Jurassic, and Cretaceous. Germany, Belgium, Poland, Russia, Italy, and the Isle of Wight have yielded material, and India has long been a famous fossil cycad locality.

LIFE-HISTORY

Most of the material from which the internal structures of the Cycadofilicales have been studied is calcified. In the Bennettitales the material is silicified. In making peels, hydrofluoric acid must be used, and cutting sections is more laborious; but the harder surface allows a higher degree of polish, and very satisfactory studies, and even photomicrographs, can be made from cut surfaces without any balsam or cover.

The stem.—If any form can be considered typical of the Bennettitales, it is the unbranched stem with a crown of leaves at the top; but branching was probably as common as in the living cycads. The axillary strobili gave the stems a very characteristic appearance so that they could not be mistaken even for those Cycadales in which the strobili are axillary (fig. 37).

The tuberous habit was common, and this, with frequent branching, gives the specimens a striking resemblance to the branching plants of *Zamia*. The stems and branches, which are so similar that it is often difficult to determine which is the main stem and which are the branches, are usually as much as 15 cm. in diameter, and specimens often reach a diameter of 25–50 cm. The branching tuberous forms are not very tall, usually not exceeding half a meter. Some columnar forms, which are not likely to be branched, have reached a meter in height. The tallest on record is *Cycadeoidea gigantea* (Seward), 1.18 M. high and about one-third that figure in diameter. The smallest known specimen is *Bennettites scotti*, 8.5 cm. in height and about two-thirds as much in diameter; this, however, was probably a bud from a larger specimen.

Williamsonia gigas was tall and slender, while *Williamsonia* (*Ano-mozamites*) *angustifolia* was slender and profusely branching.

The *Williamsonia* (*Anomozamites*) *angustifolia* type of stem shows, on the outside, what the *Dioon* type of stem shows on the inside; for the outwardly unbranched stem of *Dioon* is really profusely branched

FIG. 37.—*Cycadeoidea wielandii:* upper part of a trunk found near Hermosa, South Dakota: some of the strobili are projecting and some have fallen out, leaving cavities which are dark in the illustration. The height of the specimen is 54 cm.—From a photograph by THIESSEN.

on the inside (fig. 38). If material of this *Williamsonia* were available, just at the base of the terminal cone we should expect to find newly formed meristems which would give rise to branches. Each of these branches, with its leaves, would soon be terminated by a cone, at the base of which a new meristem would form, and so a profusely branched plant would be developed. It should be noted that the leaves are only once pinnate, and that in *Williamsoniella coronata* the leaves are simple.

In *Williamsonia gigas* the stem is outwardly unbranched and the internal structure, judging from Williamson's reconstruction, would also be unbranched.

The stems were covered by an armor of persistent leaf bases, as in most of the living Cycadales. The numerous axillary cones, often hundreds, gave the stems a striking appearance.

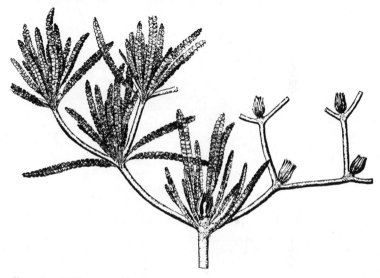

Fig. 38.—*Williamsonia (Anomozamites) angustifolia:* branching trunks with leaves and strobili at the forks; about ⅙ natural size.—After Nathorst.

The vascular system is an endarch siphonostele, the highest type found in gymnosperms, and characteristic of the Archichlamydeae and Sympetalae in the angiosperms. No seedlings have been examined and, consequently, it is not known whether a mesarch condition might be found, as in the living Cycadales.

In transverse section the stem shows the large pith, scanty wood, and thick cortex, which are so prevalent in the whole Cycadophyte phylum (fig. 39).

The scanty zone of wood, as in most of the living Cycads, shows no growth-rings. *Cycadeoidea jenneyana* is exceptional in having a zone of wood, reaching, near the base of the trunk, a radial thickness of 8 cm. Growth-rings in this specimen are very distinct. WIE-LAND[680] thinks the trunk is polyxylic, although he admits that there may have been a persistent cambium. His excellent photograph of the transverse section is so identical with the appearance of *Dioon spinulosum* and *Dioon edule*, where the rings are undoubtedly formed by a persistent cambium, that we feel certain that the same condition is present in *Cycadeoidea jenneyana*. Besides, the polyxylic condition, with its successive cambiums in the living cycads, where it is

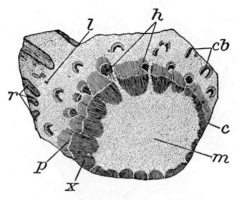

FIG. 39.—*Cycadella* sp.: transverse section of top of small trunk from Wyoming, showing large pith, woody cylinder, and cortex; *m*, pith; *x*, xylem; *c*, cambium; *cb*, leaf traces; *r*, ramentum; *h*, leaf (or peduncle) traces; *l*, base of leaf; natural size.—After WIELAND.[680]

well known, makes the successive zones or rings look very different from the growth-rings formed by a persistent cambium. SCOTT says that in *Cycadeoidea yatesii* there is evidence for the presence of two or more zones of xylem and phloem, like those in *Cycas*. Whether the rings, whatever their character, are annual, may be very doubtful, for, in the living cycads, rings looking very much like those of *Cycadeoidea jenneyana* may be formed every other year, or at intervals of 20 years or more.

The leaf-trace bundles pass directly through the cortex into the leaves, there being none of the girdling which is such a prominent feature of the living cycads. There are no bundles in the pith, nor, with axillary cones, would any be anticipated. However, there are numerous mucilage cavities in the pith, some of them several cells wide.

The histological details of xylem and phloem are beautifully preserved, but the delicate cells of the cambium are broken (fig. 40). Transverse sections at about the middle of the xylem region and the middle of the phloem region are shown in figs. 41 and 42.

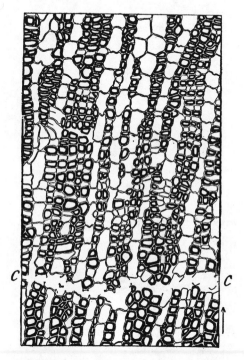

FIG. 40.—*Cycadeoidea wielandii:* c, cambium mostly broken down; above it the phloem with many thick-walled tracheids, and below, the secondary wood. ×100.— After WIELAND.[680]

Most of the tracheids are sclariform, but those of the protoxylem, next to the pith, are spiral. No pitted tracheids were observed in *Cycadeoidea wielandi*, although the preservation is so excellent that they could hardly escape notice, if present. However, LIGNIER[360] found bordered pits on the radial walls of tracheids of *Cycadeoidea micromela*, and there are some bordered pits in *Cycadeoidea painei* and *dartoni*. The markings on the tracheids should receive most critical attention, for the Cycadofilicales had so generally reached the pitted condition. The question may well be raised whether a plant whose tracheids have reached the pitted condition could give rise to

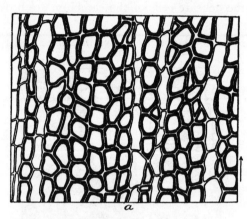

FIG. 41.—*Cycadeoidea wielandii:* transverse section of secondary wood; ×150.— After WIELAND.[680]

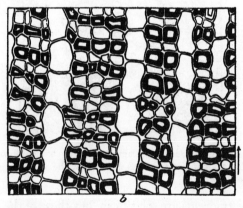

FIG. 42.—*Cycadeoidea wielandii:* transverse section of phloem showing thin-walled cells and thick-walled tracheids; ×150.—After WIELAND.[680]

a line with sclariform tracheids. Atavism is a familiar phenomenon; but, as we understand it, its influence is potent only for a short time, not persisting from one geological age to another. If the sequence, spiral, sclariform, pitted, is fundamental, we should not expect a form

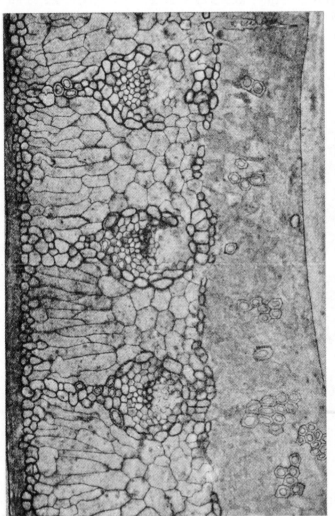

FIG. 43.—*Cycadeoidea ingens* (type): transverse section of pinnule. In the lower part only occasional, thick-walled cells are shown, not because of poor preservation, but because the natural coloring does not make them distinct; ×140.—After WIELAND.[680]

like *Cycadeoidea wielandi* to be derived from any of the Cycadofilicales which have already reached the pitted condition. But if the
sequence is due to physiological conditions, especially rate of growth,
the kind of markings would have little or no significance as far as
relationships are concerned.

Fig. 44.—*Cycadeoidea jenneyana:* tangential section of a trunk showing numerous
transverse sections of strobili among the foliage leaves; ×⅔.—After Wieland.[680]

We should anticipate much more of the pitted condition than has
yet been found; but it must be remembered that *Stangeria* still retains the sclariform tracheid of its very remote fern ancestors, and
that *Dioon*, except in young plants, has sclariform tracheids in the
protoxylem.

The leaf.—The leaves of the Bennettitales and the Cycadales are so similar that we doubt whether the two groups could be separated on the basis of the leaf alone. In both, the dominating leaf is the pinnate leaf of their filicinean progenitors. Leaves more than once pinnate are rare, found only in *Bowenia* in the Cycadales, and we have not found any record of more than once pinnate leaves in the Bennettitales, if we except the pos-

sibility that the synangia are modified pinnules. If they are modified pinnules, the microsporophylls are bipinnate. In *Williamsonia coronata* the leaves were simple and entire.

In size, the leaves are about like those of living Cycads, reaching a length of more than 3 meters in *Cycadeoidea ingens* and only about 6 cm. in *Williamsonia coronata;* most of them, however, ranged in size between these two. In the abundant material from the Lias of the Mixteca Alta of Mexico, many of the leaves of *Ptilophyllum* and *Otozamites* were less than 25 cm. in

FIG. 45.—*Cycadella ramentosa:* transverse section of ramentum: ×66. —After WIELAND.[680]

length, and in *Ptilophyllum acutifolium* var. *minor* the leaflets are less than 10 cm. long.

The venation is "parallel," which, in this phylum, means that it is dichotomous, with very little forking beyond the base of the leaflet. There are no midribs in any of the leaves, but it is interesting to note that, associated with leaves of the Bennettitales in the Mixteca Alta region, there are leaflets with midribs (*Stangerites oaxacensis* and *Sagenopteris rhoifolis* var. *mexicana*) resembling leaflets of the living African *Stangeria*. In this connection, it might be mentioned that a South African specimen, named *Zamites*, in the museum at Grahamstown, South Africa, is hardly distinguishable from the living *Dioon edule* of Mexico.

The histological structure of the leaf is typically xerophyllous, with strongly cutinized epidermis. The leaves are thick, and their internal structure shows that they were leathery and well fitted to withstand adverse conditions (fig. 43). On the upper side there are some thick-walled hypodermal cells and a well-marked palisade. Near the middle is a single row of mesarch bundles with a strong bundle sheath connected with the upper part of the leaf by sclerenchyma cells. Below the bundles is a wavy line of thick-walled cells,

FIG. 46.—*Cycadeoidea ingens:* photograph of a model in the Field Museum of Natural History in Chicago. The model is almost entirely of glass and was made by Mr. SELLA, with the aid of criticism and advice by WIELAND.

beneath which is a thick layer, extending to the lower epidermis, of thick-walled cells. In the figure, only a few of these are clearly shown, and although the preservation is good, the lack of natural coloring makes most of the cells very indistinct. In the upper part, the photomicrograph was retouched.

The root.—Scarcely anything is known about the root of this group. A paper by Dr. STOPES describes rootlets in a section identified as *Bennettites saxbyanus*, but these rootlets were probably adventitious, from an adventitious bud. They were about 1 mm. in diameter, and had abundant root hairs. There were many rootlets in the section, cut in various directions. In longitudinal and in oblique views there were three or four rather large sclariform tracheids. There was no satisfactory view in transverse section.

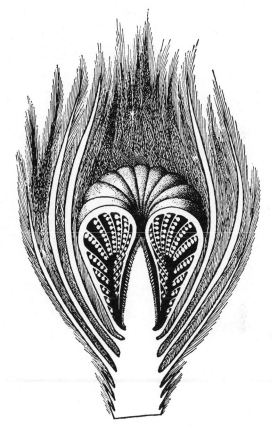

Fig. 47.—*Cycadeoidea:* diagrammatic view of unexpanded strobilus. Outside the sporophylls are numerous bracts densely covered with ramentum; about natural size.— After WIELAND.[680]

The strobilus.—The most characteristic feature of the Bennettitales is the strobilus. The strobili were borne on the upper part of the plant, usually in great numbers, hundreds having been counted in several cases. They are all axillary, in some cases a strobilus being borne in the axis of every leaf. A tangential section of a trunk of *Cycadeoidea* shows transverse sections of the bases of foliage leaves and numerous strobili surrounded by scale leaves (fig. 44). At the bases of foliage leaves and entirely covering the scale leaves is a dense ramentum consisting of scales several cells wide and often more than one cell in thickness (fig. 45). This is a dominant fern character and not at all present in the Cycadales, in which the ramentum consists

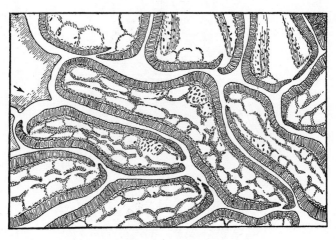

Fig. 48.—*Cycadeoidea dacotensis:* section of an unexpanded microsporophyll showing, in most cases, transverse views of the two rows of loculi. At the upper right, parts of two microsporangia are cut nearly longitudinally. Some of the loculi contain microspores; ×25.—After Wieland.[680]

of long unicellular hairs. Occasionally there is a transverse partition, but even where the ramentum is equally abundant in the Cycadales the two groups could be distinguished by this character alone.

The strobili of the Bennettitales are typically bisporangiate, with leaflike microsporophylls as loosely arranged as the megasporophylls of the living *Cycas*, and in the center a cone consisting of innumerable small megasporophylls, each bearing a single terminal ovule. The megasporophylls are slender peduncles without a trace of lateral pinnae or ovules. Intermixed with the megasporophylls are sterile leaves with a thickened top and with no lateral leaflets.

A splendid reconstruction of the bisporangiate strobilus of *Cycadeoidea ingens* has been made for the Field Museum by Mr. Sella, of the Museum staff, with suggestions and corrections by WIELAND (fig. 46). The leaflike microsporophylls surround the comparatively small ovulate strobilus.

The time of flowering has been the subject of considerable speculation. It has been noted that in some of the tallest specimens there are strobili only in the upper part, and that these strobili are of approximately the same age. Furthermore, in some there are no vegetative leaves at the extreme tip, and no indication that there would be any. If such leaves had been present, they would have been discovered, as WIELAND found them in *Cycadeoidea ingens*. From a very thorough study, WIELAND concludes that many of the Bennettitales flower but once, and then die. Such a behavior is well known in angiosperms. The century plant, *Agave americana*, flowers but once and dies; but it does not wait a hundred years. Plants from "suckers," about 3 years old, flower in 5–7 years. The palm, *Corypha umbraculifera*, attains an age of about 40 years and a height of 60 feet, when the axis is suddenly prolonged another 40 feet as an immense flower stalk bearing thousands of flowers. The plant then dies. *Yucca whipplei* flowers but once, and dies; while other species of the genus flower year after year. None of the living cycads die on account of flowering.

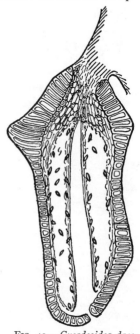

FIG. 49.—*Cycadeoidea dacotensis:* longitudinal section of sporangium showing stalk and two loculi containing microspores; ×40.—After WIELAND.[680]

The microsporophyll.—The microsporophylls retain more of the ancestral fern-leaf characters than any of the rest of the Cycadophyte line above the Cycadofilicales. They have about the same topography as the vegetative leaves, but are much reduced in size. The pinnules bear synangia on both sides, so that the pinnule looks again pinnate. If the synangia are really reduced pinnules, as WIELAND believes, the sporophylls are twice pinnate. Some strobili, younger than the one shown in fig. 46, have been sectioned, yielding younger stages in both micro- and megasporangia (fig. 47).

The microsporangia are multilocular. We should hesitate to call them "synangia," since the term implies a fusion of separate sporangia to form a single large synangium. The structure, however, is practically identical with that in the Marattiaceous ferns (fig. 48). There is an outer layer of thick-walled cells, followed by thin-walled

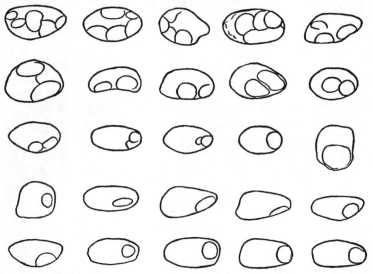

Fig. 50.—*Cycadeoidea dacotensis:* microspores indicating multicellular structure.— After Wieland.[680]

cells and then, doubtless, a tapetum. There is a cleft between the two rows of loculi, and each loculus opens into the cleft, as in *Marattia*. A complete longitudinal section of the sporangium is shown in fig. 49.

Nothing very definite is known of the internal structure of the microspore, but it seems practically certain that there were several cells. The fact that so many show a circular marking would indicate that there is a prothallial cell (fig. 50).

No pollen tubes have been observed. There is some nucellar tissue, but whether it breaks down so as to allow the pollen grains to come into direct contact with the gametophyte, as in the Cycadofilicales, is not known.

The megasporangium.—The solitary megasporangium is terminal on a slender stalk, which represents the rachis of the sporophyll. In the Cycadales, all the ovules are lateral, while, here, all are terminal (fig. 51). In the two great lines, evolution has taken two distinct

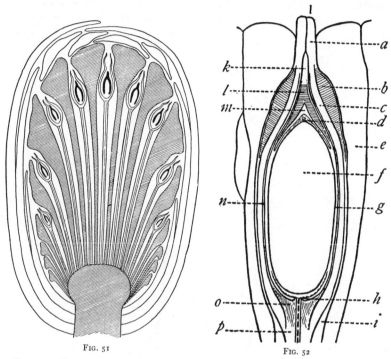

FIG. 51   FIG. 52

FIG. 51.—*Bennettites gibsonianus:* diagram of female strobilus, showing terminal seed with dicotyl embryos. The sporophylls are long and slender, and they alternate with sterile bracts (sporophylls). The whole strobilus is surrounded by bracts.—Modified by SCOTT[514] after SOLMS-LAUBACH[571] and POTONIÉ.[455]

FIG. 52.—*Bennettites morieri:* longitudinal section of a seed; *a*, micropylar tube; *b*, prismatic layer; *c*, pulpy tissue; *d*, "corpuscular" mass; *e*, interseminal scale; *f*, embryo space; *g*, remains of nucellus; *h*, chalaza; *i*, tubular envelope; *k*, micropylar canal; *l*, nucellar beak; *m*, pollen chamber; *n*, fibrous stratum; *o*, basal expansion of *n*; *p*, pedicel bundle.—After WIELAND's[680] reproduction of LIGNIER's[359] figure.

courses. Starting with sporophyll, bearing ovules both laterally and at the apex, the lateral ovules, in the Bennettitales, became sterile and disappeared; while in the Cycadales the top of the sporophyll became sterile and the lateral ones remained.

The ovules are prevailingly small, many of them not more than 5 mm. in length, and few of them exceeding a centimeter. Just what the structure is and how it compares with that of groups above and below has not yet been determined very definitely. The best illustrations available are drawn from later stages in *Cycadeoidea dartoni* and *Bennettites moreri* (figs. 52 and 53). The outer layer is thick and palisaded at the top; the middle layer, shown in black in

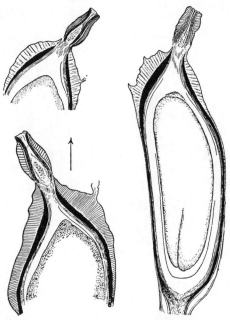

Fig. 53.—*Cycadeoidea dartoni:* longitudinal section of ripe seed with a dicotyl embryo; ×20.—After WIELAND.[687]

the figure, is stony, and the thinner inner layer is probably membranaceous. The thin line, at a little distance from the embryo, may be the megaspore membrane. The complicated micropylar end of the ovule is a striking feature.

The embryo.—It will be remembered that in the Cycadofilicales no embryo has yet been found. The almost constant presence of dicotyl embryos in the Bennettitales is in striking contrast. As shown in figs. 51 and 53, the hypocotyl is more extensive than in the living cycads, and the suspensor, if present, could not have been very prominent.

Paleobotanists agree that the Bennettitales have come from the Cycadofilicales. The leaves of some of the lower forms, like *Ptilophyllum* and *Williamsonia*, are so identical with the leaves of *Dioon*, that the similarity may not be accidental. It may mean that both Bennettitales and Cycadales inherited the leaf from some very remote ancestor; or it may be possible that some of the unattached leaves actually belong to the Cycadales. The habit of the trunk in both groups may have been similarly inherited. But the strobilus is so different in the two lines that the Bennettitales could not have given rise to the Cycadales. The lateral leaflets of the megasporophyll, entirely lost in the earliest known Bennettitales, could not have been transmitted to the Cycadales. The vertebrate paleontologist illustrates this law of evolution by saying that a tooth, lost in phylogeny, is lost for good. The Bennettitales came from the Cycadofilicales, probably in the later Carboniferous. Although no definitely recognizable material dates that far back, the first recognizable specimens are so advanced that they must have been separated from the main line for a long time.

That the Bennettitales may have given rise to any of the angiosperms we regard as not only improbable but impossible. One attempt to connect them makes the connection with the Sympetalae, a group obviously derived from the Archichlamydeae, and not only cyclic, but tetracyclic. A more recent attempt to connect them with the angiosperms, and a connection which seems more reasonable, has been with the magnolias; but, again, the superficial resemblance of the bisporangiate fructification of the Bennettitales to the magnolia type of flower does not seem adequate for establishing such a relationship, and so we must conclude that the Bennettitales were the last of their line; they left no progeny.

CHAPTER IV

CYCADOPHYTES—CYCADALES

All the forms described in previous chapters are extinct. The Cycadofilicales had already begun to decline before the end of the Carboniferous, so that it was a dwindling group which struggled through the Triassic and touched the Jurassic. The Bennettitales were dominant in the Jurassic, even forming forests, if a dense vegetation of such small plants could be called a forest; and well into the Cretaceous they were still abundant. But none of them persisted until the end of that period.

The Cycadales, like the Bennettitales, were derived from the Cycadofilicales, probably being differentiated from that group in the later Carboniferous. Consequently, throughout the Mesozoic, until the Bennettitales became extinct, the two groups must have been growing side by side. Why are the Cycadales so scantily represented as fossils, while the Bennettitales are so abundant? The strobili of the Cycadales usually begin to decay as soon as they reach maturity. Sometimes, under dry conditions, the cones shrivel and become very hard; but under such conditions, fossilization is unlikely to take place. Of course, the leaves are practically identical in the two groups, so that it is quite possible that some of the unattached leaves which have been assigned to the Bennettitales really belong to the Cycadales. The trunks also are often very similar, and the resemblance would be most striking when the Cycadales trunk bore numerous axillary strobili.

Neither the Bennettitales nor the extinct members of the Cycadales have left any fossils of such great size as some of the living Cycadales; for many reach a height of 2 meters, while 4 or 5 meters is not rare, and occasional individuals have been measured up to a height of 18 meters.

While the Cycadales have not left as complete a record in the rocks as we might wish, still, there is enough to prove their presence practically throughout the Mesozoic, and there were cycad-like leaves in the Permo-Carboniferous. Megasporophylls of *Cycadospadix hennoquei*, from the lower Liassic, differ less from those of the living *Cycas revoluta* than those of *Cycas revoluta* differ from some of the other living species of the genus. Records are more abundant in the Jurassic; and the group reached its widest distribution and greatest display in the early Cretaceous. Then it began to decline, so that the living cycads are less abundant than their predecessors.

The lack of a satisfactory geological record is partly compensated for by the fact that the cycads have come down from the remote past with so little change that, if one could be transported back a hundred million years, he would doubtless recognize some of the genera. The cycads of today may well be called "living fossils."

There is only one family, the Cycadaceae, with only nine genera, four of which belong to the Western Hemisphere, and five to the Eastern. In a recent monograph, SCHUSTER[510] recognizes 65 species; but with his subspecies, varieties, and forms—categories of no interest to the morphologist—the number is much larger. We prefer to regard a species as a norm which may vary considerably in many directions. Giving names to variants, which may never occur again, merely makes confusion and burdens the nomenclature. If all genera and species had been described by competent observers who had studied them in the field, taxonomy would not have so many species to deal with.

GEOGRAPHIC DISTRIBUTION

In the Mesozoic, the cycads were world-wide in their distribution, as cosmopolitan as *Pteris* and *Typha* are today; but now they are confined to tropical and subtropical regions, and even there they occur in scanty patches, in out-of-the-way places, so that collecting involves hard tramping, often over rocky, inhospitable ground, where natives as well as nature seem to conspire against success.

The great cycad regions of the world are Mexico and the West Indies, in the Western Hemisphere; and Australia and South Africa in the Southern Hemisphere. Only two genera occur outside of these regions: *Zamia*, in the West, and *Cycas* in the East.

Two of the western genera, *Dioon* and *Ceratozamia*, are entirely confined to Mexico, and *Zamia* is abundant there. *Microcycas* is found only in western Cuba; but here, again, *Zamia* is abundant.

The cycads grow so luxuriantly in most tropical and subtropical regions that they are popular decorative plants on lawns and in patios. Consequently, people who write from hearsay, without actually visiting the localities, may greatly increase the range of a plant.

Dioon edule.—The finest station for *Dioon edule* is at Chavarrillo, 15 miles east of Jalapa (fig. 54). It grows in the blazing sun, associated with small cacti, small acacias, bromeliads, and small oaks 30–60 cm. in height. Although plants are abundant and cone freely, the patch does not seem to be spreading.

Farther down the line, at Palmar and Colorado, there is another large stand; but there does not seem to be any extension beyond Rinconada. There are plants at Huatusco, south of Jalapa; and at Rascon, between San Luis Potosí and Tampico, *Dioon edule* is so abundant that many cattle die from eating the poisonous leaves. It has also been reported, probably correctly, as growing in rocky places in the states of San Luis Potosí, Nuevo León, and Tamaulipas. There are doubtless many other stations, but any reports not coming from experienced botanists should be checked, because the plant is so often used to decorate the patio.

Dioon spinulosum.—*Dioon spinulosum* grows much farther south than *D. edule*, appearing first about 55 miles south of Vera Cruz, and becoming more abundant southward (fig. 55). On the Hacienda de Joliet, near Tierra Blanca, there are hundreds of large plants, some of them 10–16 meters in height. South of Tuxtepec, about 100 miles south of Vera Cruz, there are forests of this species. Since it is very popular as a decorative plant, any reports of its geographic distribution should be confirmed. In the first two localities from which I obtained material, the plants were nursery specimens. The plant does not occur, except as a nursery specimen, in either of the two localities mentioned in the original descriptions.

Dioon purpusii.—This comparatively new species has a much more restricted range. It is found near the railroad at Santa Catarina; also in the Tomellin Canyon, north of Oaxaca, and in the Sierra

Mixteca, Puebla. It looks like *Dioon edule* and might be mistaken for it. Years before the new species was described, WIELAND figured

FIG. 54.—*Dioon edule:* a female plant at Chavarrillo, near Jalapa, Mexico (September, 1906). The trunk is about 1.5 meters in height, and shows the armor of leaf bases. It is about 1,000 years old.—After CHAMBERLAIN.[106]

it as *Dioon edule*, in the first volume of his *American Fossil Cycads*[680] (his fig. 101). The drawing is so accurate, even in minor details, that, from his drawing alone, there is no doubt that the plant is *Dioon purpusii.*

Ceratozamia.—This is a variable genus and several species have been described; but most of them could probably be raised from the

FIG. 55.—*Dioon spinulosum:* on the Hacienda de Joliet, near Tierra Blanca. The plant in the center is about 10 meters in height.—After CHAMBERLAIN.[109]

seeds of a single cone of *Ceratozamia mexicana*, the dominant species. *C. mexicana* is abundant a few miles out from Jalapa in the direction of the extinct volcano, Naolinco (fig. 56). On the precipitous mountain side opposite the volcano, growing in dense shade, are hundreds of mature plants. How far they extend was not determined. This species also grows at Huatusco. Colipa and Mirador are also cited as stations for species of *Ceratozamia*.

FIG. 56.—*Ceratozamia mexicana:* on the steep mountain side opposite the extinct volcano, Naolinco, near Jalapa, Mexico (September, 1906).—After CHAMBERLAIN.[114]

Microcycas.—This genus is monotypic, with *Microcycas calocoma* as the only species, and western Cuba as the only locality. It is a tall, arborescent form, often 2 or 3 meters in height, and occasionally reaching a height of 8 or 10 meters (fig. 57). The name, *Microcycas*, is unfortunate, for it is one of the largest of the cycads and does not look at all like *Cycas*. In sharp contrast with the generic name, the specific name is very fitting, for the crown of leaves is exceptionally beautiful. In striking contrast with the forms before mentioned,

Fig. 57.—*Microcycas calocoma* with male cone: near Herradura, Cuba (October, 1914).

Microcycas does not appear in cultivation in the open, and conservatories have not been able to make it flourish.

Zamia.—The remaining western genus, *Zamia*, with more than a third of all the species in the family—Schuster says 28 species—has a wide distribution, its various species ranging from Florida through the West Indies, through Mexico, Central America, the northern part of South America, and down the Andes into Chili (fig. 58). Some of the species are local, well marked, and easily recognizable, while others range widely and are so variable that identifications are uncertain. The smallest cycad known, *Zamia pygmaea*, grows in the *Microcycas* region. The leaves of adult coning specimens are some-

FIG. 58.—*Zamia floridana:* at Miami, Florida. The male cones on the right are nearly ready to shed pollen; the female cone at the left is a year older. It has reached its full size, but the seeds are not quite ripe.

times only 4 or 5 cm. long. Associated with *Z. pygmaea*, but in soil not quite so bad, is *Z. kickxii*. It is quite possible that *Z. pygmaea* might become *Z. kickxii* under equally favorable conditions. The largest species of *Zamia* are arborescent, and have leaves over a meter in length.

THE EASTERN CYCADS

The remaining five genera are oriental. Two of them, *Macrozamia* and *Bowenia*, are confined to Australia, while a third genus, *Cycas*, is abundant in Australia, but extends beyond through various islands, touching India and China, and reaching its northernmost limit in the southern part of Japan. The other two genera, *Encephalartos* and *Stangeria*, belong exclusively to South Africa.

Fig. 59.—*Macrozamia denisoni:* this large plant 18 feet (5.5 meters) in height, is on Tambourine Mountain, near Brisbane, Australia. The residents call it the "Great Grandfather Peter Tree."—From a photograph by Miss HILDA GEISSMANN.

Macrozamia.—*Macrozamia* is abundant from New South Wales to the northernmost part of Queensland (fig. 59). SCHUSTER[510] allows it 9 species; but there are certainly more, some of them, like *M. fraseri*, with its unique cones, and *M. macdonnellii*, with its immense seeds, being very sharply marked.

Perhaps the most variable species is *Macrozamia spiralis*. At Avoca, near Sydney, it forms almost impenetrable thickets, extending almost to the high-tide line of the ocean. New South Wales has

FIG. 60.—*Macrozamia moorei:* a poisoned specimen at Springsure, Queensland, Australia, showing the notch and the hole into which arsenic was placed to kill the plant.—After CHAMBERLAIN.[116]

several other species, bearing more or less resemblance to *M. spiralis* and probably related to it. Some of them extend as far west as the Blue Mountains. All of these have tuberous, more or less subterranean, stems. The most abundant species with a tuberous stem, north of this region, is *M. miquelii*, in Queensland. It is at its best around Rockhampton and Byfield.

The arborescent species flourish in Queensland. *Macrozamia denisoni*, on Tambourine Mountain, has been called the most beautiful of all cycads. It is often more than 2 meters high. *M. hopei* is the tallest of all cycads, reaching a height of nearly 20 meters. It is found in northeastern Queensland.

Macrozamia moorei, at Springsure, in Queensland, about 200 miles west of Rockhampton, is one of the most remarkable of all cycads. The range is limited, but plants are so abundant within that range that they cause great havoc among cattle, which eat the poisonous green leaves (fig. 60).

Fig. 61.—*Bowenia serrulata:* a fully grown plant at Byfield, near Rockhampton, Australia.

In the western part of Australia, *Macrozamia fraseri* may be the only species. It is tuberous or short stemmed and both micro- and megasporophylls are prolonged into spines, sometimes as much as 15 cm. long, giving the cones a very characteristic appearance.

Bowenia.—This is another genus strictly confined to Australia and, as far as we know, not occurring outside of Queensland. There are two species, *Bowenia serrulata*, at its best around Byfield and Maryvale, near Rockhampton, and *B. spectabilis*, in the Cairns region. The bipinnate leaves mark it off sharply from all other cycads (fig. 61).

Cycas.—This genus, like the American genus *Zamia*, has a wide distribution, its various species ranging beyond Australia into the

Fig. 62.—*Cycas media:* a female plant with ripe seeds, at Frenchman's Creek, on the farm of Mr. Sydney W. Snell, near Rockhampton, Australia. The trees are Eucalyptus (November, 1911).

islands north, even to the southern part of Japan; while a couple of species are found on the mainland of India and China, and one even in Madagascar.

The dominant species in Australia is *Cycas media*, most abundant around Rockhampton, but found along the Burnett and Dawson rivers, at Cape Upstart, Rockingham Bay, and Mount Elliott. It is a tall species, 2–3 meters in height, with occasional specimens reaching 6 meters (fig. 62).

Cycas kennedyana is found in the Normanby Ranges near Port Denison, and *C. normanbyana* in the mountains about the mouth of the Burdekin River. *C. cairnsiana* is in the Newcastle Range.

FIG. 63.—*Encephalartos friderici-guilielmi:* on the mountain overlooking Queenstown, South Africa. The low plant at the left is *Aloe ferox.* The big rock is dolerite.— From CHAMBERLAIN, *The Living Cycads*[120] (University of Chicago Press).

The four species just mentioned are endemic in Queensland. Three others have been described from western Australia. They are not very well known, and SCHUSTER[510] lists them as varieties of *Cycas media*.

North of Australia, in the various islands and on the mainland of China and India, are several species, some of them none too well defined. Among these, *Cycas circinalis* is the most widely distributed, and may be the most variable. It is so popular in cultivation that reported habitats need to be checked.

Widely separated from the other species is *Cycas madagascariensis*, in Madagascar. It looks like the variable *C. circinalis*.

The best known of all cycads, and the most widely cultivated, is the Japanese *Cycas revoluta*. It is endemic in the southernmost part of Japan, and is at its best around Kagoshima. It is so well marked that it is easily recognizable. In cultivation it is the most popular of all cycads, and is so hardy that it might easily become established in such places as Southern California and around the Gulf of Mexico.

Fig. 64.—*Encephalartos latifrons:* at Trapp's Valley, near Grahamstown, South Africa (February, 1912). The two cycads at the left were said not to have grown "any" in the past 40 years; the two at the right—*Encephalartos altensteinii*—were said to have grown, in that time, "about six inches."

While SCHUSTER[510] recognizes only eight species in this genus, there are doubtless more and perhaps even twice this number.

The remaining genera, *Encephalartos* and *Stangeria*, are endemic in South Africa.

Encephalartos.—There are at least 14 species of this dominant African genus, most of them in Cape Colony. *Encephalartos altensteinii*, the most familiar species in cultivation, is abundant and is found around East London, at Kentani in the Transkei, at Trapps Valley, at Kranz Kloof and other places near Durban, and as far north as Mozambique. *E. villosus* is rather abundant in the East London region, growing in the bush veldt, while *E. altensteinii* grows in rocky places in the open. It is also abundant at Kentani and occurs in Pondoland and Uganda. *E. hildebrandtii*, which resembles *E. villosus*, is farther north, extending as far as Mombasa. *E. friderici guilelmi* makes a great display on the mountains near Queens-

FIG. 65.—*Stangeria paradoxa:* near Mtunzini, Zululand, South Africa (January, 1912).—From CHAMBERLAIN, *The Living Cycads*[120] (University of Chicago Press).

town and, farther south, on the Windvogelberg at Cathcart (fig. 63). At Junction Farm at the junction of the Zwartkei and Greatkei rivers, it is associated with *E. lehmannii*, and, in the brush, there are occasional specimens of *E. villosus*. *E. caffer* makes its greatest display at van Staadens, near Port Elizabeth. *E. horridus*, a very characteristic species, is abundant at Uitenhage, not far from Port Elizabeth. *E. latifrons*, a remarkable, slow-growing species, is not abundant anywhere, but scattered specimens occur at Trapps Valley, a short distance southeast from Grahamstown (fig. 64). *E. barteri* belongs to tropical Southwest Africa, where it is found along the lower part of the Niger River. *E. septentrionalis*, the northernmost species, is in central Africa in the Niam-Niam region.

Information is rapidly accumulating for a much more thorough and accurate account of the geographical distribution of this genus than has been written.

Stangeria paradoxa.—The final genus of the family, *Stangeria*, was long classed with the ferns, being so near like *Lomaria*, a common tropical genus of the Polypodiaceae, that it was not even described as a separate genus (fig. 65). When seeds were discovered, it was named *Stangeria* and was given the specific name because it looked like a fern but was not a member of that assemblage. It is abundant in Zululand, and may occur a little farther north, and extends to the neighborhood of Port Elizabeth. It is probably monotypic, although forms growing in the bush veldt and those in the grass veldt look different. It does not get very far from the coast. In Zululand it is associated with *Encephalartos brachyphyllus*, and, in the East London region, with *E. villosus* and *E. altensteinii*.

CHAPTER V

CYCADALES—*Continued*

THE LIFE-HISTORY

Studies of the life-histories of extinct plants are necessarily incomplete because the preservation is never perfect, and delicate parts, like the gametophytes, the young embryos, and the meristems, have usually decayed before fossilization began. Consequently, the parts best known are the mature vascular structures and the harder parts of sporangia and seeds.

In the living cycads, life-history studies are handicapped only by the difficulty in getting material. There are stages in the life-history when collections should be made almost every day; for other stages, once a week is often enough; and for more than half of the year, once a month is sufficient. Since the material is tropical or subtropical, and trained histologists in those localities are scarce, the difficulty is not in the existence of material, but in securing a well-fixed series of stages. Of course, one can fix his own material, but financial considerations prevent botanists from staying a year in a cycad locality. However, cycads are easy to transport, and large cones may be in fine condition three weeks after being taken from the plant.

THE SPOROPHYTE—VEGETATIVE

The vegetative features of the life-history will be considered under the topics, "stem," "leaf," and "root."

The stem.—The cycads have sometimes been described as plants with branched leaves and unbranched stems. All have branched leaves, but there is considerable branching in the stem.

The typical habit is an unbranched stem with a crown of leaves at the top, so that the plant looks like a small palm or tree-fern (fig. 66; see also fig. 54). All of the arborescent forms are called palms by the natives. *Dioon* is the Palma de Dolores; *Microcycas* is Palma Corcha; *Encephalartos* is the Bread Palm; etc. Even in localities where tree-ferns are familiar objects, the natives do not call them ferns.

Adult plants of *Dioon, Ceratozamia, Microcycas*, and *Cycas* are always arborescent; *Bowenia* and *Stangeria* are tuberous, with all or most of the stem subterranean; while in *Zamia, Macrozamia*, and *Encephalartos*, some species are arborescent and others tuberous.

The tallest of all cycads is *Macrozamia hopei*. The Queensland botanist, F. M. BAILEY, gave the height as "20 to 60 feet," a little more than 18 meters. A similar height assigned to *Cycas media*, in

FIG. 66.—*Macrozamia moorei:* at Springsure; about 200 miles west of Rockhampton, Queensland, Australia (November, 1911).

ENGLER'S *Pflanzenfamilien*, was a mistake, since *Cycas media* does not reach more than one-third of that height. Someone probably saw the tall *Macrozamia*, thought it was *Cycas*, and so started the mistake.

Dioon spinulosum grows in the dense rainy forest and is 6–10 meters high, with occasional specimens reaching a height of 15 meters. *Microcycas calocoma* sometimes reaches a height of nearly 10 meters. None of the other genera are nearly so tall. Any arborescent cycad more than 2 meters in height may be regarded as a tall specimen.

The trunk in all of the arborescent forms is covered by an armor of leaf bases (fig. 67). The leaf does not fall off as in most deciduous plants, but loses its leaflets, bends down, and decays to a point a few centimeters from the cortex, when an abscission layer appears and cuts the rachis off cleanly, leaving a few centimeters of it to form the armor. Beneath the original abscission layer, embryonic layers ap-

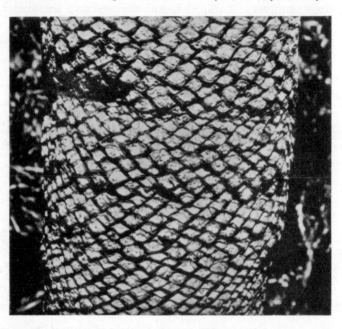

FIG. 67.—*Dioon edule:* portion of trunk of an old plant, showing armor of leaf bases. The trunk is smaller below than above. It also shows three zones, marking prolonged dormant periods.—From CHAMBERLAIN, *The Living Cycads*[120] (University of Chicago Press).

pear in succession and cut off thin membranous sheets so that finally the trunk may have a smaller diameter near the base than it has at a short distance below the crown.

In most arborescent forms the scaling-off of these thin laminae does not progress far enough to obscure the original leaf bases and, consequently, the number of leaves which a plant has borne can be counted even on plants more than a thousand years old. The age in all such forms can be determined with considerable accuracy, if the duration of the crown is known. Unfortunately, this period is seldom known. People in cycad localities know that new crowns appear every year, but have not noticed how often any individual plant forms a crown. Records of conservatory plants are worthless because leaves last much longer than in the field. The duration of the crown and the average number of leaves in a crown, under natural conditions, furnish a basis for an approximate estimate of the age.

In *Dioon edule* a new crown is formed every other year, and the average number of leaves in the crown of an adult plant is about 20, so that the average is 10 leaves a year. If the number of leaf bases is 10,000, the plant is about 1,000 years old. The number of leaves produced while the plant is young is much smaller and as it reaches the coning age it may produce a cone and a crown of leaves at the same time, thus reducing its vitality so that it may go into a dormant condition, producing neither cones nor leaves for several years. It is evident that estimates made in this way are likely to be conservative.

Plants of *Dioon edule* less than 2 meters in height, like the specimen shown in fig. 54, may be 1,000 years old. Plants in protected ravines may be much older. *Dioon spinulosum*, more than 10 meters in height, may not be more than 200 years old.

Three plants of *Encephalartos altensteinii* and two of *E. latifrons*, in front of a residence at Trapps Valley, South Africa, under practically field conditions, had been under observation for 46 years in 1912. The owner said that the *E. altensteinii* might have grown 6 inches, but that the *E. latifrons* did not seem to have grown at all, although all of the plants had had green leaves all the time and had occasionally produced cones.

There seems to be no way of estimating the age of those tuberous forms which have no persistent armor of leaf bases. Naturally, the tuberous forms are comparatively small, but it is possible that they may reach a great age. The stem of *Bowenia serrulata* is more or less spherical, and is often 20 cm. in diameter, with occasional specimens twice that size. *Bowenia spectabilis* does not reach so great a diameter, but is often 30 cm. in length (figs. 68, 69). *Stangeria* and the tuberous species of *Zamia* have the same general shape of stem as *Bowenia spectabilis*.

The smallest of all cycads is *Zamia pygmaea*, with adult stems 1 or 2 cm. in diameter, and rarely reaching 3 cm.

In transverse section the stem shows a large pith and large cortex with a scanty zone of wood between (fig. 70). The vascular cylinder is an endarch siphonostele in the adult plant, but the seedling shows

FIG. 68.—*Bowenia spectabilis:* plant with a female cone. *a*, apogeotropic root. The elongated, fusiform stem contrasts sharply with the short, broad stem of *B. serrulata.*—After CHAMBERLAIN.[113]

FIG. 69.—*Bowenia serrulata:* short, broad stem with numerous branches at the top, some bearing male cones.—After CHAMBERLAIN.[113]

a distinct mesarch condition, and there is some centripetal wood in cone axes and in the stalks of sporophylls.

The amount of xylem in most stems is surprisingly small. A mature plant of *Zamia floridana*, with a stem 15 cm. in height and 6 cm. in diameter, had a zone of xylem 2 mm. wide. The zone of phloem had the same diameter. A plant of *Ceratozamia mexicana*, 30 cm. high and 15 cm. in diameter, had a zone of xylem 3 mm. wide and phloem 2 mm. wide. *Dioon edule*, 60 cm. tall and 21 cm. in diameter, had zones of xylem and phloem each 5 mm. in width.

Dioon spinulosum is exceptional in the amount of wood. A stem 6 meters in height and 33 cm. in diameter had a zone of wood 10 cm. in width, with phloem 1.4 cm. in width (fig. 71). What the amount of wood might be in plants with twice that height and diameter has not been determined. The strong medullary rays are a conspicuous feature of the transverse section.

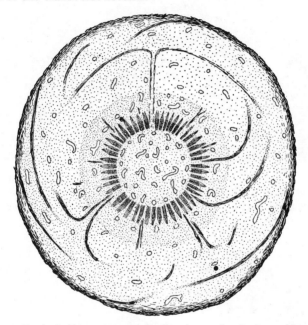

Fig. 70.—*Zamia floridana:* transverse section of stem, showing large pith and cortex and scanty zone of wood. Parts of leaf traces are also shown.

A strange feature in the anatomy of most cycad stems is the absence of growth-rings. Stems of *Zamia, Stangeria,* and *Ceratozamia,* which may be more than 50 years old, show no trace of growth-rings. On the other hand, in *Dioon spinulosum* and in *D. edule,* growth-rings are so well marked that they can be seen and counted without a lens (fig. 72). The rings are formed by a persistent cambium and they look like the familiar annual rings of dicotyls, but they are not annual or even seasonal. In *D. spinulosum* they are formed every other year, the stimulus which produces a new crown of leaves making a growth-ring in the stem. In *D. edule* even the stimulus which results in the formation of a new crown of leaves or a cone is not sufficient to make a new ring, but when the plant has gone into a prolonged resting period of several years, the stimulus which brings

FIG. 71.—*Dioon spinulosum:* transverse section of trunk, showing large pith and cortex and prominent medullary rays. The growth-rings show faintly. The zone of wood is the broadest ever described in a cycad.—From CHAMBERLAIN, *The Living Cycads*[120] (University of Chicago Press).

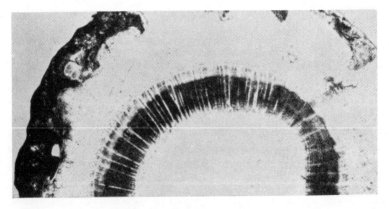

FIG. 72.—*Dioon spinulosum:* the growth-rings are quite clear at the right.—After CHAMBERLAIN.

it out of its resting period produces a new ring, so that the rings may appear at intervals of 10, 20, or even more years. The rings are due to the alternation of larger and smaller cells, as in dicotyls, but the difference in size, under the microscope, is so slight, that it might almost escape notice (fig. 73).

Stems with a vascular cylinder developed from a persistent cambium of the familiar dicotyl type are called "monoxylic." When there is more than one zone, each with xylem and phloem, the stem is polyxylic (fig. 74). *Cycas*, some species of *Macrozamia*, and some of *Encephalartos* are of this type. The zones are formed at irregular intervals of, probably, many years, and may mark the number of times the plant has had prolonged dormant periods. Where the zones succeeding the first stelar zone originate is not settled definitely. JEFFREY[303] claims they arise in the pericycle, while MILLER[394] claims that pericycle is indistinguishable from the endodermis and the rest of the cortex. SISTER HELEN ANGELA[170] found cambiums in the cortex of *Ceratozamia*, thus proving that embryonic tissue can arise in the cortex. In some angiosperms, like the beet and some other members of the Chenopodiaceae, similar zones arise from a well-marked pericycle. In *Boerhavia* (Nyctaginaceae) the zones are particularly well marked. The problem is hard to settle because it would kill a valuable plant to get material.

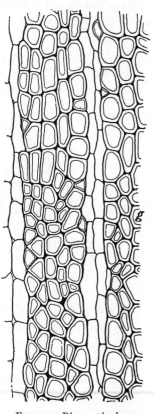

FIG. 73.—*Dioon spinulosum:* histology of the growth-rings; the slow growth, corresponding to the summer wood in an ordinary dicotyl, is at *g*.—After CHAMBERLAIN.[109]

A stem of *Cycas media*, 3 meters in height, showed at the base three zones of xylem and phloem. A piece of stem of *Cycas pectinata* Griff., 20 cm. in diameter, had 14 zones, doubtless a very high number.

The protoxylem, in seedlings, has spiral markings, but in older plants, where elongation is extremely slow, even the protoxylem consists of scalariform tracheids. The secondary xylem consists of tracheids with bordered pits, except in *Zamia* and *Stangeria*, which still retain the scalariform tracheid of their remote fern ancestry. In cone axes and in sporophylls the scalariform tracheid is also retained, but probably not without exception.

The pitting is usually multiseriate, sometimes with as many as four or five rows of pits. SIFTON,[557] in 1920, investigated pitting in the cycads and discussed the literature. He believes the bordered pit is derived from the scalariform and cites transitions in *Dioon spinulosum* as evidence. The pitting at the ends of tracheids is more primi-

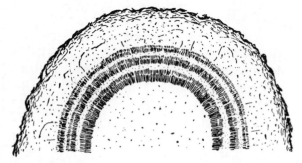

FIG. 74.—*Cycas media:* transverse section of stem, showing three zones of wood

tive than that throughout the rest of its length. He also found tertiary thickenings on the walls of tracheids, resembling those which are so characteristic of taxads. This subject will be considered more fully when dealing with the Coniferophytes.

SIFTON claims that bars of Sanio are present in both primary and secondary wood, while HALE[230] claims that they do not occur in cycads. Differences in interpretation, rather than in observation, seem to be responsible for the discrepancy.

The whole subject of markings on cell walls needs investigation, and a thorough cytological study may yield more reliable results than the usual examination of mature structures. Dr. GRACE BARKLEY'S[32] work on *Trichosanthes anguina* showed how the spiral thickening arises from the alternation of dense protoplasm with small vacuoles and less dense protoplasm with large vacuoles. That the simple pit was in some way connected with vacuoles in the proto-

plasm was already known. Intermingled with the tracheids are sometimes rows of thin-walled cells, as in *Dioon spinulosum* (fig. 75).

The rays in *Dioon spinulosum* are usually 1 cell wide, but often 2
cells, and occasionally 3 cells, wide. Longitudinally, they vary from
1 cell to 20 cells or more (fig. 76). In *Cycas media* some of the rays
are even 6 or 7 cells in width, and are correspondingly long. The
cells of the rays contain a large amount of starch but, instead of the

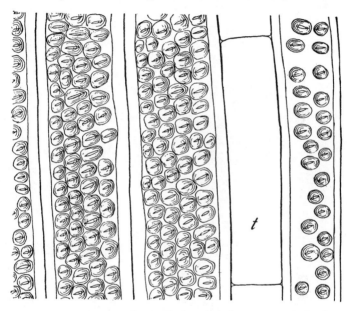

Fig. 75.—*Dioon spinulosum:* longitudinal section of mature wood, showing multiseriate bordered pits, and also one of the thin-walled cells (*t*); ×390.—After CHAMBER-
LAIN.[109]

starch, a cell may include a large crystal of calcium oxalate. The
thin-walled cells of the xylem, which also contain starch, are usually
in contact with the rays (fig. 76).

The cambium, with a little of the xylem and phloem, is shown in
fig. 77. The bast tracheids have the same width as the other cells of
the phloem. While the phloem has not been studied critically in
enough forms to warrant a generalization, it may be that such a comparative study of Cycadofilicales, Bennettitales, and Cycadales
would be worth while.

The large ray, or leaf gap, is immensely larger, in *Dioon spinulo-*
sum 20 or more cells in width and 50 or more in height. The gap contains the leaf trace and, above it, a mucilage duct (fig. 78). The re-

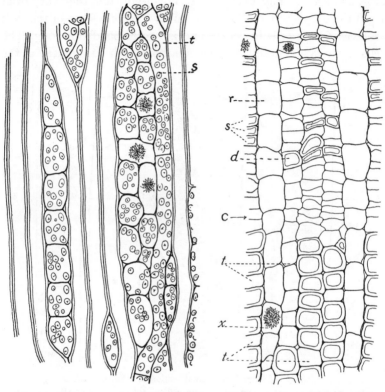

FIG. 76.—*Dioon spinulosum:* longitudinal
tangential section of mature wood, showing
thin-walled cells of the xylem (*t*) containing
starch (*s*), the xylem tracheids, and the small
medullary rays containing starch and calcium
oxalate crystals; ×125.—After CHAMBER-
LAIN.[109]

FIG. 77.—*Dioon spinulosum:* transverse section of stem, showing cambium (*c*); thin-walled cells (*t*), containing starch (*s*); calcium oxalate crystals
(*x*); phloem with some thick-walled
tracheids (*d*); and medullary rays (*r*);
×125.—After CHAMBERLAIN.[109]

ticulate arrangement of the tracheids, characteristic of the cycads,
is well shown in the figure.

The leaf trace, as it appears near the base of the leaf gap, is small,
but in the cortex the trace becomes very conspicuous. The girdling
of leaf traces in the cycads has long attracted attention, especially

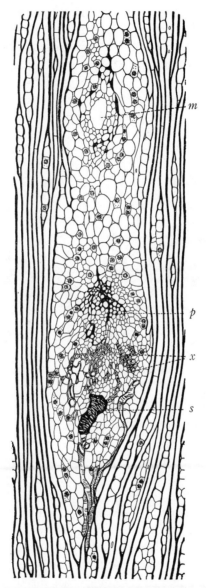

FIG. 78.—*Dioon spinulosum:* longitudinal section of mature wood, showing a leaf gap with a leaf trace connected with the base of the gap by tracheids; above the leaf trace is a mucilage canal; there are many small medullary rays, mostly one cell wide. The dark spots are calcium oxalate crystals. *m*, mucilage duct; *p* and *x*, phloem and xylem of leaf trace; *s*, scalariform tracheid.—After Dr. La Dema M. Langdon.[343]

since the Bennettitales have a leaf trace passing straight from the stele to the leaf. The most critical studies of the leaf trace have been made by THIESSEN,[614] DORETY,[172] and LANGDON,[343] (figs. 78, 79, 80, and 81). The leaf traces pass through the cortex, not horizontally, but rising a little, so that in a thin transverse section the girdling feature might be overlooked. The leaf trace often passes half-way around the stem, so that it enters the leaf almost opposite the starting place. The traces from the leaf gaps keep joining the girdling trace as it passes through the cortex, making the trace larger and

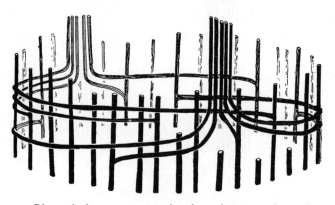

FIG. 79.—*Dioon spinulosum:* reconstruction of vascular system of stem of a seedling, showing the girdling of the leaf traces. The two groups of five bundles each (parallel at the top), are passing out to two leaves.—After SISTER HELEN ANGELA DORETY.[172]

larger as it nears the leaf. The trace, as it appears in a thick transverse section, is shown in fig. 79.

The traces consist almost entirely of scalariform tracheids. This feature and their union with the xylem of the stem is shown in fig. 81.

Such a girdling of the leaf trace is not confined to cycads, being found in many angiosperms which have "radial" leaves.

A curious feature of the stem, when one has an opportunity to see a longitudinal section of the entire trunk of a genus which has terminal cones, is the *cone dome*. The first cone borne by such a plant is actually terminal, but all succeeding cones, although apparently terminal, are really lateral. The meristem is entirely used in the formation of the cone, and a new meristem appears at the base of the peduncle, and from the new meristem crowns of leaves are formed until another cone is produced, when a new meristem appears at the base of the peduncle of the second cone, and the process is repeated every time a cone is produced (fig. 82). A median longitudinal section of the upper part of a large trunk of *Dioon spinulosum* shows very clearly these domes, each one of which was, in its turn, the apex of the plant (fig. 83). This structure, as presented diagrammatically by Dr. F. GRACE SMITH,[565] bears a striking resemblance to *Williamsonia* (*Anomozamites*) *angustifolia* (fig. 84).

Naturally, there are no cone domes in the female plant of *Cycas*, and in those species of *Macrozamia* and *Encephalartos* which have axillary cones. There should be cone domes in the male plant of *Cycas*. What the condition may be in *Encephalartos* and *Macrozamia*, when they bear a single apparently terminal cone, remains to be seen.

The leaf.—The beautiful crown of graceful leaves makes the cycad look like a palm of the *Phoenix* type, for the leaves are pinnate in all except *Bowenia*, in which they are bipinnate. In most cycads the leaves come in crowns (fig. 85). The leaves are formed in spiral succession, but it is only when the leaves are very young that there is any noticeable difference in size. In a young crown of a dozen leaves, while the oldest leaf is 30 cm. long, the youngest may measure only 4 or 5 cm.

FIG. 80.—*Dioon spinulosum:* semidiagrammatic view of vascular system of top of stem of a seedling, showing the girdling of leaf traces of the first leaf, and also how the leaf trace is built up by traces from the leaf gaps: l^2, and l^3, ventral strands apparently united with the two dorsal strands.—After Dr. LA DEMA M. LANGDON.[343]

The length of the leaf varies from about 3 meters in *Cycas circinalis* down to 5 or 6 cm. in *Zamia pygmaea*. *Dioon spinulosum* has beautiful leaves, often 2 meters in length, and in many cycads the leaves are a meter long. The number of leaflets on each side of the rachis varies from more than a hundred in species with large, long leaves down to 3 or 4 in the smallest leaves. In seedlings, even of those species which have a hundred leaflets when mature, there may be only one or two pairs of leaflets. The number then increases gradually with the age and size of the plant.

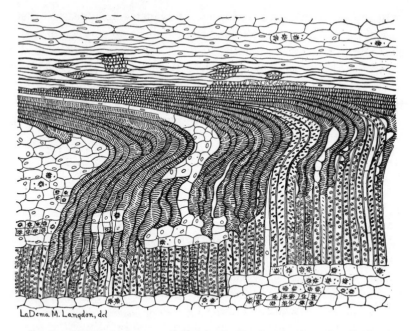

LaDema M. Langdon, del

FIG. 81.—*Dioon spinulosum:* radial longitudinal section, showing union of leaf traces with the vascular cylinder. Most of the tracheids of the leaf trace are scalariform; those of the cylinder are pitted; ×55.—After Dr. LA DEMA M. LANGDON.[343]

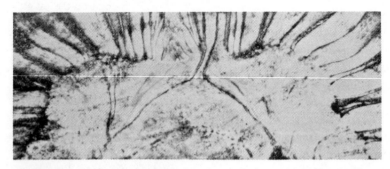

FIG. 82.—*Dioon edule:* photograph of surface view of apex of stem, showing a cone dome with its bundles going to a cone, and, to the left of it, a similar series of bundles going to the new apex, which is producing leaves; below is a cone dome with some of the bundles cut across.—After CHAMBERLAIN.[111]

Leaflets vary greatly in size. In *Ceratozamia longifolia* they reach 40 cm. in length and 2.5 cm. in width; in *Dioon spinulosum*, 8.5–20 cm. in length and 10–17 mm. in width; in *Dioon edule*, 11–15 cm. in

FIG. 83.—*Dioon spinulosum:* photograph of a surface view of the top of a large plant cut longitudinally through the middle. The second cone dome from the top shows the peduncle of the cone, and part of the peduncle can be seen in the cone dome just below it, and in the lowest cone dome; one-half natural size.—After CHAMBERLAIN.[111]

length and 4–8.5 mm. in width. The widest leaflets are those of *Zamia skinneri*, 19–29 cm. long and 3–10 cm. wide. The narrowest is in the Cuban *Zamia angustissima*, with leaflets about 7 cm. long and 1 mm. wide.

The vernation, in *Cycas*, is circinate both in the rachis and the leaflets (fig. 86). In *Zamia, Ceratozamia, Bowenia*, and *Stangeria* the rachis is somewhat circinate (subcircinate) but sometimes looks almost reflexed. In *Dioon, Macrozamia*, and *Encephelartos* both rachis and leaflets are perfectly straight (fig. 87). In the family, as a whole, there is more of the erect vernation than of the circinate, the pre-

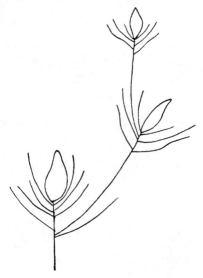

FIG. 84.—*Zamia floridana:* diagram of apex of stem, showing relation of cones, crown, and axis, with the axes much lengthened.—After Dr. F. GRACE SMITH.[565]

vailing type in ferns. It is interesting to note that both *Cycadeoidea* and *Cycadella* have the erect type of vernation.

The leaves of the various genera are so characteristic that they can be identified by this feature. SISTER MARY ALICE LAMB[336] constructed a key based entirely upon the leaf. Only two genera, *Cycas* and *Stangeria*, have a midrib in the leaflet. In *Cycas*, there is only a midrib without any side veins; while in *Stangeria* there are side veins from the midrib. *Bowenia* has a bipinnate leaf, marking it off easily from all the rest. In *Macrozamia* there is an obvious gland at the base of the leaflet in most species, and a histological examination might show it in the rest. In *Dioon* the bases of the leaflets are as wide or even wider than the middle of the leaflet. In *Microcycas*, the

FIG. 85.—*Dioon spinulosum:* new crown of leaves nearly erect; the previous crown nearly horizontal. In the greenhouse of the University of Chicago.

FIG. 86.—*Cycas revoluta:* young crown, showing circinate vernation of both rachis and leaflets. In the greenhouse of the University of Chicago.

leaflets are reflexed on the rachis. The other three are not so easy. In *Ceratozamia* the leaflets are always entire (integerrima), a character very rare in *Zamia* and found only in a part of the species of *Encephalartos*. By adding the histological characters of the leaf, any indefiniteness in the identification could be removed.

The leaflets of young and adult plants are usually quite different, so that some botanists regard the juvenile form as evidence in favor

FIG. 87.—*Dioon edule:* young crown, showing perfectly erect vernation. In the greenhouse of the University of Chicago.

of the theory of recapitulation, which means that ontogeny recapitulates phylogeny, or the history of the individual recapitulates the history of the race.

Dioon spinulosum, in the seedling and in young plants, has a leaf with a long naked petiole and lowest pair of leaflets nearly as large as the rest; while in older and adult plants the leaflets are more and more reduced until, at the base of the leaf, they are scarcely more than spines.

In *Dioon edule* leaflets of seedlings and young plants have a spiny margin, especially near the tip, while in the adult plant the margins are entire (fig. 88).

If the theory of recapitulation holds, it would mean that *Dioon spinulosum*, with its spinulose leaflets, is the ancestral form and that *D. edule* shows the spinulose leaflets, in its younger stages, on account of its spinulose ancestry.

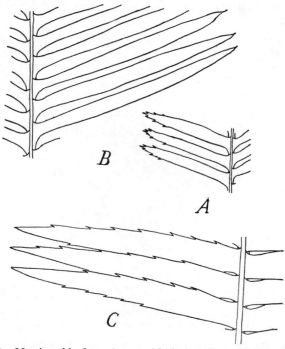

Fig. 88.—Margins of leaflets: *A*, part of leaf of seedling of *Dioon edule*, showing spiny leaflets; *B*, adult leaf with entire margins; *C*, adult leaf of *Dioon* spinulosum with spiny leaflets.—From Chamberlain, *The Living Cycads*[120] (University of Chicago Press).

In most, and perhaps all, of the cycads, the leaves of young plants differ from those of the adult, in some the change taking place after the plant is 50 or more years old. Taxonomists have been trapped into identifying two species from leaves taken from a single plant of *Encephalartos altensteinii*, just as it passes from the spiny to the entire leaflet condition. Some of the leaves, at that time, will have spiny leaflets, while in others the leaflets will be perfectly entire, as in *E. caffer*. A bud coming from a wound in an old *E. altensteinii* plant shows typically spiny leaves.

The leaves of all the cycads have a strongly xerophytic structure (fig. 89). The cells of the epidermis have thick walls and are heavily cutinized. The stomata are sunken and are mostly confined to the under surface, except in *Bowenia* and *Macrozamia*. In *Microcycas* there is not much thickening of the hypodermal cells, except above and below the bundles and near the margins of the leaflets; in *Macro-*

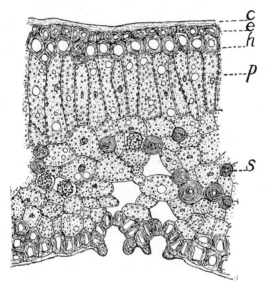

FIG. 89.—*Dioon edule:* transverse section of part of leaflet. *c*, cuticle; *e*, epidermis; *h*, hypodermis; *p*, palisade; *s*, suberized cell.—From CHAMBERLAIN, *The Living Cycads*[120] (University of Chicago Press).

zamia moorei the hypodermal cells are thick walled throughout; and in *Encephalartos altensteinii* the thick-walled hypodermal region is several cells thick.

There is usually a well-marked palisade layer and a more or less spongy parenchyma beneath. The bundles are usually surrounded by thick-walled cells, and such cells often extend from the bundle to the hypodermal cells above and below. Many of the thick-walled tracheids around the bundles, and nearly all thick-walled tracheids scattered through the thin-walled cells between bundles, are bast fibers.

Altogether, the structure is such that the leaves are strong and leathery. Many of them keep their fresh, green color a long time after being cut off from the plant, so that they are popular for decorative purposes in cycad regions, and the beautiful leaves of *Cycas revoluta* have become a standard nursery stock for funeral wreaths and for Palm Sunday.

The root.—The primary root may be very large, even as large as the stem; and in the seedling the root is much larger than the stem which, at this stage, is rather inconspicuous (fig. 90). After the seedling has become thoroughly established, the stem begins to grow more rapidly, and in the adult plant is usually much larger than the root.

Roots may attain a great length. A root of *Dioon spinulosum*, at a distance of 12 meters from the stem, hanging exposed over a rock, was still 3 cm. in diameter when it entered a crevice and could not be followed any farther.

The root is tetrarch. Secondary growth begins early and more or less irregularly, so that the topography, as seen in transverse sections, differs markedly from that of familiar dicotyl roots.

All cycads have remarkable apogeotropic roots (fig. 91). These grow up, instead of down, branch dichotomously and profusely, forming coralloid masses above ground. The vascular structure is about the same as in normal roots, but bacteria, or "bacterioids," get in very near the tip and cause some distortion, which seems to prepare the way for the entrance of a blue-green alga, *Anabaena*. The alga multiplies rapidly, so that there is a blue-green zone midway between the vascular cylinder and the epidermis (fig. 92). While the

FIG. 90.—*Dioon edule:* seedling; all the part bearing secondary roots is the primary root. The stem, bearing the leaf and scale leaves, is so small at this stage that it is hidden by the emergent part of the cotyledons. — From CHAMBERLAIN, *Elements of Plant Science*[125] (McGraw-Hill Book Co.).

zone is usually only one cell wide, the cells are so enlarged radially
that the zone is easily visible to the naked eye. These roots are almost universal in seedlings and are
much more prevalent in the greenhouse than in the field.

THE SPOROPHYTE—REPRODUCTIVE

No plants are more absolutely
dioecious than the cycads (fig. 93).
SCHUSTER reports one case in *Cycas
revoluta* where a plant was cut into
two longitudinal pieces, which were
taken to different places. It is claimed
that one piece produced a female
strobilus and the other, a male. On a
lawn in Australia there were several
plants of *Cycas revoluta*. It was reported to me that one of these produced a female strobilus and, a few
years later, a male strobilus. It is
also claimed that a bud from a female plant of *Cycas circinalis*, in the
Garfield Park Conservatory at Chicago, reached the coning stage and
produced a male cone. In 30 years
of study in the field and in green-
houses I have never seen anything
to indicate that the cycads are not
absolutely dioecious.

It will be remembered that in the
Bennettitales the strobili are prevailingly bisporangiate. The reduction from the bisporangiate condition to the dioecious is a general
tendency in plants.

FIG. 91.—*Cycas revoluta:* coralloid
masses of root tubercles on erect
(apogeotropic) roots.—From CHAM-
BERLAIN, *The Living Cycads*[120] (University of Chicago Press).

*The female strobilus.**—The largest cones that have ever existed

* The term "strobilus" is used to include both the crowns of loose sporophylls, like
the female sporophylls of *Cycas* and the male sporophylls of *Cycadeoidea*, and compact

are found in the living cycads (fig. 94). Cones of *Macrozamia denisonii* are often 70 cm. in length, with a weight of 30 kilos; and they sometimes reach a length of nearly a meter with a weight of 38 kilos. A cone of *Encephalartos caffer* in the park at Port Elizabeth, South Africa, weighed 42 kilos, and cones of this species, even when two or three are borne at the same time, reach a weight of 20 kilos. In *Dioon spinulosum* the cone reaches a length of 50 cm. and a weight of 15 kilos. The cones of *Dioon edule* are smaller, about 30 cm. in length and weighing five or six kilos. *Microcycas* has a large slender cone occasionally reaching 94 cm. in length and a weight of 9.5 kilos, but most of its cones are not nearly so long or heavy. Cones of other cycads are smaller. In *Ceratozamia* the average cone is about 26 cm. in length, and in the remaining genera considerably shorter. *Zamia pygmaea* has the smallest cones, about 2 cm. long and 1.5 cm. in diameter.

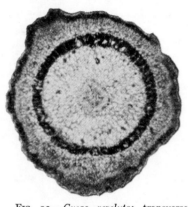

FIG. 92.—*Cycas revoluta:* transverse section of root tubercle, showing prominent algal zone; ×20.—After *Life*.[355]

The evolution of the compact cone from a loose crown of sporophylls is shown very clearly in the living cycads.

In *Cycas revoluta* the female strobilus consists of a crown of sporophylls arising spirally in acropetal succession and as loosely arranged as the male sporophylls of *Cycadeoidea* (fig. 95). The upper part of the sporophyll has numerous leaflets, one or two of which are occasionally replaced by small ovules. The ovules are not transformed leaflets, but the leaflet is probably very much shortened, and bears a terminal ovule. Below the leafy portion there are usually three pairs of ovules, sometimes two pairs, and occasionally four pairs. Both sporophylls and ovules are covered with yellowish hairs, but as the

cones. As long as the terms "male" and "female" are applied to the $2x$ generation in animals, there should be no objection to applying the same terms to the corresponding generation in plants.

ovules get large, some of the hairs are lost, and the ripe seeds have a soft orange-red color.

In the various species of *Cycas* there can be traced a gradual reduction in the size of the sporophyll, a reduction of the leaflets until the sporophyll has merely a serrate margin, and a reduction in the number of ovules to a single pair, the number characteristic of all the other genera (figs. 96 and 97).

FIG. 93.—*Dioon edule:* two male plants at the left and a female plant at the right. Chavarrillo, Mexico (September, 1906). The taller plants, to the top of the leaves, are about 7 feet high.—From CHAMBERLAIN, *Elements of Plant Science*[125] (McGraw-Hill Book Co.).

In *Dioon edule* the sporophylls have lost even the serration, but are broad and loosely compacted into a cone (fig. 98). The final stage, with much reduced sporophylls and very compact cone, is well illustrated by *Zamia* (fig. 99).

The various genera show various reductions from the leafy character to a peltate sporophyll bearing scarcely any resemblance to a leaf (fig. 100). In *Macrozamia* the rachis of the sporophyll remains as a more or less prolonged, tapering spine, especially in the upper part of the cone. In *Ceratozamia* and *Encephalartos* the terminal

part of the rachis is suppressed, but there are often serrations representing the pinnae. In the rest, reduction has gone still farther, so
that the sporophyll is merely a thick peltate structure bearing scarcely any resemblance to a leaf.

Fig. 94.—*Macrozamia denisoni:* female cone nearly a meter (37 inches) long, and
weighing 38.5 kilos (85 pounds).—From a photo taken on Tambourine Mountain, near
Brisbane, Australia, by Miss Hilda Geissmann.

It will be remembered that in the Bennettitales the strobili are
prevailingly bisporangiate. The reduction from the bisporangiate
condition to the dioecious is a general tendency in plants. The re-

duction of the sporophyll from the leafy condition to the peltate structure, which reaches its extreme in *Zamia*, can be traced in great detail through the various genera and species of the living cycads.

There is no doubt that *Cycas revoluta* shows the most primitive sporophyll condition in the family, producing a crown of sporophylls just as it, and the other cycads, produce a crown of foliage leaves, still leaving in the center a meristem to produce more leaves or

FIG. 95.—*Cycas revoluta:* strobilus consisting of a loose crown of sporophylls still retaining many pinnae in the upper portion.

sporophylls. Thus, the original meristem continues from the embryo to the death of the plant. Proliferation is seen, occasionally, at the top of a male cone, and sometimes in other genera, where vegetative leaves, greatly reduced, but sometimes bearing leaflets, appear instead of sporophylls.

The megasporangium.—The megasporangia, or ovules* as they are usually called, are all erect and have a single massive integument. In *Cycas circinalis* and *Macrozamia denisonii* they reach a length of

* The term "ovule" (little egg) was mistakenly devised to apply to the entire megasporangium. It is short, convenient, and in general use but, like the term "cell," has nothing else to recommend it.

6 cm., about the size of the largest seeds of *Trigonocarpus*. Most cycads have seeds from 3 to 5 cm. in length. *Zamia kickxii* has very small seeds, only a centimeter long, while *Zamia pygmaea*, with seeds from 5 to 7 mm. in length, has the smallest which have been measured.

The principal features of the ovule are well illustrated by a longitudinal section (fig. 101). Only the upper part of the nucellus is free

Fig. 96.—*Cycas circinalis:* crown of sporophylls not yet expanded. The apex of the sporophyll has become merely serrate, there are no separate pinnae, as in *Cycas revoluta*.

from the integument. After the ovule reaches its full size, as in the illustration, the stony layer, with a fleshy layer on each side of it, is very conspicuous. Later, as the female gametophyte grows, it absorbs most of the inner fleshy layer, so that it disappears, except as a dry papery membrane closely applied to the megaspore membrane. Usually two strong vascular strands enter the ovule. The outer

FIG. 97.—*Cycas circinalis:* a later stage, after sporophylls have expanded.—Garfield Park Conservatory, Chicago.

strands branch immediately, before they reach the level of the stony layer, and, from that point, extend almost to the micropyle without any further branching. The number of these outer bundles is quite

FIG. 98.—*Dioon edule:* sporophylls loosely compacted into a cone, 30 cm. in length.—After CHAMBERLAIN.[108]

constant for any species and usually does not exceed a dozen. The inner strands, after reaching the inner fleshy layer, fork repeatedly so that they are much more numerous than the outer bundles (fig.

102). Usually they end before they reach the nucellus, but sometimes extend beyond the free portion of the nucellus into the inner fleshy layer of the integument.

The outer fleshy layer remains fleshy and, in the ripe seed, becomes variously colored, bright red in *Encephalartos altensteinii*,

FIG. 99.—*Zamia floridana:* a very compact cone, with megasporophylls so regularly arranged that they appear to be in vertical rows.

pale yellowish in *Encephalartos horridus*, orange-red in *Zamia floridana*, blood red in *Zamia latifoliolata*, salmon pink in *Microcycas*, and nearly white in *Dioon* and *Ceratozamia*. The color seems to be constant for any given species.

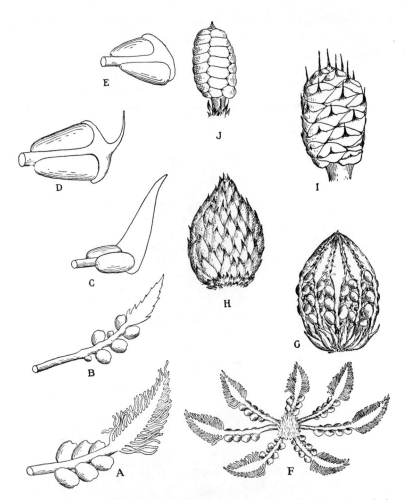

Fɪɢ. 100.—Diagram showing the reduction of the megasporophyll and the evolution of the cone. *A, Cycas revoluta,* with leaflike megasporophyll; *F*, megasporophylls in a loose crown, not compacted into a cone; *B, Cycas media,* leaflets of the megasporophyll reduced to serrations; *G*, the grouping of megasporophylls in early stages makes the crown of sporophylls look like a cone; *C, Dioon edule,* the leaflet character is lost, and *G*, the sporophylls, are compacted into a loose cone; *D, Macrozamia miquelii,* the midrib of the leaf represented by a spine, and *I*, the sporophyll compacted into a tight cone; *E, Zamia floridana,* sporophylls with hardly any resemblance to a leaf, and *J*, compacted into a very tight cone.—From Cʜᴀᴍʙᴇʀʟᴀɪɴ, *Elements of Plant Science*[125] (McGraw-Hill Book Co.).

The upper part of the ovule, at the time of fertilization, is shown in detail in a later figure (fig. 147). This figure shows the nucellus with pollen tubes which have digested their way completely through. The sharp beak is characteristic. At this stage the inner fleshy layer has become a thin, dry membrane, sticking to the inner border of the stony layer. There are many mucilage ducts in the outer fleshy layer and many cells (shaded in the drawing) filled with tannin.

The younger stages in the development of the ovule have not been studied very thoroughly on account of the difficulty in getting material. In most cycads these stages occur while the young cone is still covered by scale leaves and there is uncertainty whether a cone or a crown of leaves is developing. Naturally, in conservatories, it would be difficult or impossible to get permission to cut out the top of a rare plant. There are few, if any, trained histologists in cycad regions, and when a histologist reaches such a place, on a hasty trip, the young stages might not be available. The most thorough study was made by Dr. F. GRACE SMITH,[565] who, after sending repeatedly and getting little except to learn the approximate time for various stages, went and spent a month in the *Zamia floridana* region, and fixed material. Previously, LANG[341] had figured a row of three cells in *Stangeria*, the lowest of which was cer-

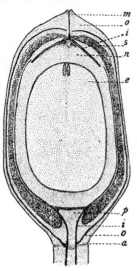

FIG. 101.—*Dioon edule:* longitudinal section of ovule, shortly after pollination; *m*, micropyll; *n*, nucellus; *e*, endosperm; *s*, stony layer; *p*, basal papilla; *i*, inner vascular bundles; *o*, outer vascular bundles; *a*, abscission layer; ×2.—After CHAMBERLAIN.[106]

tainly a megaspore, and TREUB[645] had found a similar stage in *Ceratozamia*. Dr. SMITH found, quite regularly, a row of four megaspores in *Zamia*, three of which aborted, while the fourth germinated and formed the functioning female gametophyte (figs. 103, 104, 105).

The formation of the megaspore brings to a close the 2x generation, which in all plants, from the Bryophytes up, and also in many Thallophytes, is also the sporophyte generation. The reduction of chromosomes, which, of course, takes place during the formation of megaspores from the megaspore mother cell, has not yet been described, but counts in microsporogenesis and in other phases of the life-history have constantly shown that the x and $2x$ numbers are 12 and 24.

As the megaspore germinates, the cells next to the developing female gametophyte become differentiated into a layer of "spongy tissue," looking like sporogenous tissue on account of the dense cell

Fig. 102.—*Dioon edule: A*, transverse section of ovule near the middle; *B*, inner vascular system, treated with eosin and photographed after the female gametophyte and part of the inner fleshy layer had been removed; *C*, ovule photographed from above; *o*, outer bundles (the eosin has diffused some in *A*, and considerably in *C*); *m*, micropyle; *s*, stony layer; *i*, inner vascular system; *p*, basal papilla; *e*, female gametophyte; *n*, inner fleshy layer; ×2.—After CHAMBERLAIN.[106]

contents. This layer nourishes the gametophyte in early stages, then weakens and finally becomes almost indistinguishable. Such a layer, very highly developed in cycads, is prevalent in gymnosperms.

The male strobilus (fig. 106).—The male, or microsporangiate, strobilus is not so large as the female and there are no leafy sporophylls like the megasporophylls of *Cycas revoluta*. All of the strobili are compact cones, even in *Cycas*. Occasionally there is a slight proliferation of the axis, producing a few much reduced leaves, but the cone ripens, dies, and any further development comes from a new meristem. This applies to stems bearing a single terminal cone, as in *Dioon* and many others. When cones are axillary, as in *Macrozamia moorei*, the original apical meristem persists from the embryo to the death of the plant.

While the cones do not reach the great length and weight of some of the female cones, they are nevertheless the largest living male

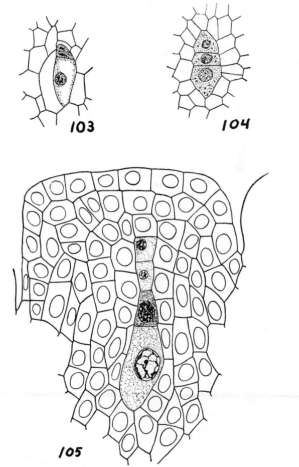

FIGS. 103–105.—Megaspores of cycads. Fig. 103, *Stangeria paradoxa;* the lower cell of the row of three is the functioning megaspore; ×250.—After LANG.[341] Fig. 104, *Ceratozamia mexicana*, similar stage; ×266—After TREUB.[645] Fig. 105, *Zamia floridana*, row of four megaspores; ×930.—After Dr. F. GRACE SMITH.[565]

cones and are probably larger than those of their geological ancestors.

The largest cone described is that of *Macrozamia denisonii*, which in extreme cases reaches a length of 80 cm. and a diameter 20 cm.

In *Encephalartos altensteinii* the longest reported was 60 cm., with a diameter of 12 cm. Other measurements are, *Cycas circinalis*, 45 cm.; *Cycas revoluta*, 40; *Dioon spinulosum*, 40; *Dioon edule*, 30; *Dioon purpusii*, 20; *Zamia floridana*, 10; *Bowenia serrulata*, 5; and *Zamia pygmaea*, 2 cm.

These are the maximum measurements. The average cones are not much more than half as long. Measurements of the same cone, taken 48 hours apart, might be very different; for just before shedding the pollen, the cone elongates immensely and rapidly, so that the sporangia are freely exposed.

The microsporophylls are spirally arranged in acropetal succession, but the arrangement is so absolutely regular that, in surface view, they often look as if they were in vertical rows, like the grains of corn on a cob (fig. 107, and see also fig. 106).

FIG. 106.—*Dioon edule:* male cone, photographed at Chavarrillo, a short distance east of Jalapa, Mexico. September, 1906. One-third natural size. After CHAMBERLAIN.[108]

While the arrangement is spiral and acropetal, so that the sporophylls at the top are the last to be formed, they are the first to ripen their pollen, probably because the ripening depends largely upon drying, and

these sporophylls are farthest from the water supply. A large
cone may shed its pollen from the upper sporophylls several

FIG. 107.—*Zamia portoricensis:* male cones of various ages on one plant. The microsporophylls, although in strictly spiral arrangement, look as if they were in vertical
rows. The University of Chicago greenhouse (January, 1933).

days before the lower ones dehisce (fig. 108). Like the cones, the
microsporophylls vary greatly in size; in *Cycas circinalis*, from 3 to 5
cm. in length and from 12 to 23 mm. in width; in *Dioon edule*, from

10 to 28 mm. in length and 7 to 19 mm. in width; in *Ceratozamia mexicana*, from 10 to 15 mm. in length and 7 to 8 mm. in width; in *Zamia floridana*, about 6 mm. long and 5 mm. wide; and in *Zamia pygmaea*, about 4 mm. long and 3 mm. wide.

FIG. 108.—*Encephalartos villosus:* top of male cone, with sporophylls at the top spreading apart and exposing the sporangia. The University of Chicago greenhouse.— From a photograph by SEDGWICK.

The microsporangia.—The sporangia, always on the abaxial surface of the sporophyll, are arranged radially in sori, the number varying from 5 in the *Cycas* region of the family down to 2 or 3, with occasional single sporangia in the *Zamia* end of the family (figs. 109, 110).

The sorus arrangement is the typical fern arrangement. There are no "synangia," like those of all the Marattiaceae except *Angiopteris*.

The number of sporangia on a sporophyll is largest in the *Cycas* region, and decreases to the *Zamia* end of the family. The numbers of sporangia on a sporophyll, averaged from several counts are as follows: *Cycas media*, 1,160; *Dioon spinulosum*, 770; *Encephalartos caffer*, 567; *Macrozamia miquelii*, 503; *Dioon edule*, 295; *Microcycas calocoma*, 245; *Cera-tozamia mexicana*, 191; *Stangeria paradoxa*, 153; *Bowenia serrulata*, 67; and *Zamia flori-dana*, 25. Sporophylls near the top and near the bottom of the cone have fewer sporangia, in *Zamia*, often only 2 or 3 on each side, with a sterile area between. By hunting, one can sometimes find a sporophyll with only one microsporangium on each side, so that it looks like a small megasporophyll with its two ovules. The more reduced sporophylls at the extreme top and bottom of the cone are entirely sterile.

Fig. 109.—*Dioon edule:* side view and view of ab-axial surface. The sori are mostly in fours and threes; ×⅘.—After CHAMBERLAIN.[108]

In histological structure the microsporangia bear a striking resemblance to those of *Angiopteris* (figs. 111, 112). In both, the spores are very numerous, the stalk is massive, there are several layers of wall cells between the epidermis and tapetum, dehiscence is similar, and there is some ramentum. In the cycad, the ramentum is unicellular, with rarely a cross wall; while in the fern, two or three cross walls are common. The tapetum consists of very small cells in the cycad and of rather large ones in the fern. The structure of the sporangia, in both cases, is much like that of the eusporangiate ferns and of the Cycadofilicales of the Carboniferous. In all the cycads the microsporangium is strictly unilocular, in striking contrast with the multilocular (synangium) type of the Bennettitales.

The development of the sporangium is of the eusporangiate type. There is a hypodermal archesporial cell or, in large sporangia, there may be a row or plate; the archesporial cell divides, forming a primary wall cell and a primary sporogenous cell; from these, the thick wall and numerous sporogenous cells are produced. The tapetum becomes clearly distinguishable rather late, so that it cannot always be determined with certainty whether it is coming from the progeny of the primary wall cell or from that of the primary sporogenous cell. But, whatever its origin may be, it is in contact with spores which it is to nourish.

As the spore mother-cells enlarge, the tapetum breaks down and appears as a mass of nucleated protoplasm surrounding the growing mother-cells, which absorb not only the tapetum but also the wall cells between the tapetum and the epidermis. The epidermal cells become very much thickened, especially at the bottom and along the sides, while remaining thin at the top, where the cell contents break through and escape (fig. 113).

FIG. 110.—*Ceratozamia mexicana:* four microsporophylls; *a*, with sporangia not yet dehisced; *b*, sporangia at the upper part dehisced and the pollen still holding together in balls; *c*, later stage, with nearly all of the pollen shed. The sorus arrangement (mostly threes) is more easily seen in the later stages; ×2.—After CHAMBERLAIN.[112]

The spore mother-cells round off and each divides twice to form four microspores, thus bringing the $2x$, or sporophyte, generation to a close and initiating the x, or gametophyte generation. In the first mitosis 12 pairs of chromosomes are easily distinguished, and in the anaphase of the second division the number 12 is easily counted.

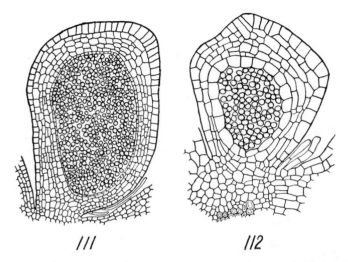

/// 112

FIG. 111.—*Dioon edule:* longitudinal section of microsporangium, showing numerous microspores and typical structure of a eusporangiate sporangium. Two ramental hairs, each with one transverse wall, are shown on the lower left part of the sporangium.— From CHAMBERLAIN, *The Living Cycads*[120] (University of Chicago Press).

FIG. 112.—*Angiopteris evecta:* a typical eusporangiate sporangium, much like that of the carboniferous Cycadofilicales.—From CHAMBERLAIN, *The Living Cycads*[120] (University of Chicago Press).

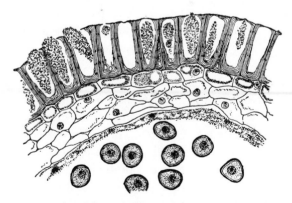

FIG. 113.—*Stangeria paradoxa:* section of part of microsporangium with micro-spores. The cell walls of the outer layer are becoming very thick; the tapetal cells have broken down into a tapetal plasmodium. Finally, all the cells between the spores and the outer layer will be absorbed by the growing microspores.

CHAPTER VI

CYCADALES—*Continued*

The reduction of chromosomes, in both megaspore mother-cells and in microspore mother-cells, brings back the original x number, which is the only number in plants below the level of sexuality. Since the terms gametophyte and sporophyte are coincident with x and $2x$ generations, in plants from the Hepaticae through the angiosperms, and in many Thallophytes, students are likely to think the terms are synonymous. It is customary to call the x generation the gametophyte because, in the higher plants, it produces only gametes; and the $2x$ generation, the sporophyte, because, in the higher plants, it is the only generation producing spores.

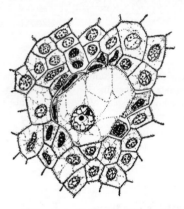

Fig. 114.—*Zamia floridana:* Enlarging megaspore; ×930.—After Dr. F. Grace Smith.[566]

THE FEMALE GAMETOPHYTE

The megaspore is the first cell of the female gametophyte. It enlarges considerably, absorbing some of the neighboring cells before it divides (fig. 114). By the time the first division of the nucleus has been completed, there is a great change in the surrounding cells, which form a layer, quite common in gymnosperms, called "spongy tissue" by Strasburger (fig. 115). The earlier free nuclear divisions are simultaneous, and the nuclei are crowded outward by a large central vacuole, so that most of the protoplasm, containing the free nuclei, is in a thin peripheral layer (fig. 116). Free nuclear division, in *Dioon edule*, continues until there are about 1,000 free nuclei, before walls begin to form.

Cell walls appear first at the periphery, and wall formation proceeds toward the center until the entire gametophyte becomes cellular (fig. 117). Long before the cellular stage is reached, a nutritive layer, one or two cells thick, is developed in contact with the gametophyte. It has been called the endosperm jacket, and is so conspicuous that it can be seen with the naked eye. It is shown in both the preceding figures. It functions like a tapetum, passing nutritive material from the cells next to it into the growing gametophyte.

The arrangement of cells in the young gametophyte is extremely regular, radiating from the center to the periphery, as shown in fig. 117.

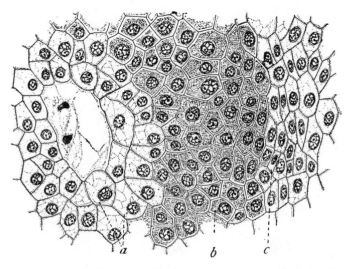

FIG. 115.—*Zamia floridana:* First division of megaspore; *a*, actively nutritive cells; *b*, tissue of closely packed cells; *c*, flattened cells; ×930.—After Dr. F. GRACE SMITH.[566]

Soon after this stage, when the gametophyte has reached a diameter of about 3 mm., some of the cells at the micropylar end become larger, and their nuclei move from their central position to the peripheral end of the cell (figs. 118–122). These are archegonium initials. They are very numerous in comparison with the number which develop up to the fertilization stage. In most of them the nucleus does not divide at all, and, in *Dioon edule*, not more than ten ever reach the fertilization stage, and the usual numbers are only three, four or five. In other cycads there may be a couple more or a couple less. *Microcycas* is exceptional. CALDWELL[88] found scores, and some-

times hundreds of archegonia, some of them on the sides of the gametophyte, and some even at the base. They are often as crowded as
in the Cupressaceae. Dr. LILLIAN REYNOLDS,[470] studying the development of the archegonia in *Microcycas*, found the large numbers
reported by CALDWELL, but found that only the group at the micropylar end of the gametophyte progressed up to the ventral canal
mitosis, and that only in connection with this group was there any
archegonial chamber.

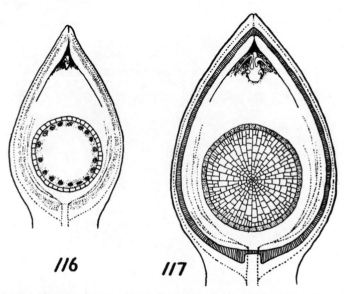

FIG. 116.—*Dioon edule:* ovule soon after pollination, free nuclear stage of the female
gametophyte.—From CHAMBERLAIN, *The Living Cycads*[120] (University of Chicago
Press).

FIG. 117.—*Dioon edule:* the female gametophyte has become cellular throughout.—
From CHAMBERLAIN, *The Living Cycads*[120] (University of Chicago Press).

In *Dioon edule* the archegonium initials can be seen early in November (figs. 118–122). They soon divide, forming the central cell
and the primary neck cell, which divides almost immediately, so that
December material shows the two neck cells characteristic of all the
cycads.

The central cell enlarges rapidly without a corresponding increase
in the amount of protoplasm. Consequently, there is a large vacuole

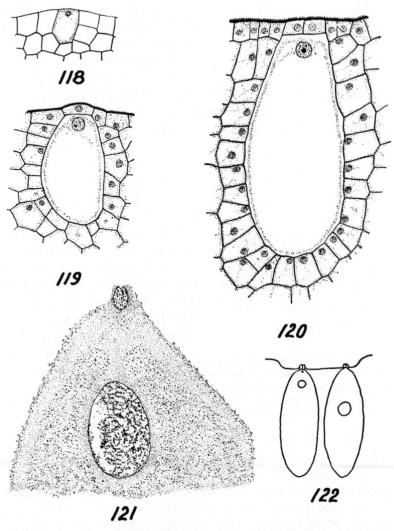

Figs. 118–122.—*Dioon edule:* development of the archegonium: fig. 118, archegonium initial; fig. 119, primary neck cell and central cell; fig. 120, the two neck cells; fig. 121, nucleus of central cell has divided, forming the ventral canal nucleus and the egg nucleus; fig. 122, mature archegonia showing archegonial chamber; figs. 118–120, ×98; fig. 121, ×50, fig. 122, ×8.—From CHAMBERLAIN, *The Living Cycads*[120] (University of Chicago Press).

pressing the protoplasm against the wall of the cell. This single large vacuole is filled with a colorless sap. Material from the outside passes into the central cell, the amount of protoplasm increases rapidly, and soon the entire cell is filled with a beautifully vacuolate protoplasm, with very large vacuoles in the central portion and smaller and smaller ones toward the periphery. There is a gradual gradation in the size of vacuoles from the large ones, more than 500 microns in diameter, down to the smallest ones, which can be seen with a 1.5 mm. oil immersion objective and a 20× eyepiece; and probably the gradation continues beyond the resolving power of present-day microscopes.

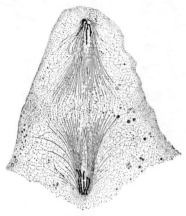

The central cell and its nucleus grow for about 6 months before the nucleus divides, the division taking place about the middle of April. The achromatic figure in this division is rather scanty, and there is not the slightest trace of the formation of a cell wall between the two nuclei (fig. 123).

Fig. 123.—*Dioon edule:* mitosis giving rise to the ventral canal nucleus and egg nucleus, showing that there is no cell plate between the two nuclei; ×350.—After Chamberlain.[106]

The ventral canal nucleus soon disorganizes, and, at the time of fertilization, is usually unrecognizable. Occasionally, however, it enlarges and goes through the same kind of development as the egg nucleus. Sedgwick[537] observed several cases of this sort in *Encephalartos villosus*, and suggested that the egg nucleus might be fertilized by the ventral canal nucleus, as has been observed several times in *Ginkgo, Pinus,* and *Picea.* The fact that embryos have been found in conservatory material where no male cones were present, indicates that such a fertilization may occur. Hemsley's[241] reported hybrids between *Ceratozamia longifolia* and *C. mexicana,* in which 3-year-old pollen was used, also suggests such a fertilization; for cycad pollen probably does not retain its vitality more than a month—probably not so long.

The failure of wall formation at the ventral canal mitosis indicates a more advanced stage in the reduction of the archegonium than that found in *Ginkgo, Pinus*, and other forms which develop a definite wall between the two nuclei.

It is interesting, in this connection, to recall the reduction of the archegonium from forms with long necks, numerous neck canal cells, and a definite ventral canal cell, as in *Marchantia;* through forms like *Riccia*, with four neck canal cells, a ventral canal cell and an egg cell; through forms with only one neck canal cell and a ventral canal cell and an egg cell, like *Marsilia*, where the next step brings the condition in *Ginkgo*, with no neck canal cell, but with a ventral canal cell and an egg cell. In this series one finds occasional binucleate neck canal cells and, in related forms, a smaller number of neck canal cells, so that there is first the failure of a wall to be formed between two nuclei, and then the failure of the division itself. In this reduction, the cycads have gone a step farther than *Ginkgo*, which still retains the wall between the ventral canal nucleus and that of the egg. It is only when viewed in this way that it becomes a matter of any evolutionary importance whether there is a ventral canal cell and an egg cell, or merely two nuclei not separated by a wall.

Comparative morphology leaves no doubt that the neck canal cells and the ventral canal cell are homologous with the egg, so that the archegonium, phylogenetically, contained several eggs.

The neck itself keeps pace with the reduction of the neck canal cells until, in the cycads, there are almost always just two neck cells; but in *Encephalartos villosus* SEDGWICK[537] found that the neck cells rather frequently divide. One of his figures shows six neck cells.

The neck cells grow rapidly and, in later stages, become very turgid.

To return to *Dioon edule*, which seems to be a typical cycad: the nutrition of the egg is practically the nutrition of the central cell, for the division of the nucleus of the central cell to form the ventral canal nucleus and the egg nucleus takes place only a few days before fertilization. So the process may be called the nutrition of the egg.

For the first two or three months after the appearance of the archegonium initials, food materials are received from the surrounding cell by the usual method of transferring substances from one cell to another; but, as the central cell becomes large, a definite layer of cells, called the "archegonial jacket," appears. As the jacket becomes more and more differentiated, the egg membrane thickens and finally becomes so tough that it retains its form and connection with the suspensor, even when embryos half the length of the seed are dissected out. In the ripe seed this resistent egg membrane can still be recognized. In an early stage it is easy to see that it has numerous large pits into which the turgid protoplasm of the egg presses. For some time the pits are covered by a thin membrane, the middle lamella between the wall of the jacket cell and that of the egg. The cells of the female gametophyte are full of starch, proteid, and probably other materials which find their way through the archegonium jacket and into the egg in the usual manner.

But the growing egg becomes so turgid that the papillae, or haustoria, as they may be called, break the thin membrane, which closes the pit, thus leaving the haustoria of the egg in direct contact with the protoplasm of the jacket cell, so that materials can pass from the jacket cell into the egg as readily as from one part of a cell to another (figs. 124–29).

The turgidity of the female gametophyte, and, later, the turgidity of the central cell, and, still later, the egg cell, is extreme. In trimming material for fixing, if one cuts too near the jacket, the young gametophyte breaks through. At the fertilization period, and for a month before that time, if one cuts too near the jacket, there may be a rupture several millimeters in length. If one cuts into the endosperm too near the archegonial jacket, there will be a small rupture of the egg membrane and cells nearest to it, and the liquid contents of the egg will spurt out, sometimes to a distance of 20 cm.

Shortly before the nucleus of the central cell divides, the tissues around the archegonial region grow rapidly, leaving the archegonia in a depression called the "archegonial chamber."

Immediately after the mitosis which gives rise to the ventral canal nucleus and the egg nucleus, the ventral canal nucleus begins to disorganize and soon disappears, while the egg nucleus moves toward the center of the egg, increasing immensely in size, until it sometimes reaches a diameter of 500 microns, easily visible to the naked eye. During this time the chromatin, easily distinguishable in the late telophase, becomes obscured by other nuclear contents until it becomes unrecognizable.

The contents of the egg become very dense. Most of the vacuolate structure of the protoplasm disappears, apparently by the breaking down of the thin sides of the vacuoles, resulting in a more or less

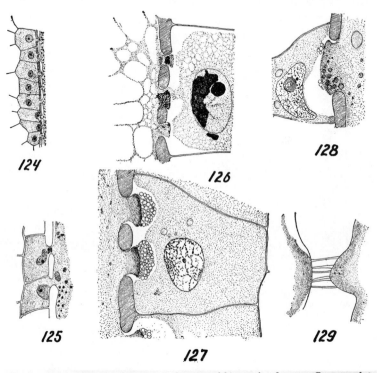

FIGS. 124–129.—Pits in the egg membrane and haustoria: fig. 124, *Cycas revoluta*, ×150; fig. 125, the same, ×375; fig. 126, *Dioon edule* before the haustorium has broken the pit closing membrane; in figs. 127 and 128, the membrane has been broken and material is passing directly from the jacket cell into the haustorium, ×800; fig. 129, *Encephalartos lehmanii*, shallow pit with protoplasmic continuity between the haustorium and the jacket cell; ×1100. Figs. 124 and 125, after IKENO;[280] figs. 126–128, after CHAMBERLAIN;[106] fig. 129, after STOPES and FUJII.[591]

fibrillar appearance. Starch, proteids, and oil can be identified. In the living condition, at this stage, the outer border of the egg, which may be called the "*Hautschicht*," is as colorless as water, while the interior is slightly turbid.

As in all seed plants, the megaspore, with its contained female gametophyte, is never shed from the sporangium. The spore coats of the heterosporous ferns, the ancient ancestors of the cycads, were very thick. As the megaspore became retained, its spore coats became thinner, but are easily recognized even in rock sections of the extinct Cycadofilicales (figs. 16, 19, 20). In the Cycadales, the megaspore membrane stains brilliantly with safranin. THOMSON[633] found

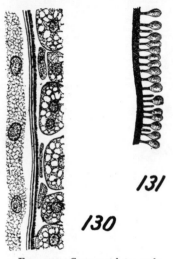

that the membrane consists of two layers, which may be called the endospore and exospore, the outer of which is suberized, while the inner consists of a substance closely related to pectin.

The inner layer is dense and homogeneous. The outer layer consists of club-shaped bodies with enlarged ends, so that under moderate magnification there seem to be three layers, a middle layer being the stalks of the club-shaped bodies (figs. 130, 131).

The membrane, in *Dioon edule*, is strongly developed as early as November, and continues to increase in thickness up to the germination of the seed, when it reaches a thickness of 10 microns. In fresh material, one might mistake the jacket of the female gametophyte for the membrane, but the jacket is coarser and can be stripped off entire with forceps. The membrane is more delicate, but pieces several millimeters in length can be stripped off. The

FIG. 130.—*Cycas revoluta:* endospore and exospore about equal in thickness. Thickness of entire membrane is 4.5 microns.—After R. B. THOMSON.[633]

FIG. 131.—*Dioon edule:* The megaspore membrane; the inner part is dense and homogeneous, while the outer part consists of ovoid, stalked bodies; ×900.—After CHAMBERLAIN.[106]

membrane is thicker at the middle of the gametophyte than at the top or bottom.

As the archegonial chamber develops, the membrane in that region is ruptured, so that the pollen chamber and archegonial chamber form a continuous cavity (figs. 132, 133; see also fig. 147).

THE MALE GAMETOPHYTE

The microspore is the first cell of the male gametophyte. It has a very definite polarity and two very definite spore coats. The exine is thick at the bottom, moderate on the sides, and thin at the top; while the intine is thin at the bottom and top and very thick on the sides (figs. 134–37).

The microspore, in all the cycads, begins to germinate while still contained in the microsporangium. At the first mitosis, a prothallial cell is cut off. This cell does not degenerate, as in most gymnosperms,

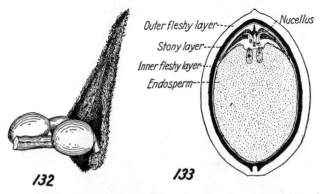

Outer fleshy layer
Stony layer
Inner fleshy layer
Endosperm
Nucellus

132

133

Fig. 132.—*Dioon edule:* megasporophyll with two ovules; one-half natural size.

Fig. 133.—*Dioon edule:* section of ovule at the stage shown in fig. 132; ×2. Both figs. 132 and 133 from CHAMBERLAIN, *The Living Cycads*[120] (University of Chicago Press).

but becomes very active, although it never divides. The other cell divides, forming a generative cell and a tube cell. At this three-celled stage the microspore is shed from the sporangium.

There have been many reports of insect pollination, but in a rather extensive field study in which all of the genera have been examined, most of them at the time of pollination, nothing has been observed which would indicate anything but the wind pollination so characteristic of the whole group of gymnosperms. The pollen is light and dry, and easily blown by the wind. The entire mass of pollen in a microsporangium, for a while, hangs together in one mass, being held by a kind of membrane formed by the disorganized wall and tapetal cells. When this breaks, the dry pollen is shed. As soon as the microsporophylls begin to crack apart, insects arrive and can be seen crawling over the sporangia and doubtless feeding on the pollen. While the insects are so abundant in the male cones, they are rare in the female cones, except that a beetle is common about species of *Encephalartos*. This beetle, however, bores into the female gametophyte, destroying many of the seeds rather than furthering seed

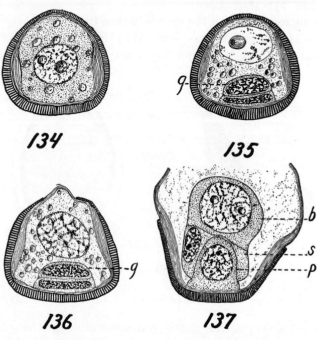

Figs. 134–137.—*Dioon edule:* fig. 134, microspore; fig. 135, germinating microspore; *p*, prothallial cell; *g*, generative cell: fig. 136, exine ruptured by the young pollen tube: fig. 137, later stage, with more starch: the generative cell has divided, forming a stalk cell (*s*) and body cell (*b*). The prothallial cell (*p*) is protruding into the stalk cell; figs. 134–136, ×1260; fig. 137, ×1000.—After CHAMBERLAIN.[108]

production. Many of the insects observed are flying species, but fertilization more than a hundred meters from a male plant is rare, and, in collecting material, it is well to select female cones within 10 or 20 meters of a male plant. Nucelli from a female cone within 4 or 5 meters of a male cone may show 15 or 20 pollen tubes, while those at 100 meters may show only 2 or 3, and female cones at a distance of 200 meters may show only 2 or 3 good seeds or none at all. Any claim that there is any insect pollination should be supported by the most critical field study.

At the time of pollination a large pollination drop appears at the micropyle. Cells at the top of the nucellus break down and some of their contents ooze out as a mucilaginous drop. The pollen grains fall on the drop and, as it dries, are drawn into the young pollen chamber below. Further drying seals the chamber, and the top becomes very hard, forming the nucellar beak.

Pollen germinates readily in sugar solutions, in thick juice of pear preserves, and in many syrups. The pollen tube soon appears, and grows to several times the length of the pollen grain, but the generative cell does not divide. Cultures kept for a month show no division; but in material taken in the field, probably not more than a week after pollination, the division has taken place, giving rise to a stalk cell and a body cell, the name "stalk cell" being given from a supposed homology with the stalk cell of the antheridium of Pteridophytes.

The pollen tube, coming from the upper end of the pollen grain, grows into the nucellus, and acts as a haustorium, conveying food material to the basal end of the tube. In *Ceratozamia*, in addition to the usual haustorial pollen tube, there are numerous haustoria extending downward from the base of the pollen tube. The genus could be identified by this feature as positively as by the two horns on the sporophyll, which give it its name. The pollen tube is a haustorium, not a sperm-carrier as in angiosperms.

There is no further cell division for a long time, the division of the body cell taking place almost immediately before fertilization. The interval between pollination and fertilization is about four months in *Cycas revoluta*, five months in *Zamia floridana*, and about six months in *Dioon edule*.

During this long period the pollen tube digests its way downward, enlarging the pollen chamber until it finally extends completely through the nucellus and the pollen tubes hang free in a cavity which is partly pollen chamber and partly archegonial chamber (fig. 147).

When the body cell, or spermatogenous cell, is first formed, no blepharoplast or centrosome has been demonstrated; but, as the body cell enlarges and elongates, first one and then two very small

blepharoplasts appear. They are at the side of the nucleus opposite
the prothallial cell, and one of them soon moves around to the opposite side of the nucleus. They remain in this position and grow rapidly. As the elongated body cell increases in size, it gradually becomes
spherical, and the two blepharoplasts move 90 degrees, so that a
line drawn through them would be perpendicular to the long axis of
the pollen tube (figs. 138, 139). The blepharoplasts are at first very

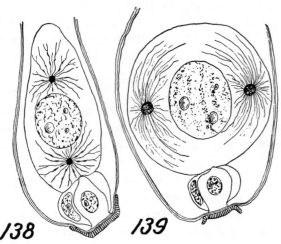

FIGS. 138 and 139.—*Dioon edule:* fig. 138, December material, body cell elongated
and blepharoplast parallel with the long axis of the pollen tube; fig. 139, May material
with blepharoplasts rotated until they have become transverse to the long axis of the
pollen tube; ×237.—From CHAMBERLAIN, *The Living Cycads*[120] (University of Chicago
Press).

dense and homogeneous, but later become very vacuolate and reach
an immense size, from 16 to 18 microns in diameter in *Dioon edule*,
and 20–27 microns in *Ceratozamia mexicana*, the largest yet known.

The radiations surrounding the blepharoplasts are very conspicuous and often extend to the wall of the cell.

Shortly before fertilization the body cell divides, and in each of the
two resulting cells a single sperm is developed. As the sperm grows,
the radiations begin to disappear and the blepharoplast breaks up
into a great number of small granules (fig. 140). Some of these become attached to a beaklike protuberance of the nucleus, which increases immensely in size and rotates so that the mass of granules,

fusing into a band, is drawn out into a spiral with several turns (fig. 141). From this spiral band, lying just beneath the *Hautschicht*, thousands of cilia are developed. They pierce the *Hautschicht* and extend into the cell cavity. The topography of the nucellus with its pollen tubes during these stages is shown in figs. 142 and 143.

In all of the cycads, except *Microcycas*, there are two sperms in each pollen tube. In *Microcycas*, according to CALDWELL,[88] there

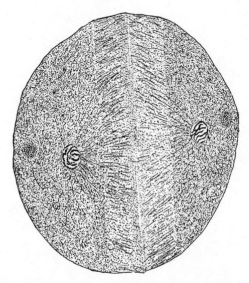

FIG. 140.—*Stangeria paradoxa:* the body cell has divided to form two sperms, and each blepharoplast has broken into numerous granules which will form the spiral band. The nuclei of the sperms are still comparatively small (January 11, 1913). ×400.

are usually 16 sperms. Dr. DOROTHY DOWNIE found 8 to 11 body cells, so that the number of sperms would range from 16 to 22.

Spermatogenesis in *Microcycas* was studied in great detail by Dr. DOWNIE[173] and the results not only show how the large number of sperms originates, but suggest what is probably the real nature of the generative cell and stalk cell (figs. 144 and 145). After the prothallial cell has been formed, the next mitosis gives rise to a tube cell and a generative cell. The latter divides in the usual way, forming a stalk cell and a body cell; but from this point, the behavior is peculiar to *Microcycas*. The stalk cell divides, giving rise to another body cell, which later gives rise to two sperms, while the cell beneath it divides again, producing another body cell, and the process is repeated until as many as 8 and sometimes even 11 body cells have been formed, each of which produces two sperms.

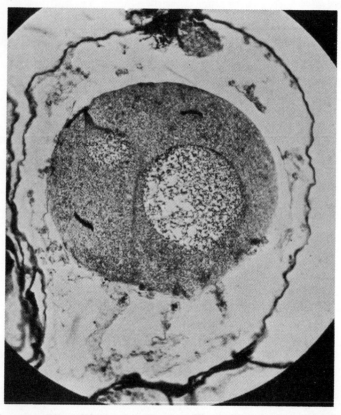

Fig. 141.—*Dioon edule:* two young sperms. The nuclei of the sperms have become larger, and, in the one at the left a part of the spiral band can be seen attached to the beak of the nucleus; ×350.

Dr. Downie[173] regards the generative cell as the primary spermatogenous cell, and the stalk cell as a spermatogenous cell still active in *Microcycas*, but having lost the division potentiality in other gymnosperms. This interpretation seems to be sound from the standpoint of comparative morphology and phylogeny.

Sperms of cycads are remarkably large (fig. 146). In *Dioon edule*, while still in the pollen tube, they measure about 200 microns in diameter and 275 microns in length. After leaving the tube, they

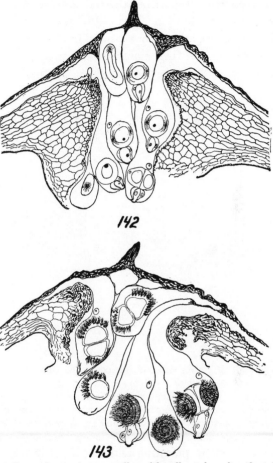

142

143

FIG. 142.—*Stangeria paradoxa:* nucellus with pollen tubes after the tubes have broken entirely through the nucellus. In one pollen tube, the body cell has divided to form the two sperms (January 19, 1913); ×50.—From CHAMBERLAIN, *The Living Cycads*[120] (University of Chicago Press).

FIG. 143.—*Stangeria paradoxa:* two sperms have been formed from each body cell (February 2, 1913); ×50.—From CHAMBERLAIN, *The Living Cycads*[120] (University of Chicago Press).

increase in size, reaching a diameter of 230 microns and a length of 300 microns. Consequently, they are easily visible to the naked eye.

The 2 sperms begin to move while still within the sperm mother-cells, but soon the peripheral part of the wall between them breaks down and leaves them free within the wall of what was called the "body cell" before its division. This cell increases in size, and the sperms, which stick together, move around in the cavity. The cilia, at first, move slowly and then more vigorously, so that the pair of sperms roll about in the rather small space. The movement of the

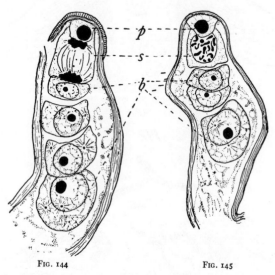

FIG. 144   FIG. 145

FIGS. 144 and 145.—*Microcycas calocoma:* fig. 144, pollen tube with four body cells, and stalk cell in telophase of division to form another; fig. 145, pollen tube with three body cells and stalk cell in prophase of division to form another; *p*, prothallial cell; *s*, stalk cell; *b*, body cells. No centrosomes have been found in the stalk cell or in the body cell immediately after its formation; ×1280.—After Dr. DOROTHY G. DOWNIE.[173]

cilia is accompanied by pulsating and amoeboid movements, and when the apex of a sperm strikes the wall, there is a sudden, convulsive movement which makes one think of *Vorticella*. They swim for an hour or more in the cavity of the body cell before they separate, and then for another half-hour before they escape into the general cavity of the pollen tube. When free from each other, the general movement is straight ahead, with a rotation upon the longer axis. They swim up into the tube as far as the diminishing diameter will permit, and then come back. When a nucellus is inverted, with a

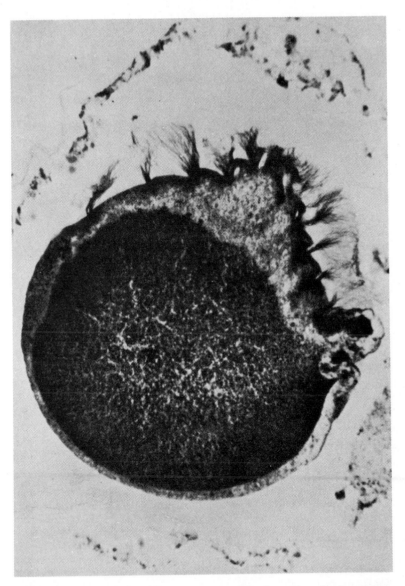

Fig. 146.—*Ceratozamia mexicana:* photomicrograph of a section of a sperm, showing the large nucleus, thin sheath of protoplasm, and numerous cilia; ×360. The photomicrograph was made by Miss Ethel Thomas.—From Chamberlain, *The Living Cycads*[120] (University of Chicago Press).

drop of strong sugar solution and still further protected by a bell jar, the movements have continued for 5 hours. How much longer they

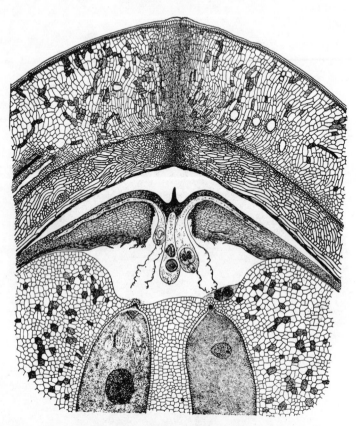

Fig. 147.—*Dioon edule:* a reconstruction, from several sections, of an ovule at the time of fertilization. The pollen tube on the left shows the body cell still undivided; the one in the middle shows two sperms and the remains of the prothallial and stalk cells; the one on the right shows the two sperm mother-cells and the spiral ciliated band beginning to develop. Two pollen tubes have discharged their sperms. A sperm has entered the egg on the left; the one on the right still shows the ventral canal nucleus. Two sperms, in the thick liquid discharged from the pollen tube just above them, are ready to enter the egg. The dark line below the nucellus is the megaspore membrane.—After CHAMBERLAIN.[106]

would move under natural conditions is conjectural. Efforts to keep the sperms alive after escaping from the pollen tube were not successful. In weak sugar solutions they almost explode. In a 10 per cent solution, they quickly die; in a 20 per cent solution, they live a little longer.

FERTILIZATION

Some have imagined that the archegonial chamber is a cavity in which the sperms swim for a while before entering the egg. This view is entirely incorrect. At the time of fertilization the pollen chamber and the archegonial chamber are merely moist. There is not a trace of any free liquid. In studying the living condition and in fixing material for detailed study, hundreds of ovules have been cut, and always there is the moist membrane, but nothing more.

A careful study of a drawing will help to understand the process of fertilization in a cycad (fig. 147).

In the later stages of the development of the sperms, the basal end of the pollen tube becomes very much swollen and so turgid that it finally bursts, discharging the sperms, with liquid from the pollen tube, into the archegonial chamber. This liquid is the only medium in which the sperms can move while in the archegonial chamber.

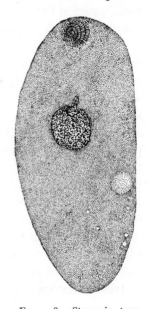

FIG. 148.—*Stangeria paradoxa:* fertilization; the sperm nucleus is entering the top of the egg nucleus; the ciliated band is at the top of the egg; ×42.—After CHAMBERLAIN.[119]

As before noted, the egg becomes extremely turgid during the final stages of its development, in fact, so turgid that the contents of the egg would spurt out into the archegonial chamber were it not for the turgid neck cells. The liquid discharged from the pollen tube has such a high pressure that sperms discharged from the pollen tube into a 30 per cent solution of cane sugar move about freely. The liquid from the pollen tube, coming into contact with the neck cells, lowers their turgidity, and some of the contents of the upper part of the egg escape into the archegonial chamber, leaving large vacuoles at the top of the egg. A sperm is then drawn into the egg so violently that the protoplasm, with its ciliated band, is torn off and left near the top of the egg, while the nucleus moves downward to unite with the egg nucleus. The ciliated band remains in the top of the egg throughout the free nuclear stages of the embryo, and sometimes can be distinguished still later. The cilia become indistinguishable from the protoplasm of the egg, as if they actually become a part of the egg protoplasm; but the dense band, from which they arise, seems solid as long as it can be recognized.

The behavior of the chromatin, from the entrance of the sperm up to its contact with the egg nucleus, has not been satisfactorily described in any gymnosperm. Both nuclei are filled with a substance which stains deeply with iron haematoxylin, but most of that substance is certainly not chromatin (fig. 146). STRASBURGER called it *metaplasm*, because he did not regard it as chromatin or as protoplasm. Even after the sperm nucleus begins to enter the egg nucleus the metaplasm is conspicuous, and the chromatin does not seem to be recognizable (fig. 148).

The term "fertilization" is used rather loosely and perhaps it is better not to attempt to define it too closely. Any stage with the sperm inside the egg is likely to be called fertilization, and any stage with the two nuclei in contact passes for fertilization. Details are more thoroughly worked out in Coniferales, and so the subject will be treated again, especially in *Pinus*, *Abies*, and *Juniperus*.

CHAPTER VII

CYCADALES—*Continued*

EMBRYOGENY

Just where fertilization is completed and embryogeny begins, is indefinite; but the stage shown in fig. 148 is certainly regarded as a stage in fertilization, while the stage shown in fig. 149 shows the first division of the nucleus of the fertilized egg and, consequently, is a $2x$ mitosis. So somewhere between the stages shown in these two figures fertilization has been completed, and the sporophyte generation has started.

Around the first mitotic figure there is a fibrillar area many times as large as the figure itself. The fibrillae seem to be the same as the spindle fibers and radiations of later figures. The chromosomes, at metaphase of the first mitosis, are not hard to count, but it is surprising to find that the number is 12, the same number counted at the mitosis which gives rise to the ventral canal nucleus and the egg nucleus, and also at various stages in the development of the gametophyte. The anaphase of this mitosis was not found, but anaphases of later mitoses showed 24 chromosomes, and root tips showed the same number. The microspore has 12 chromosomes, so there is no doubt that in *Stangeria*, and probably in the rest of the cycads, the x and $2x$ numbers are 12 and 24. HUTCHINSON'S[275] work on the first division in *Abies*, which will be considered in the proper place, offers an explanation of the condition found in *Stangeria*.

FIG. 149.—*Stangeria paradoxa:* first division of the nucleus of the fertilized egg. At the top is the spiral band of the sperm which fertilized the egg, and also three sperms which got through the neck but failed to penetrate the egg; ×42.—After CHAMBERLAIN.[119]

Free nuclear stage.—Following fertilization there is a period of free nuclear division. The divisions are simultaneous, so that the number of nuclei is, theoretically, 2, 4, 8, 16, 32, 64, 128, 256, 512, and, in some cases, 1,024. The earlier divisions are very regular and the numbers of nuclei are about what should be anticipated; but, in *Dioon edule*, the eighth, ninth, and tenth divisions are irregular, some of the

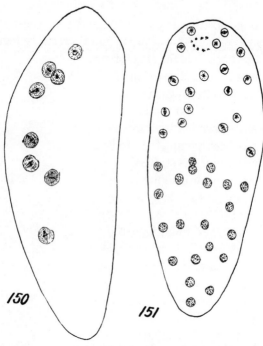

FIGS. 150 and 151.—*Stangeria paradoxa:* free nuclear stage of embryo; fig. 150, 8-nucleate stage, showing simultaneous mitoses in two groups of nuclei; very definite polarity with simultaneous mitoses in both groups of nuclei; fig. 151, polarity with mitoses in upper group but not in the lower; ×42.—After CHAMBERLAIN.[119]

nuclei failing to divide, especially in the upper part of the embryo. The number beyond the 256 nucleate stage is likely to be less than the theoretical estimate, because some of the nuclei fail to divide.

In *Stangeria* there is often a distinct polarity, the nuclei being in two groups (figs. 150, 151). If the nuclei in the lower group divide, those at the top do also; but those at the top may divide without a corresponding division in the lower group. A glance at the illustrations of free nuclear division in *Stangeria* will show that the nuclei in the upper part of the embryo, during the earlier mitoses, may become much more numerous than in the lower part.

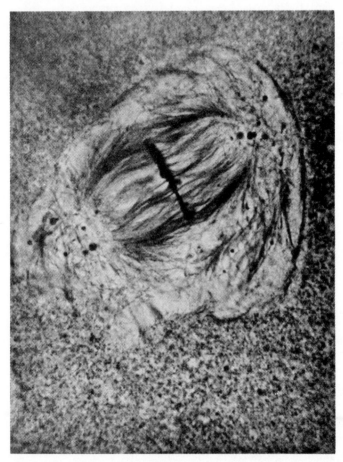

Fig. 152.—*Zamia floridana:* photomicrograph of a small portion of a section showing an early free nuclear division; ✕413. Negative by Miss Ethel Thomas.—From Chamberlain, *Methods in Plant Histology* (5th ed.) (University of Chicago Press).

During the earlier mitoses, the spindle fibers and polar radiations are very striking, but there are no centrosomes at any stage (fig. 152).

The number of nuclei reached in the free nuclear period varies.

In *Dioon edule* the egg often reaches a length of 5 mm., and the number of free nuclei is about 1,000—theoretically 1,024. In *Zamia floridana*, with an egg about 3 mm. in length, the number is quite regularly 256. In *Bowenia serrulata*, LAWSON[352] reports 64, the lowest number ever found in a cycad. In other gymnosperms, with much smaller eggs, the number comes down to 4, and in *Sequoia* a wall is formed at the first mitosis.

In the homosporous ferns there is no free nuclear period, and none in living heterosporous ferns, although it is probable that there was

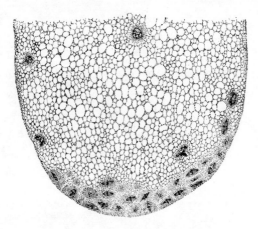

FIG. 153.—*Stangeria paradoxa:* simultaneous division of nuclei in lower part of embryo; ×140.—After CHAMBERLAIN.[119]

a free nuclear period in extinct heterosporous ferns, and, in our opinion, there was an extensive free nuclear period in some of the Cycadofilicales. A free nuclear period arose as a consequence of the enlarging eggs. The mass of protoplasm became so large that the early mitotic figures could not segment it.

In *Cycas* and *Stangeria* the nuclei at the base of the embryo undergo a vigorous simultaneous division after the nuclei of the rest of the embryo have ceased to divide (fig. 153). The suspensor, and all the rest of the embryo below it, come from this second period of simultaneous division.

Formation of cell walls in embryo.—After the nuclei have increased in number until there is a comparatively small amount of proto-

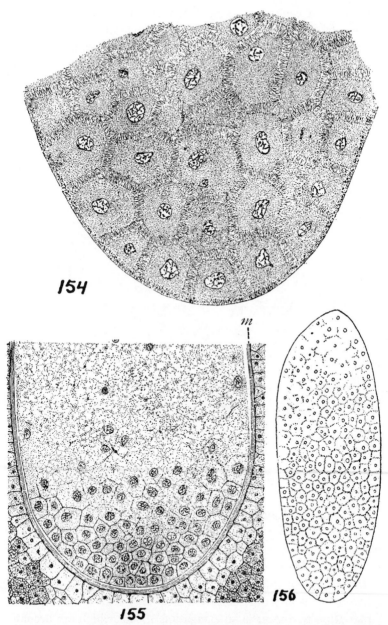

FIGS. 154–156.—*Dioon edule:* evanescent segmentation; fig. 154, lower part of embryo; fig. 156, diagram of entire embryo; fig. 155, lower part of embryo, showing permanent walls at the bottom and free nuclei above; *m*, the thick membrane of the egg; fig. 154, ×200; fig. 156, ×20; fig. 155, ×108.—After CHAMBERLAIN.[110]

plasm about each one, segmentation begins. In some cycads, like *Dioon* and *Stangeria*, an evanescent segmentation throughout the entire embryo takes place before the permanent walls appear (figs. 154–56). In early stages they are stronger at the base of the embryo and weaker and weaker above (figs. 156, 157).

Following the free nuclear period, in the type of embryogeny which we should regard as the most primitive, the embryo becomes

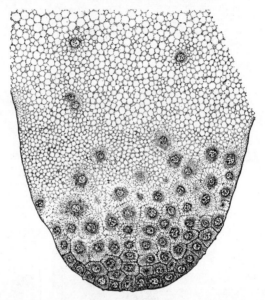

Fig. 157.—*Stangeria paradoxa:* permanent walls forming below; above, weaker walls and then free nuclei.—After CHAMBERLAIN.[119]

cellular throughout, as in some species of *Cycas*,[646] *Encephalartos*, and *Macrozamia*[116] (fig. 158). In these, the cells break down in the central portion, leaving two or three layers of cells at the outside. In others, including those with evanescent segmentation, the upper part remains in the free nuclear condition, while cell division continues in the basal region.

Differentiation into body regions.—Hundreds of cells are formed before there is any differentiation into body regions. The first differentiation to appear is an elongation of cells which are becoming the suspensor. Mucilage cavities also appear at this time (figs. 159–

61). The body regions differentiate very slowly, the cellular condition, except in the suspensor region, being somewhat uniform even after the topography of cotyledons and coleorhiza become easily recognizable (fig. 162). That the dermatogen has not yet become completely differentiated, even after the appearance of cotyledons, is shown by the frequent occurrence of periclines.

The suspensor is a remarkable feature of the cycad embryo. In an early cotyledon stage the suspensor is not a simple structure derived from a single embryo, but is made up of the suspensors of all the embryos which have come from the fertilized eggs of that group. In some of the embryos, the suspensor elongates but little; in others, it elongates more; and in the embryo which is to be the only one to reach full development the later stretches of the suspensor belong only to the mature embryo. In a good preparation the various embryos, each at the end of its own suspensor, can be seen in spite of the coiling and twisting of the compound structure made up of all the suspensors (fig. 163). In *Ceratozamia*, in the living condition, the suspensors can be pulled out to a length of 7 or 8 centimeters. Whatever the primary function of this suspensor may be, it certainly thrusts the growing embryo down into the gametophyte.

Fig. 158.—*Cycas circinalis:* young embryo, indicating that the entire egg may have segmented and that the central portion has broken down; ×25. —After Treub.[646]

Another remarkable feature of the cycad embryo is the coleorhiza. It appears early in the development of the embryo, and in later stages, after the embryo has reached the full length of the seed, it becomes extremely hard.

The mature seed is rather uniform throughout the family (fig. 164). There is an outer, fleshy seed coat which is white or creamy, or which may be variously colored, with red or various combinations

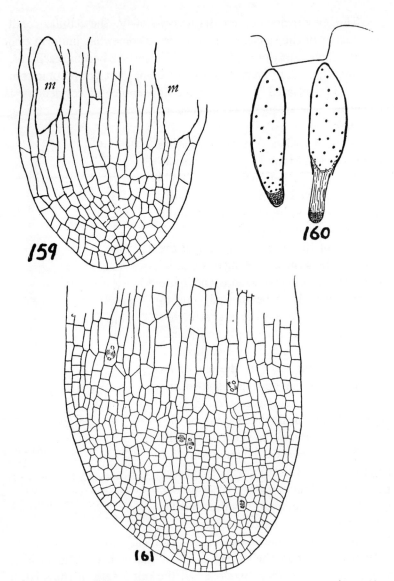

FIGS. 159–161.—*Dioon edule:* fig. 159, embryo showing mucilage cavities (*m*) and beginning of suspensor; fig. 161, later stage, but with dermatogen not yet fully differentiated; fig. 160, diagram with embryo at the left a little more advanced than that in fig. 159, and the one at the right, in the same stage as that in fig. 161.—After CHAMBERLAIN.[110]

of red and orange predominating. Beneath the fleshy layer is a hard, tough, stony layer; and, within this, the inner, fleshy layer, which

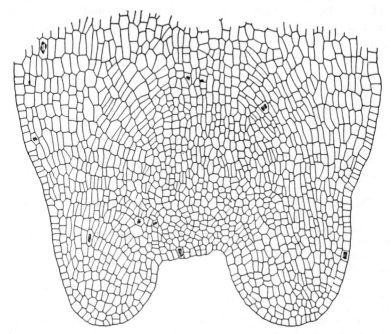

FIG. 162.—*Dioon edule:* early cotyledon stage of embryo; the enlarged portion back of the cotyledons is the coleorhiza; periclines show that the dermatogen is not yet fully differentiated.—After CHAMBERLAIN.[110]

soon gives up most of the cell contents to the female gametophyte and growing embryo. This layer, containing the inner vascular system, becomes a dry, papery membrane. Just underneath the top of it the remains of the nucellus can be seen, forming a dry, papery cap. The embryo, now extending the whole length of the seed, inside the seed coats, has two cotyledons, which are not always equal in size; one leaf with usually one or more scale leaves; and the long suspensor coiled and packed against the micropylar end.

FIG. 163.—*Ceratozamia mexicana:* young embryos with suspensors; the rounded bodies at the top are the tough egg membranes; ×1.5. —After CHAMBERLAIN.[112]

Occasionally there are more than two cotyledons, three being reported for *Encephalartos;* and *Ceratozamia* has regularly only one. The cotyledon situation in *Ceratozamia* is particularly interesting. SISTER HELEN ANGELA,[167] noticing a few tracheids in the part of the embryo opposite the cotyledon, suspected that they might represent the missing cotyledon. *Ceratozamia* is unique in that the cone decays and sheds its seeds before the cotyledon stage. She revolved seeds on a clinostat during the entire embryogeny, and all these seeds developed two cotyledons, while more than 100 seeds, grown in the usual way, had only one cotyledon, which developed on the side next to the ground. In all cases, the cotyledons, in the basal region, form a continuous cotyledonary tube. At the tips, cotyledons are sometimes lobed or divided, giving an impression that there are more than two.

FIG. 164.—*Dioon edule:* mature seed: The darkly shaded part at the top is the coleorhiza (*c*); the two cotyledons and first leaf are shown; the dotted part is a female gametophyte; the hatched part is the stony layer (*s*) of the seed, outside of which is the outer fleshy layer (*o*); *m*, micropyle; natural size. From CHAMBERLAIN, *The Living Cycads*[120] (University of Chicago Press).

THE SEEDLING

There is no resting stage in a cycad seed: development is continuous from fertilization to the death of the old plant. Seeds do not long retain their vitality. Those with the hardest stony layer and toughest outer fleshy layer may be germinated a year after they fall out from the cone. Seeds of *Macrozamia moorei*, which have an exceptionally thick and hard stony layer, have germinated after 2 years. If a seed rattles when shaken, the chances are against any germination.

Germination of the seed.—Cycad seeds are nearly always elongated. When they fall out from the cone they do not sink into the ground, but lie on the surface. To secure the best germination in the greenhouse, they should not be covered with soil, but pressed in lightly— about half-way—with the long axis of the seed parallel with the surface of the soil.

As the embryo within the germinating seed elongates, it fractures the stony coat, the hard coleorhiza protecting the delicate young root-tip (figs. 165–67). After the coleorhiza has fractured the stony coat, the root tip digests its way through the coleorhiza and begins to turn down. Entering the soil, it grows rapidly, while the stem remains inconspicuous. Usually only one leaf appears. Part of the cotyledon protrudes from the seed but the greater part remains inside, absorbing all of the female gametophyte and passing it on to

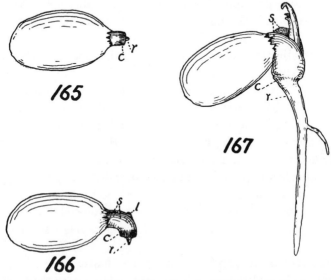

FIGS. 165–167.—*Dioon edule:* seedling; fig. 165, the coleorhiza has fractured the stony coat and the root tip has digested its way through the base of the coleorhiza; fig. 166, the root end is turning down: about two-thirds of the protruding part is cotyledon and the lower part is coleorhiza, with the root visible at the base; fig. 167, later stage with 3 leaves between the cotyledons; *c*, coleorhiza; *r*, root; *s*, cotyledons; all natural size.—From CHAMBERLAIN, *The Living Cycads* (University of Chicago Press).

the seedling. The cotyledons then become dry, but the stony coat of the seed, with the withered cotyledons inside, remains attached to the plant for a year or even longer.

Anatomy of the seedling.—Many have studied the anatomy of the cycad seedling and have described its principal features. THIESSEN,[614] MATTE,[391] and SISTER HELEN ANGELA DORETY[172] have presented the most detailed accounts. THIESSEN's account of *Dioon edule* and SISTER HELEN ANGELA's of *Dioon spinulosum* have already been mentioned in connection with the girdling of the leaf trace.

THIESSEN[614] found that the vascular cylinder of the stem is very short, so that it may be called a vascular plate rather than a cylinder (fig. 168). The plate is squarish and has a protoxylem group at each corner, from each of which a strand extends downward, forming the protoxylem of the tetrarch root. Four strands extend in the opposite direction, soon forking and entering the cotyledons, so that each cotyledon gets four strands. For each of the first leaves four strands leave the vascular plate at or near its four protoxylem points.

An interesting feature is the change from the endarch to the exarch condition. The cotyledonary bundles, as they leave the vascular plate, are endarch; but, farther along in the cotyledon, they become mesarch. The leaf traces also, when leaving the vascular plate, are endarch; but, in the leaf base, centripetal xylem appears, so that the bundle becomes mesarch. From this point the centripetal xylem increases and the centrifugal decreases until the bundle becomes entirely exarch before it reaches the region of leaflets. Beyond this point the bundles are exarch.

The vascular cylinder of the embryo is a protostele; but in older stages it gradually becomes an endarch siphonostele, except in *Microcycas*.[169]

SISTER HELEN ANGELA[169] also found that in *Microcycas* the vascular strands of cotyledons and leaves are endarch near the base and exarch in the upper portions. The vascular plate, from its first appearance, is an endarch siphonostele, probably the only siphonostele in early stages of a cycad seedling (fig. 169).

MATTE,[391] and others who have studied the embryogeny of the cycads, agree that the stem consists of leaf bases. This would mean that the adult stem is a mass of leaf bases, in which secondary growth has produced the familiar trunk. This interpretation is suggestive and may have a wider application.

The seedling usually has just one leaf. Leaf after leaf appears at irregular intervals, and it is likely to be several years before leaves begin to appear in crowns. It is rare for a cycad to produce a cone before the tenth year, and some are probably much older before the coning stage is reached. The demarcation between seedling and adult plant is as indefinite as that between baby and boy—and between boy and man.

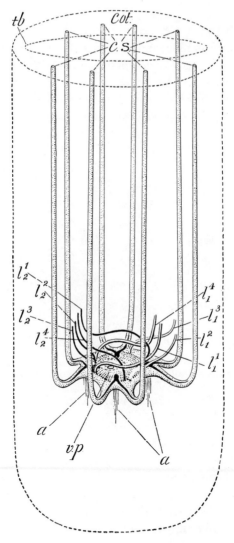

Fig. 168.—*Dioon edule:* semi-diagrammatic reconstruction of vascular system of embryo, showing girdling: *cot*, cotyledon; *tb*, tubular part of cotyledon; *cs*, cotyledonary strands; l_1^1 to l_1^4, four strands of first leaf; l_2^1 to l_2^4, strands of second leaf; *vp*, vascular plate; *a*, xylem from protoxylem of the plate to form protoxylem of primary root. —After Thiessen.[614]

HYBRIDS

Hybrids between *Ceratozamia longifolia* and *C. mexicana* were claimed as early as 1882; and there was also a claim that hybrids had been secured between *Ceratozamia robusta* and *C. brevifrons*. In both cases, seeds were secured which germinated. But, as HELMSLEY[241] remarked, "There is only one thing certain in all this, and that is the uncertainty of the so-called species." Doubtless, HELMSLEY was

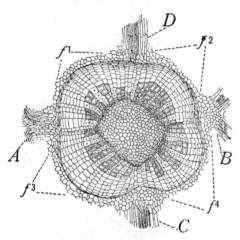

FIG. 169.—*Microcycas calocoma:* transverse section of stem just above the cotyledonary plate, showing the siphonostele condition: *A*, *B*, *C*, *D*, the four cotyledonary strands; f^1, f^2, f^3, f^4, the leaf traces still in procambial condition.—After SISTER HELEN ANGELA DORETY.[169]

right, for all of these so-called species could probably be raised from seeds of a single cone of *Ceratozamia mexicana*.

In the first-mentioned cross, pollen from a male cone of *Ceratozamia longifolia* was preserved for 3 years and then used to pollinate *C. mexicana*. It is possible that the mere irritation of dead pollen in the pollen chamber might stimulate development; but it is certain that the 3-year-old pollen was dead.

However, the cycads hybridize freely. Of more than a dozen successful pollinations made at the University of Chicago, two will be described here.

Zamia latifoliolata × *Zamia pumila*.[123]—On December 20, 1921, I pollinated female cones of two plants of *Zamia latifoliolata* with pollen of *Z. floridana*. The sporophylls of the female cones were tightly closed, and it is more than doubtful whether any of the pollen survived the usual spraying. A week later sporophylls of both female cones opened and Dr. PAUL J. SEDGWICK pollinated them with *Zamia pumila*. One cone produced three seeds, and the other, four. All were planted, and four of the seven have developed into vigorous F_1 plants, two of them female and two male. The first of these four

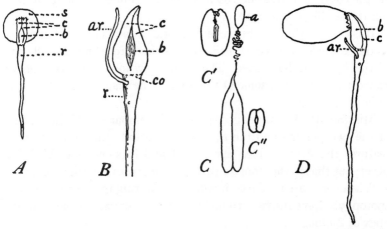

FIG. 170.—*Ceratozamia mexicana* × *Zamia monticola*, F_1 seedlings: *s*, seed; *c*, cotyledons; *b*, bud; *r*, primary root; *ar*, apogeotropic root; *co*, coleorhiza; *a*, egg membrane: *A*, *B*, and *C*, with two cotyledons: *D*, with only one; *C'*, embryo in female gametophyte; *C''*, transverse section of embryo with two cotyledons.—After CHAMBERLAIN.[123]

to cone produced a small male cone which shed its pollen in January, 1928. So, the male cone appeared while the plant was only 6 years old.

In 1929 three of the F_1 plants produced cones, one female and two males. One of the males shed all of its pollen before the sporophylls of the female opened; but the second male cone was still shedding pollen at the right time, and from this pollination good seeds were secured and several F_2 plants are thriving.

Ceratozamia mexicana × *Zamia monticola*.[123]—A generic cross between *Ceratozamia mexicana* and *Zamia monticola* was particularly successful. One cone was pollinated March 23, 1924, and another, on a different plant, on April 25, 1924. From these two cones more than a hundred seeds were secured, and now (December, 1934) more than fifty thriving F_1 plants look as if they were large enough to produce cones. It will be remembered that, normally, *Ceratozamia* has only one cotyledon, while *Zamia* has the usual two. In 1925, when the seedlings were being repotted, a careful examination was made and of the fifty-six which had survived up to this stage, forty-seven showed two cotyledons; three had one cotyledon, and in the other six the cotyledon situation could not be determined without sacrificing the seedlings (fig. 170).

It is evident that, in this generic hybrid, *Zamia* is dominant as far as the cotyledons are concerned. At this time (1934) not a single one of the F_1 plants has coned. The leaves now look like *Ceratozamia mexicana* leaves, and some of them would be diagnosed as *C. longifolia*.

Miss SOPHIA PAPADOPOULOS[434] made a comparison of the leaflets of the two parents and the F_1 generation, and found that in some features the F_1 resembled one parent and in some resembled the other; but that in the stomata there were features of both parents.

When cones are produced it will be interesting to find whether the sporophylls have the two strong horns of *Ceratozamia* or the truncate apex of *Zamia*.

CHAPTER VIII

CYCADALES—*Continued*

A study of the life-history of any group should make the investigator try to determine what its ancestry may have been and try to find whether it has left any progeny.

The "living fossil" character of the Cycadales makes them particularly favorable for a study of phylogeny, because the ancestors, which must have flourished in the Upper Carboniferous, are the best known of any fossil plants.

Without going into any detailed discussion, it may be assumed that the Cycadales have come from the Filicales either directly or through the Cycadofilicales. It is true that the lycopod line was very well represented in the Carboniferous, but paleobotanists agree that this line has not given rise to either the Cycadales or the Bennettitales.

The fern leaves of that period are nearly always pinnate, more often twice or thrice pinnate than once pinnate; and the Cycadofilicales are similar, with more than once-pinnate leaves prevailing. As far as the leaf is concerned, the cycads might have come from either group.

But, as shown in an earlier chapter, we think it has been proved, as far as anything can be proved in phylogeny, that the Cycadofilicales came from the Filicales. Lines of evolution do not progress at the same rate: one organ may progress rapidly while another remains stationary. The cycads retain the swimming sperm, but have lost the wall between the ventral canal nucleus and the egg nucleus; while in the pines the sperms have lost the swimming character but still keep the wall between the ventral canal nucleus and the egg nucleus. In *Stangeria*, the leaf is so fernlike that the genus was placed in the Polypodiaceae, of the true ferns—even in the genus *Lomaria;* but it has lost the wall between the ventral canal nucleus and the egg nucleus. Extremely rapid changes may take place in reproductive structures without any noticeable changes in the leaves. Most of the apples on the market today were unknown 30 years ago; but there has been little corresponding change in the leaves.

Since this is true, there is no occasion for surprise if the leaf of the true ferns is carried over into the Cycadofilicales, with little or no change, while the reproductive structures become so modified that they form the basis for a great phylum.

As we have already remarked, leaves, stems, and roots might originate independently in different groups. Nearly all botanists believe that the land flora had an aquatic ancestry, and no one doubts that algae preceded vascular plants. When algae transmigrated to the land, it became necessary to develop protective, conductive, and supporting structures, which had not been produced while the plant was surrounded by water. By mutation, by smaller variations, by natural selection, or in some other way, an efficient conducting system was developed.

Later, more algae may have transmigrated to the land, and, having similar conditions to contend with, may have made similar responses and developed a vascular system much like that of the previous transmigrants.

Because two systems of this sort resemble each other, it has been assumed that one of them transmitted it to the other. Paleobotanists are dependent, to a great extent, upon the evidence of vascular anatomy. Resemblances may be due to heredity, but it is possible that some of the similar structures may owe their similarity to environment.

And so there is a logical possibility that the leaves of Filicales and Cycadofilicales may owe their similarity to similarity of conditions. But we doubt whether details in venation and margins would be so identical if developed in this way. There are such things as environmental anatomy and hereditary anatomy. The former is more quantitative than qualitative and much more subject to change. If environmental anatomy were as powerful as hereditary, corn seeds and pumpkin seeds planted in the same hill should not produce such different plants.

We believe that the striking similarity of the leaves of Filicales and Cycadofilicales is due to heredity, so that the Cycadofilicales represent only the further evolution of some of the Filicales.

The strongest evidence for the derivation of the Cycadofilicales from the Filicales, as we have remarked before, is furnished by the seed. The *Evolution of the Seed* would make a good title for a book. One would have to transport himself back to the days of fairies and giants, of wonderful lamps and carpets, to believe that the seed originated without any ancestry.

The heterosporous Pteridophytes of today show unmistakably their homosporous ancestry; and it is only reasonable to suppose that heterosporous forms of ancient times arose from homosporous in the same way, some of the sporogenous cells failing to reach full development and giving up their substance to nourish the one or more spores which thus reached a higher stage in evolution. Megaspores became larger and larger until a free nuclear period arose within the spore, the gametophyte being retained within the spore, just as the spore itself, later, became retained within the sporangium. This, we believe, was the mode of origin of the seed habit. Naturally, it might take place without any great accompanying changes in the leaf.

In *Selaginella*, a lycopod, but nevertheless showing what probably took place in the heterosporous ferns, the megaspore is shed with its contained female gametophyte in various stages of development. Usually, the gametophyte has passed the free nuclear stage and entered the stage of cell formation. In *Selaginella apus*, a semi-aquatic species, archegonia may be formed and fertilization may take place before the megaspore falls out from the sporangium. In extreme cases there is little dehiscence of the sporangium and the megaspore remains inside, so that the shoot with its cotyledons and stem tip, and the root, break through the sporangium. In this extreme case the term "seed" is strictly applicable to *Selaginella*. Very probably, such a situation was common in the Carboniferous, where so many "seedlike" structures are found.

The line between ferns and advanced members of the Cycadofilicales, like *Trigonocarpon*, was as sharp as the line between ferns and seed plants of today. The place where it would be hard or impossible to draw the line would be where the enlarging megaspores were just beginning to be retained within the sporangium, sometimes falling out—when the plant must be classed as an heterosporous fern—and sometimes remaining inside the sporangium—when the plant must be classed as a seed plant. When some sporangia on a plant shed the

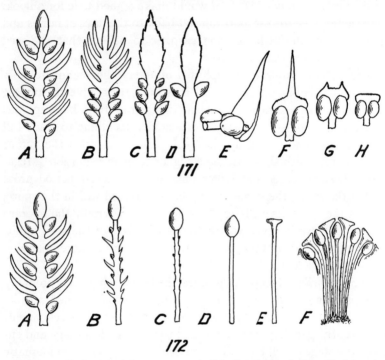

FIG. 171.—Reduction of the megasporophyll in Cycadales: *A*, theoretical ancestor of *Cycas*; *B*, *Cycas revoluta*; *C*, *Cycas circinalis*; *D*, occasionally in *Cycas media*, and usually in *Cycas normanbyana*; *E*, *Dioon edule*; *F*, *Macrozamia*; *G*, *Ceratozamia*; *H*, *Zamia*.

FIG. 172.—Reduction of the megasporophyll in Bennettitales: *A, B, C*, stages in the reduction in some hypothetical ancestor; *D*, the usual condition found in fossils; *E*, the sporophyll has become entirely sterile; *F*, fertile and sterile sporophylls with about the arrangement found in *Bennettites gibsonianus*.

megaspore, while others on the same plant retained it, as sometimes happens in *Selaginella apus*, only a taxonomist, by carefully selecting small portions of the frond, could get satisfactory specimens for his herbarium.

The reduction of the megasporophyll in the Cycadofilicales has already progressed so far that it suggests the *Cycas revoluta* type. In *Lyginopteris*, the tips of leaflets are regularly sterile, while the seeds are borne farther back. In *Neuropteris*, while many of the seeds are terminal, some are lateral. From such a type, both the

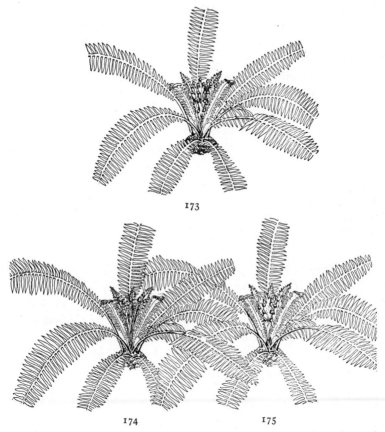

173

174   175

FIGS. 173-175.—Theoretical form (fig. 173) which might have given rise to the Bennettitales by the abortion of lateral ovules (fig. 174), and to the Cycadales, by the abortion of terminal ovules (fig. 175).

Cycadales and Bennettitales condition could be derived; the Cycadales by the abortion of the terminal sporangium, and the Bennettitales by the loss of the lateral sporangia (figs. 171, 172).

We can imagine that the ancestor of both the Bennettitales and the Cycadales looked something like fig. 173. Inside the crown of vegetative leaves is a crown of much reduced leaves, the male sporophylls, bearing sporangia, much as they are borne in a fern. Inside the crown of male sporophylls is a crown of still farther reduced leaves, the female sporophylls, bearing the ovules. The change from the bisporangiate condition to the dioecious is one which can be seen in all stages of transition in living angiosperms; and the evolution of the compact cone from a loose crown of sporophylls is seen in the living cycads.

From the condition shown in fig. 173, the Bennettitales may have developed as in fig. 174; and the Cycadales as in fig. 175.

From the Cycadofilicales to such a form as *Cycadospadix hennoquei*, the transition is not hard to imagine; and *Cycadospadix* might well have been included in the living genus, *Cycas*, for its megasporophyll differs less from that of *Cycas revoluta* than the sporophyll of *C. revoluta* differs from those of some of the other species of the genus (fig. 176). *Cycadospadix milleriana*,[465] with sporophylls loosely arranged, but stopping the growth of the axis, shows a condition intermediate between the loose crown of sporophylls of *Cycas revoluta*, and the compact cone (fig. 177).

The theory that the Cycadales may have come from the Bennettitales has already been referred to. The trunk and leaves are similar in the two lines and some of the Cycadales, like the Bennettitales, have axillary strobili. But the ovules, even in the earliest known Bennettitales, have followed a very different line of evolution. They have, in all cases, retained the terminal ovule and lost the lateral ones; while all of the Cycadales, even those known only as fossils, have lost the terminal ovule and retained the lateral. The Bennettitales could not have transmitted what the line had already lost. The multilocular microsporangium of the Bennettitales is so different from the unilocular sporangium of the Cycadales that they could hardly be related. Lines characterized by unilocular and multilocular sporangia may have been as distinct in the Paleozoic as they are in *Angiopteris* and *Marattia* today. Both types, in the Paleozoic, may have developed heterospory; and the heterospory of the fern may have progressed into the seed habit of the Cycadofilicales, so that one section of the Cycadofilicales may have given rise to the Bennettitales, and the other, to the Cycadales.

Have the Cycadales left any progeny? *Something* has left some progeny; for an abundant progeny, both gymnosperm and angiosperm, is very visible and very much alive. What groups could have been responsible?

If we consider only the nine living genera of cycads, the answer is easy: They are not responsible; they are the last of their race, restricted in geographical distribution, restricted in numbers, and struggling for their very existence.

What progeny exists for which an ancestry should be found? The only possibilities are the Cordaitales, Ginkgoales, Coniferales, Gnetales, and the angiosperms. We do not believe that any of these owe their origin to the cycads, but shall venture some speculations in dealing with the Coniferophytes.

FIG. 176.—*Cycadospadix hennoquei:* a megasporophyll rather closely resembling that of *Cycas revoluta.*—After ZEILLER.[717]

FIG. 177.—*Cycadospadix milleriana:* megasporophylls collected into a loose cone, which must have stopped the growth of the axis. The axis could not have persisted as in the female plant of *Cycas revoluta.*—After RENAULT.[465]

We should feel considerable confidence in concluding that the line, Filicales, Cycadofilicales, and Cycadales, is a genetic line, as thoroughly established as any line extending over so great a period.

TAXONOMY

The ideal taxonomy should be based upon life-histories and phylogeny. Unfortunately, the taxonomy of the Cycadales has suffered more than that of most groups, because the people who have made most of the descriptions have never studied cycads in the field. *Microcycas*, so large that one can climb around among its branches, and not looking at all like *Cycas*, would never have received such a name if the taxonomist had seen it in the field. But even such misnomers are not so bad as names given to commemorate those whose names would otherwise be lost; or those who would be remembered without spoiling the name of a plant. It is to be hoped that the growing practice of decapitalization will discourage commemorative names in botany, as it has in zoölogy and geology. How much better *Encephalartos horridus* and *Ceratozamia mexicana* than *Smithia jonesiana* and *Wangia yenii.*

Cycads, in the field, vary with age and with other factors. One who has studied cycads in the field would hesitate to determine most of the species from herbarium specimens.

The latest monograph is that of SCHUSTER.[510] There is a splendid bibliography and some original work, but what seems to be a total lack of study in the field. The keys are in Latin, as taxonomists claim they should be. The rising generation knows little or no Latin, but must know English, German, and French. Keys in any of these three languages would be more useful to nearly all of the people who might want to do some identification.

Cycads have several characters which could be made the basis for taxonomic keys. Most of them are composite, using both vegetative and reproductive features. In cultivation, where individuals are few and coning is rare, a key based entirely upon vegetative features would be desirable. SISTER MARY ALICE LAMB[336] devised a key to the genera based upon the leaves. Only *Cycas* and *Stangeria* have a midrib in the leaflet; and *Cycas* has only a midrib with no lateral veins, while *Stangeria* has a midrib with lateral veins. *Bowenia* is the only cycad with twice-pinnate leaves. *Dioon* is the only cycad with the insertion of the leaflet as broad as any other part of it. *Macrozamia* is the only one with a gland at the base of the leaflet; but in some species of this large genus the gland is obscure or may be absent. However, its presence identifies most of the species as belonging to this genus. In *Microcycas* the leaflets are reflexed on the rachis; in the rest they are either flat or turn up a little. Of the other three, *Zamia* has the rachis subcircinate in vernation; while in *Encephalartos* and *Ceratozamia* it is erect. In *Ceratozamia*, the leaflets are long, narrow, and taper gradually to a point, and are always entire (*integerrima*). In *Encephalartos* the margin of the leaflet is very jagged in some species and the lower leaflets are more and more reduced until, at the base, they become mere spines. In *Ceratozamia* there is no such reduction.

With the addition of histological characters the key devised by SISTER MARY ALICE LAMB could be made sufficiently complete for identification of the genera. In the large genera, she studied several species.

A key based upon the male gametophyte could probably be devised. Some of the genera can be determined, at a glance, by the cones. The two strong horns of *Ceratozamia*, the long spine of *Macrozamia*, the elongated peltate top of *Microcycas*, the loose cone of *Dioon*, and the crown of megasporophylls in *Cycas* provide an easy identification. With all characters available, it is easy to make keys.

For the convenience of students the following key, somewhat modified from PILGER'S key in ENGLER and PRANTL, *Pflanzenfamilien*, may be as good as any:

KEY TO THE GENERA OF CYCADACEAE

A. Leaflets with a midrib, but no side veins. Megasporophylls in a crown, through which the axis continues to grow. Sporophylls with several ovules along the sides—Oriental.................... 1. *Cycas*

B. Leaflets with a midrib and pinnate side veins. Sporophylls, each with 2 ovules, forming a cone —Africa... 2. *Stangeria*

C. Leaflets parallel veined, no midrib. Megasporophylls in cones, each with 2 ovules
  a) Leaflets bipinnate—Australia.................... 3. *Bowenia*
  b) Leaflets once pinnate
    1. Ovules on stalklike protrusions of the megasporophyll and arranged in a loose cone— Mexico.................................... 4. *Dioon*
    2. Ovules sessile. Ovules with
      (*a*) shield-shaped top with two strong horns—Mexico........................... 5. *Ceratozamia*
      (*b*) Sporophylls shield shaped, without horns
        (1) Cones small; sporophylls in longitudinal rows; leaves developed singly; mostly small plants— America............................. 6. *Zamia*
        (2) Cones large; leaves in crowns; mostly large plants—Africa............. 7. *Encephalartos*

(c) Sporophylls with a long median spine
—Australia.............................. 8. *Macrozamia*

(d) Male sporophylls with a flat top; female sporophylls with a shield shaped
top—Cuba.............................. 9. *Microcycas*

The "sporophylls in longitudinal rows," as given for *Zamia* is, of course, entirely wrong. The arrangement is strictly spiral, but so regular that the sporophylls appear to be in rows. This appearance is not at all confined to *Zamia*.

When the plants have cones, the genera can be identified positively. *Stangeria* and *Microcycas* are monotypic. *Bowenia* has only two species, both easily recognized. *Dioon* has three, and perhaps four, species, all easily recognizable. *Ceratozamia* has two, and, possibly, three good species and a lot of variants which taxonomists classify as species, subspecies, varieties, or forms, categories of no interest to the morphologist, except that they show how a plant may vary. The other genera, *Cycas*, *Encephalartos*, and *Zamia*, have numerous species, some of which have not been described adequately and never will be accurately described until there has been a prolonged and detailed field study. Until such a study has been made, the descriptions of species, subspecies, varieties, and forms in the more difficult regions of a genus will continue to degenerate into descriptions of individuals, which burden the literature, while the plants may or may not ever occur again.

Although the family has persisted from the Upper Paleozoic up to the present time, there is not sufficient material to make a key to the extinct members.

CHAPTER IX

CONIFEROPHYTES—CORDAITALES

The other great line of gymnosperms is the Coniferophytes, comprising four groups, the Cordaitales, Ginkgoales, Coniferales, and Gnetales, whose relation to each other is obscure.

As contrasted with the Cycadophytes, they are, prevailingly, much larger plants, with profusely branched stems and simple leaves. A transverse section of the stem shows a large pith, rather scanty zone of wood in some forms, and a fairly large cortex. But, while these features recall the Cycadofilicales, there are, within the order, forms with rather small pith, extensive zone of wood, and small cortex, approaching the condition characteristic of the Coniferales. Like the Cycadofilicales, they are all phyllosiphonic.

The living forms belong as dominantly to the temperate zone as the Cycadales belong to tropical and subtropical regions. Many flourish where the winter temperature becomes colder than 40°F. below zero.

The geological history goes back as far as that of the Cycadophytes, probably much farther back. A provisional diagram is shown in fig. 2. In this diagram no attempt has been made to show the relation of the six families under which we shall treat the Coniferales; and we have not tried to attach the Gnetales to anything.

The four great groups of the Coniferophytes will be treated separately.

GRAND D'EURY,[222] C. E. BERTRAND,[52] and RENAULT[465] were pioneers in the investigation of this order. Among later investigators whose names have become prominent are SCOTT, OLIVER, P. BERTRAND, GORDON, and others. Excellent textbooks, which are contributions to knowledge as well as presentations of known material, have been written by SCOTT,[533-534] SEWARD,[546-548] SOLMS-LAUBACH,[573] and POTONIÉ.[455]

The Cordaitales formed the world's first great forests. Many of them were tall trees reaching 30 meters in height, and growing in dense stands. Although the trunks sometimes reached a diameter of nearly a meter, and often two-thirds that size, the great height made them appear slender, an appearance accentuated by the branching which was confined to the top of the plant. The leaves range from two centimeters to a meter in length, and are as uniformly simple as the leaves of the Cycadophytes are compound. While some of the large leaves are 20 cm. in breadth, the prevailing type is uniformly rather narrowly lanceolate. The top of the plant must have looked some- what like the modern Screw Pine, *Pandanus*. GRAND D'EURY'S restoration, as modified by SCOTT,[533] is shown in fig. 178.

DISTRIBUTION

The Cordaitales were most abundant in the Carboniferous, but how far below and how far above that horizon they may extend depends upon the diagnosis of araucarioid stems in the pre-Carbonif- erous deposits, and of leaves in the Triassic and Rhaetic. KRÄU- SEL[328] thinks that these lower horizon stems and higher horizon leaves cannot be assigned to this group with much confidence. WIELAND thinks they go back to the Silurian or earlier, developing into great forests in the Devonian, culminating in the great swamp- forests of the Carboniferous, declining in the Permian, and becoming extinct in the Liassic.

In the Carboniferous, stems, leaves, roots, and reproductive structures are well known, and there has been an assembling of stem, leaf, root, and reproductive structures, as in the famous *Lyginopteris*. Consequently, in this horizon, isolated parts can be assigned to the group with considerable certainty. Where only the wood is avail- able, as in the lower horizons, it is a matter of individual opinion whether a certain trunk or piece of wood may belong to this group or not. It must be admitted that investigators who have made the most thorough studies of the histological characters of the wood of both living and extinct forms are the ones who lay greatest stress upon the reliability of diagnoses based upon the microscopic struc- ture of wood. The assigning of leaves to the group is also a matter of opinion. When we remember that, on the basis of the leaf alone, it is impossible to determine whether a certain leaf belongs to the

Bennettitales or Cycadales, there should be some hesitation in asserting that some particular leaf must belong to the Cordaitales.

All investigators agree that the group can be recognized with certainty from the lowest Carboniferous (Culm) through the lower

FIG. 178.—*Dorycordaites* sp.: restoration showing stem, leaves, roots, and fructification. SCOTT's modification of GRAND D'EURY's figure is principally a shortening of the trunk, which would have required a couple more pages to show it on the same scale as the roots and the branching top.—After GRAND D'EURY and SCOTT.[533]

Permian (Rothliegendes), with its greatest development in the Pennsylvanian.

Geographically, the distribution was world-wide in the Carboniferous. Material has been collected in the Carboniferous and Permian of Europe, North America, and China; in the Permian of Russia and Siberia; and in the Permo-Carboniferous of India, Australia, South Africa, and South America.

LIFE-HISTORY

While the life-history has not been worked out as thoroughly as that of the Cycadofilicales, the structure of the wood and leaves has been studied in detail, and something is known of the reproduction.

SCOTT[533] treats the order, Cordaitales, under three families, the Poroxylae, Pityeae, and the Cordaiteae, which, for the sake of the usual family ending, might be called the Poroxylaceae, Pityaceae, and the Cordaitaceae. The first family has only one genus, *Poroxylon;* in the second, the principal genera are *Pitys*, *Callixylon*, and *Dadoxylon;* in the third, *Cordaites* is the best-known genus, but *Mesoxylon, Parapitys, Mesopitys*, and others have received attention. Some of the names suggest resemblances to members of the second family.

KRÄUSEL,[329] in *Die natürlichen Pflanzenfamilien*, arranges the material, provisionally, under four families, based largely upon the endarch or mesarch character of the primary bundles and their distribution.

THE SPOROPHYTE—VEGETATIVE

The stem.—The stem, in most forms tall and slender, and branching only at the top, with dense clusters of leaves, suggests that the plants grew in crowded stands, forming a deep shade.

In the reconstruction of the Carboniferous swamp-forest in the Field Museum of Natural History, at Chicago, a Cordaites with large leaves was chosen to represent this important group (fig. 179). The general appearance, as the spectator views the realistic scene, is probably correct, but in another reconstruction the *Dory-Cordaites* leaf is combined with the *Eu-Cordaites* fructification, as in the well-known restoration of GRAND D'EURY.

In transverse section, the topography of the stem of some species of *Cordaites* resembled that of a cycad, with large pith, scanty wood, and large cortex, as in *Cordaites (Mesoxylon) sutcliffii* (fig. 180). In *Mesoxylon multirame* the topography of the stem bears a striking resemblance to that of a cycad, except that there is a differentiation of the cortex into two regions, as in so many of the Cycadofilicales. The double leaf trace is very distinct (fig. 181). In others, there is less pith and cortex and more wood (fig. 182).

FIG. 179.—*Cordaites* sp: tip of a branch with long leaves and branches bearing strobili. Detail from the restoration of an entire tree in the Carboniferous swamp-forest reconstruction in the Field Museum of Natural History at Chicago.

Cordaites seldom shows any growth-rings, and such rings are rare in Carboniferous woods, indicating that the weather was uniform throughout the year. Near Jalapa, Mexico, there are places where some particular dicotyl may not show any growth-rings; while the same species, 10 miles away, may have well-defined annual rings. In this case, the rings are absent where the forest is wet throughout the year; while, a few miles away, outside the forest, there is a well-marked alternation of wet and dry seasons, a condition which produces growth-rings.

Coenoxylon (probably Permian) has distinct growth-rings. PEN-HALLOW[449] divided the species of *Dadoxylon* (lower Carboniferous)

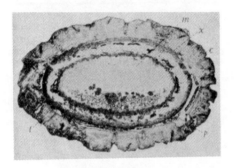

FIG. 180.—*Cordaites sutcliffii:* transverse section of stem; *m*, pith; *x*, xylem; *p*, phloem; *c*, cortex; *t*, leaf trace.—From a photograph by LAND of a section made by LOMAX. From COULTER and CHAMBERLAIN, *Morphology of Gymnosperms*[154] (University of Chicago Press).

into two groups, one characterized by the presence, and the other by the absence, of growth-rings. A similar treatment of the plants of the Jalapa region would be interesting, for individuals would probably change from one group to another, if they should be moved to the corresponding locality.

In the specimen shown in fig. 182 there are distinct growth-rings, and so many of them that it seems necessary to interpret them as regularly recurrent, perhaps seasonal. When only one or two rings appear, where rings are not usually present, they may be due to injury. If most of the top of the plant should be broken off, the growth might nearly stop; and as a new top developed, growth would be resumed, resulting in the formation of a ring, just as in *Dioon edule* a ring is formed when a prolonged dormant period is followed by a resumption of growth.

ELKINS and WIELAND[186] figured distinct growth-rings in *Calli-xylon oweni*, from the upper Devonian of Indiana. While these rings are too distinct to be overlooked, there might be rings a little less distinct, which might escape notice, just as growth-rings in some of the woody monocotyls escaped for so long. We suspect that there

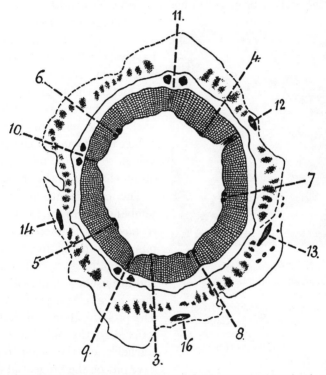

FIG. 181.—*Mesoxylon multirame:* transverse section of stem, showing large pith, scanty wood, large cortex, and 13 of the 16 leaf traces which may be found in a section. The leaf traces are numbered from within outward.—After SCOTT.[533]

are seasonal differences in some of the big cacti. Some of the beautifully silicified pieces of trunks of *Callixylon oweni* were more than 5 meters in length and nearly a meter in diameter, and the entire trees may have been from 30 to 40 meters in height.

Cordaites, the dominant genus, has an endarch siphonostele, with spirally marked tracheids bordering on the pith. The first formed protoxylem cells are small and are followed by cells of greater diameter, still with the spiral markings; then come scalariform tracheids, and finally the pitted tracheids of the secondary wood; so that there is a gradual transition from the earliest spiral elements to the pitted tracheids of the secondary wood (fig. 183). Such a sequence can be seen in seedlings of *Dioon spinulosum*, but not in older plants, where even the earliest protoxylem has scalariform tracheids.

FIG. 182.—*Cordaites* sp.: transverse section of stem with large zone of wood, small pith and cortex, and numerous growth-rings.—From a photograph by LAND of a section made by LOMAX. Natural size. From COULTER and CHAMBERLAIN, *Morphology of Gymnosperms*[154] (University of Chicago Press).

Other genera, as *Mesoxylon*, *Pitys*, *Callixylon*, and others, have various amounts of centripetal xylem. In *Poroxylon*, all of the metaxylem is centripetal, so that the bundle is exarch (fig. 184). The general tendency is to reduce the amount of centripetal xylem, so that the mesarch condition changes to the endarch.

The multiseriate pitting, resembling that of the living genus *Araucaria*, is characteristic. The pits are bordered, in two, three, and sometimes even five rows, and are usually so crowded that they have a hexagonal outline. The pits are almost entirely restricted to the radial walls, but tracheids of the older regions have pits on the tangential walls.

The medullary rays are narrow, usually only one cell wide; but in *Pitys* and its allies they are wider, the middle of the ray reaching a width of several cells.

The pith, in the *Cordaites* section of the order, is very characteristic. It cracks transversely, but remains intact at the periphery, where it borders on the xylem, giving the whole pith the appearance of a pile of concave discs. So it was called a discoid pith. In many fossils, the pith drops out, and was first discovered and described as a distinct genus, ARTIS describing it as *Sternbergia*, and STERNBERG returning the compliment by naming it *Artisia*.[533]

The leaf.—Taking the group as a whole, the leaves are in striking contrast with those of the Cycadophytes. They are much smaller, even the largest seldom exceeding a meter in length and 20 cm. in width; while the smallest are needle-like and only a couple of centi-

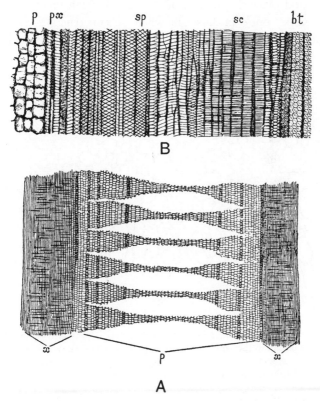

FIG. 183.—*Cordaites (Araucarioxylon) brandlingii: A*, longitudinal radial section of stem, showing discoid pith (*p*), and wood (*x*); ×7. *B*, longitudinal radial section from the pith to the beginning of secondary wood; *p*, pith; *px*, first protoxylem; *sp*, later spiral and *sc*, scalariform tracheids of primary wood; *bt*, pitted tracheids of secondary wood; ×95.—After SCOTT.[533]

meters in length. They are leathery, with a highly xerophytic structure. The margins are entire, and the venation dichotomous, with so little forking of the veins beyond the base of the leaf that botanists regarded them as parallel-veined leaves, and promptly made the monocots older than the dicots by the sure evidence of geological history. A prominent paleobotanist once proved that the monocots must be older than the dicots, because an ancestor must be older than its progeny. Now that it is generally believed that dichotomous venation is the most ancient type, the monocots can take a more natural place as progeny of the dicots. Such recent mistakes should temper one's enthusiasm when he constructs phylogenies, especially when dealing with extinct plants where only scattered fragments are available.

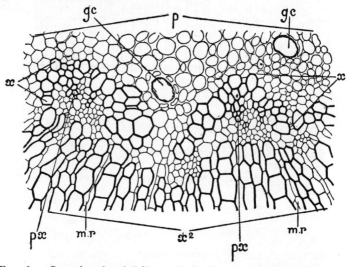

Fig. 184.—*Poroxylon edwardsii* (Permo-Carboniferous): transverse section of stem. Both bundles belong to the same leaf trace; *p*, pith; *gc*, mucilage canals; *px*, protoxylem; *x*, centripetal metaxylem; x^2, secondary xylem; *mr*, medullary rays; ×66.—After BERTRAND and RENAUD, in SCOTT'S, *Studies in Fossil Botany*.[533]

The name "*Cordaites*" was originally applied to the leaves, and the *Cordaites* section is still subdivided on leaf characters. *Cordaites*, the *Eu-Cordaites* of GRAND D'EURY, includes those in which the leaves are broad, with rounded apex and with strong veins mixed with weaker ones. They were most abundant in the middle part of the Upper Carboniferous. The *Poa-Cordaites* forms had linear, grasslike leaves, up to 40 cm. in length, with veins about equal. The *Dory-Cordaites* section contains those with broad lanceolate leaves with acute apex, and rather fine equal veins. They are most abundant in the Upper Carboniferous and Lower Permian.

Taking the group as a whole, the internal structure of the leaf is highly xerophytic[464] (fig. 185). The epidermal cells are rather thick walled, and the hypodermal cells on both sides of the leaf have very thick walls and are grouped into ribs. There is a strong bundle sheath connected with the ribs of the hypodermal layer, and be-

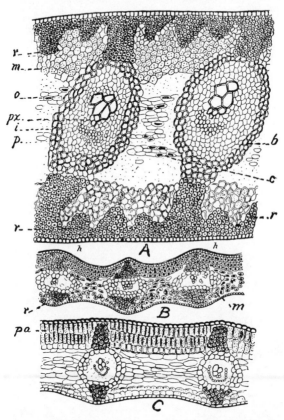

Fig. 185.—*A, Cordaites angulostriatus; B, C. rhombinervis; C, C. lingulatus; r,* ribs of thick-walled cells; *m,* mesophyll; *o,* centrifugal metaxylem; *i,* centripetal metaxylem; *px,* protoxylem; *p,* phloem; *b,* bundle sheath; *c,* elongated cells connecting bundles; *pa,* palisade: *A,* ×60; *B* and *C,* ×50.—After RENAULT.[465]

tween bundles the cells are often elongated, as in some transfusion tissues. Some forms have a well-marked palisade layer, as in *C,* of fig. 185. The veins are mesarch, even when the stem is endarch.

GORDON'S discovery of needle-like leaves in connection with

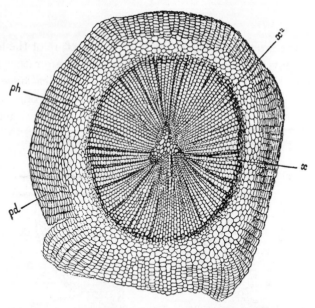

Fig. 186.—*Amyelon radicans:* (probably root of one of the Cordaitales) from the lower Carboniferous of England; x, protoxylem of triarch primary xylem; x^2, secondary xylem; ph, phloem; pd, secondary cortex; $\times 23$.—After Scott.[533]

Fig. 187.—*Amyelon* sp.: (probably root of Cordaites) transverse section of tetrarch root showing growth-rings; $\times 9$.—From a photomicrograph by Land of a section by Lomax. From Coulter and Chamberlain, *Morphology of Gymnosperms*[154] (University of Chicago Press).

Pitys is important, for it is this type of leaf which became dominant, and which has persisted in living forms.

The root.—Not so much is known about the roots of Cordaitales. No roots, showing internal structure, have ever been found in such close association with stems and leaves, and agreeing so well in histological details, that there is no doubt about their connection. Many of them are splendidly silicified, showing even the cambium and secondary cortex, with cells lined up in rows as definite as those produced by a phellogen in a living plant (fig. 186).

An older root, assigned to *Cordaites*, shows definite growth-rings (fig. 187). This specimen has tetrarch primary wood; in others, the primary wood is diarch.

The protoxylem has spiral markings, the metaxylem is scalariform, and the secondary wood has multiseriate pitted tracheids like those of the stem.

THE SPOROPHYTE—REPRODUCTIVE

As in other fossil plants, not so much is known about the reproductive portion of the life-cycle.

FIG. 188.—*Cordaianthus gemnifer Grand d'Eury:* female fructification of *Cordaites* from Mazon Creek, Illinois, U.S.A.—From NOÉ, *Pennsylvanian flora of Northern Illinois.*[415]

The strobili.—Some of the Cordaitales are monoecious and some dioecious, but there are none of the bisporangiate strobili which are so prevalent in the Bennettitales. Impressions of long rigid shoots with ovules in the axils of bracts have long been known in European Carboniferous deposits; and more recently Noé[415] has found similar specimens in the Carboniferous of Illinois (fig. 188). Long ago, Grand d'Eury,[219] combining such elongated spikes with the abun-

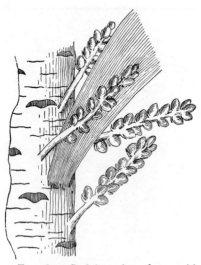

dant lanceolate leaves, made a restoration which has been copied ever since (fig. 189). His restoration of the complete plant (fig. 178) has the *Eu-Cordaites* type of fructification combined with pointed lanceolate leaves of *Dorycordaites*. The fructification which belongs with *Dorycordaites* has a long axis with ovules borne on slender drooping pedicels (fig. 190).

Some monoecious forms have been found with the shoots attached to the stem (fig. 191). The individual strobili, more or less definitely arranged in two rows, are about a centimeter in

FIG. 189.—*Cordaites:* piece of stem with base of one leaf and four fruiting spikes. Several broad leaf scars are shown; two-thirds natural size.—After Grand d'Eury.[219]

length. In some impressions it has not been possible to distinguish between male and female strobili.

The male strobilus.—The male strobilus consists of a stout axis with numerous bracts and some sporophylls bearing one, two, or even four microsporangia (fig. 192). A more detailed view shows that the sporangia had not yet shed their pollen (fig. 193).

The female strobilus.—The female strobilus also has a stout axis, with even more bracts than the male, and comparatively few ovules (fig. 194). The ovule is borne on a short spur shoot in the axil of a bract, thus making the strobilus compound. There are no compound strobili in the Cycadophytes, nor in the male strobili of Coniferophytes, except in the Gnetales.

The nucellus of the ovule was free from the integument throughout (fig. 195).

THE GAMETOPHYTES

Even less is known about the gametophytes than in the Cycadofilicales, but some silicified material has been sectioned.

The male gametophyte.—The male gametophyte is better known than the female, probably on account of the protection afforded by the exine. Sections show that the interior was multicellular. The best views are seen in sections of the upper part of the nucellus

FIG. 190.—*Samaropsis pitcairniae* (*Dory-Cordaites*): part of fruiting branch, bearing winged seeds; natural size.—After CARRUTHERS.[91]

FIG. 191.—*Cordaianthus pitcairniae:* piece of stem with a shoot bearing male strobili on the left, and one with female strobili on the right; natural size.—After GRAND D'EURY.[219]

(fig. 196). It has been suggested that since pollen grains in the micropylar canal are larger than apparently mature pollen grains in the microsporangium, there is growth after shedding. This is hardly probable in forms with a thick spore coat. In well-known living anemophilous forms, the dry pollen swells when it becomes wet. Just so, in these fossil forms, the pollen would be likely to swell upon reaching the pollination drop. The pollen grains in the micropylar canal, of course, are mature; but whether the cells are vegetative or spermatogenous is not certain. It is very likely that there was both vegetative and spermatogenous tissue in the pollen grains. If well-preserved material in late stages should be found and sectioned, it seems safe to predict that it will show that the Cordaitales had swimming sperms.

The female gametophyte.—Nothing is known about the female gametophyte, except that it must have been elongated. The ovule is so highly developed that the megaspore membrane must have become too thin to give much protection.

The embryo.—As in the Cycadofilicales, no embryo has yet been found. Immense numbers of American coal balls, with well-pre-

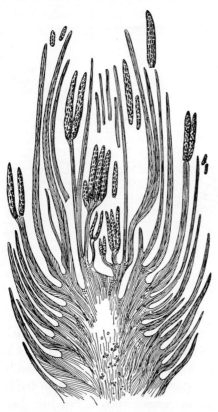

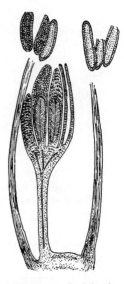

FIG. 192.—*Cordaianthus penjonii:* longitudinal section of male strobilus showing bracts and sporophylls bearing terminal microsporangia; ×10.—After RENAULT.[465]

FIG. 193.—*Cordaianthus penjonii:* the sporophyll in the middle bears four microsporangia. The one at the right has shed its pollen; ×23.—After RENAULT.[465]

served structures, have been collected and still remain to be sectioned. They may contain the missing stages in the life-history.

PHYLOGENY

The Coniferophytes have been contrasted with the Cycadopnytes as having branched stems and unbranched leaves, while the Cycadophytes have branched leaves and unbranched stems. In external appearance this contrast is very prevalent.

In the Cycadophytes, the large pith, scanty wood, and large cortex are characteristic from the first appearance of the phylum to

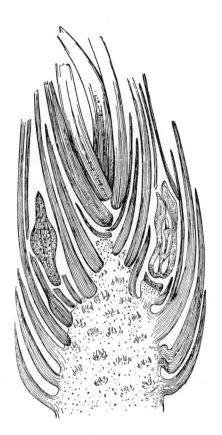

FIG. 194.—*Cordaianthus williamsonii:* longitudinal section of female strobilus, showing sterile bracts and two ovules; ×10. —After RENAULT.[465]

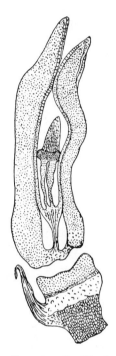

FIG. 195.—*Cordaianthus williamsonii:* longitudinal section of ovule, showing the nucellus free from the integument. The lower part of the nucellus was much decayed before silicification occurred, but it still shows that there was an elongated female gametophyte; ×35. —After RENAULT.[465]

its living members. In the Coniferophytes, the earlier members also have a large pith, scanty zone of wood, and a large cortex; but there is a tendency, even in the Cordaitales, to reduce the pith and cortex and increase the proportion of wood. The later fossil members and all the living members have a small pith, large zone of wood, and a comparatively small cortex.

Whether these resemblances in stems mean genetic relationship is conjectural. *Helianthus*, *Sambucus*, and *Cucurbita* have a large pith, scanty zone of wood, and small cortex; but that does not mean that any one of them inherited the condition from another or that any of them got it from any gymnosperm. Phylogenetic anatomy is one of the best indicators of genetic relationships; but it is not always easy to distinguish between phylogenetic anatomy and ecological anatomy. Environment is a powerful factor. If there had been no changes in this factor, the Cordaitales should still be with us, and their life-stories would be as well known as that of *Pinus*.

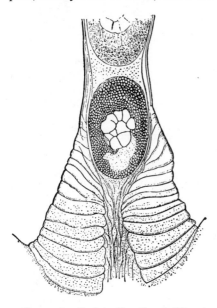

FIG. 196.—*Cordaianthus Grand d'Euryi:* section of beak of nucellus; wedged in the passageway are two large pollen grains, the lower one showing part of the surface of the exine and also the multicellular interior; ×225.—After RENAULT.[465]

While the leaf is peculiarly sensitive to changes in conditions, and may change from simple to compound in the lifetime of an individual, we should regard the compound leaf as an outstanding character of the Cycadophytes; and the simple leaf as just as strong a characteristic of the Coniferophytes.

The two phyla existed side by side in the Paleozoic, and the Cordaitales have been recognized much farther back than the Cycadofilicales; but it is more than doubtful whether the Cordaitales were the ancestors of the Cycadofilicales. Both must have come from heterosporous Pteridophytes. There was so much variety among the Paleozoic Pteridophytes that it is not necessary to make both come from the same section of that group. Some Pteridophyte with compound leaves and a stem with large pith, scanty wood, and large cortex, may have given rise to the Cycadophytes; while another, with similar stem structure, but with simple leaves, may have been the ancestor of the Coniferophytes.

When the life-histories of the Paleozoic forms become better known, there will be a firmer foundation for theories, and theorizing will not be so easy. With only a few facts to reconcile, any theory will do; but when facts become numerous, a theory reconciling all the facts is more difficult to formulate.

CHAPTER X

CONIFEROPHYTES—GINKGOALES

This order is still represented by one living genus, *Ginkgo*. Its ancestry can be traced back to the Paleozoic, and, like the cycads, it may be called a living fossil, for it still retains the swimming sperm which characterizes the ferns and which probably characterized all of the Paleozoic seed plants.

Leaves are abundant in the Permian, and leaves which may belong to the order, but which may belong to the Cordaitales, were abundant in the Carboniferous. From the Triassic the order developed rapidly and can be traced with confidence, reaching its greatest abundance and widest distribution in the Jurassic; but before the end of the Jurassic, it began to wane, and is now represented by the single genus, *Ginkgo*.

EXTINCT MEMBERS

As extinct members of this order, aside from *Baiera*, which all recognize as nearly related to the living *Ginkgo*, PILGER, in *Die natürlichen Pflanzenfamilien*, lists seven genera as more or less probably related, and six more as more or less doubtfully belonging here.

The living genus, *Ginkgo*, is not rare in the Liassic, and in the middle Jurassic was abundant and world-wide in its distribution. Several extinct species have been described, but, since they are based principally upon leaves, it seems just as well to put all of them under *Ginkgo biloba*. Its leaves vary so much with age, position on the tree, and environment, that most, if not all, of the leaf impressions which have tempted taxonomists to make more species could be duplicated by leaves of the living species.

Baiera[465] was abundant in the lower Permian of Europe and North America. In the Jurassic it was not so abundant as Ginkgo. Impressions have been found in the Rhaetic of South Africa. The genus became extinct in the Lower Cretaceous.

Usually only the leaves are found, and they are very seldom attached. They differ from the living *Ginkgo* in being more deeply incised and in having narrower lobes. The venation is as distinctly

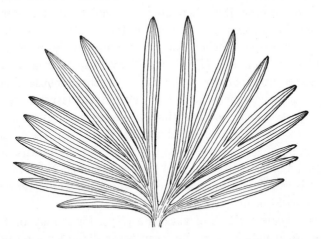

Fig. 197.—*Baiera gracilis:* the leaf is bilobed, but each of the two lobes is repeatedly dichotomous; natural size.—After Renault.[465]

dichotomous as in the ferns (fig. 197).

The seeds are borne on a branching axis, usually with several seeds on an axis. Some of the figures, which seem to give the shape very accurately, do not show any collar (fig. 198*A*).

The microsporangia were in strobili consisting of several sporophylls, each with several microsporangia. In younger stages, the sporo-

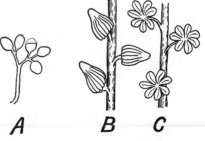

Fig. 198.—*Baiera münsteriana: A*, five unripe seeds; *B*, portion of male strobilus with three sporophylls bearing several microsporangia, shortly before shedding pollen; *C*, similar specimen at a later stage. Rhaetic from Bayreuth.—After Schimper-Schenk.[501]

phylls, with their microsporangia, closely resemble those of the living *Ginkgo*, except that there are generally six or more sporangia on a sporophyll (fig. 198*B* and *C*).

GINKGO

Probably no other living tree can trace its ancestry so far back as *Ginkgo*, for, as we have noted, it can be recognized in the Liassic. It is doubtful whether it exists today in the wild state. Travelers claim that they have seen it growing wild in the forests of western China, where, they say, it reaches a height of more than 30 meters, with a diameter of 1.3 meters. If extinct in the wild state, it must have become so recently, perhaps in the last two or three thousand years, or the date may have been much later, even in the last hundred years; for the passenger pigeon is extinct, although people now living can remember when it was so abundant that immense flocks cast shadows like big clouds. *Ginkgo* was kept alive by priests in China and Japan, who cultivated it in temple grounds. Now, in cultivation, it is world-wide and hardy even where the winter temperature reaches 20°F. below zero.

It is a beautiful tree of various aspects, for it may be tall and slender; or it may have a trunk a meter in diameter, soon breaking into widely spreading branches, so that the breadth may exceed the height. Whether it ever reaches the reported 30 meters in height is doubtful. A botanist should identify the tree which is being measured.

THE LIFE-HISTORY

The life-history, especially its spermatogenesis and embryogeny, has been so thoroughly investigated that the principal features are well known.

The stem.—In most cultivated specimens the trunk is strongly excurrent and the outline steeply pyramidal: but as the tree gets old—50 or 60 years—it is likely to broaden, so that the outline is rounded at the top. If the top of a young tree is cut off, the branches spread widely; so that the trunk of a tree a meter in diameter may not be more than twice that height before it breaks into large spreading branches (figs. 199, 200).

As in many Coniferophytes, there are two kinds of branches, the long branch and the short spur. The first growth is always of the first type; and as the branch, or the main axis, increases in length, it grows for a year as a long branch before any spurs appear. The

FIG. 199.—*Ginkgo biloba:* Young trees with strongly excurrent trunks

Fig. 200.—*Ginkgo biloba:* ovulate tree at Imperial University of Tokyo.—From a photograph by MIYAKE.

long branch grows rapidly, even half a meter in a year, while a spur
2 or 3 centimeters long may be several years old. A spur with its leaf
scars and scale leaf scars, and with half a dozen leaves coming out
from the top, at nearly the same level, recalls the cycad trunk, with
its armor and crown of leaves.

A spur, even after reaching an age of 5 or 10 years, instead of producing a crown of leaves, may grow out into a long slender shoot with
widely scattered leaves.

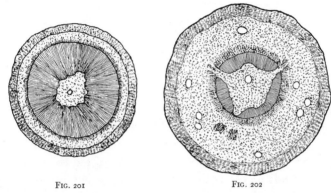

FIG. 201   FIG. 202

FIG. 201.—*Ginkgo biloba:* transverse section of long shoot; ×8
FIG. 202.—*Ginkgo biloba:* transverse section of spur shoot; ×8

In transverse section, the topography of the long shoot and the
spur is very different (figs. 201 and 202). The long shoot has a comparatively small pith and cortex, its wood is harder, and there are
not so many mucilage cavities. Even in old spurs, where the quanti-
ty of wood is at its maximum, it is not difficult to cut sections. In
both shoots there is an abundant development of secondary cortex.

Annual rings, while not so prominent as in *Pinus* and other gymnosperms of the Chicago region, are well marked. Chicago is near
the northern limit for *Ginkgo*. Seeds planted in the open scarcely
ever survive the first winter. The seedlings are kept inside the first
winter and then, for several years, are put out earlier and earlier in
the spring and taken in later and later in the autumn, until they are
rugged enough to be set out permanently. Even then the tree is not
as hardy as most native trees, for a few weeks of mild weather, too
early in the spring, will cause the buds to swell. When cold weather

follows, as it usually does, many leaves fall, and those remaining on the tree do not reach their full size and are likely to fall early in the autumn. Such an untimely swelling of the buds is usually accompanied by the formation of a growth-ring; not a strong ring which might cause uncertainty in estimating the age, but nevertheless a ring which can easily be seen.

Mucilage cavities are abundant. They are found in the pith and in the primary cortex of the stele, in the root, in the petiole and blade of the leaf, in the seed and its peduncle, and in the sporangium. They seem to be absent from the secondary cortex. Tannin cells and calcium oxalate crystals are also abundantly and widely distributed.

The vascular cylinder of the stem is an endarch siphonostele. The protoxylem consists exclusively of spiral elements, which are much more abundant in the spur shoots than in the long shoots. In the long shoots, in transverse section, in the radial direction, there are from one to five spiral elements; while in the spur shoots there may be as many as ten, with five or more quite common. In both shoots, the spiral elements border directly upon the pitted tracheids.

The tracheids of the secondary wood have one or two rows of bordered pits on the radial walls, not crowded as in the *Cordaites* group, but more or less scattered. Their arrangement is either opposite or alternate. The last tracheids of a year's growth have tangential pitting, where they border upon the spring wood of the next year, a feature of considerable interest, because paleozoic stems of the *Cordaites* type, when they have rings, do not show any radial pitting.

Bars of Sanio are easily demonstrated in the secondary wood, but do not occur in the primary wood[301] (fig. 203). The pits are often so scattered that no bars are formed. The trabeculae of Sanio also occur, but are easily distinguished from the bars, because they cross the lumen of the tracheid, while the bars are covered by a secondary thickening of the cell wall.

The medullary rays are characteristically short in vertical extent, many of them being only one cell in height, and they are nearly always only one cell in width. Rays one cell wide and two cells high predominate in the trunk and in the long shoots, but some rays are three, four, or even five cells in height. In the spur shoots the rays, although only one cell wide, range from one to sixteen cells in height, with rays three to six cells high very common (figs. 204 and 205). The rays remain alive for a long time, retaining their nuclei, protoplasm, and starch for 30 years or more.

With the exception of the medullary rays, there are no parenchyma cells, like the thin-walled cells of the cycads, interspersed with the woody tracheids.

The leaf.—The beautiful leaf, with its symmetrical dichotomous venation, has given *Ginkgo* its colloquial name, the Maidenhair Tree, because the leaves on the spur shoots resemble those of *Adiantum*, the Maidenhair Fern. The leaves on the long shoots are mostly bilobed, the feature which suggested the specific name; but the leaves on the spurs usually have only a wavy margin, with none of the deep lobing. Leaves at the top of the tree, on first-year long shoots, and especially the leaves of seedlings, are very deeply lobed; and besides the two deep primary lobes may have two or three secondary lobes on each side, so that they approach the deeply and narrowly lobed leaves of the extinct *Baiera* (figs. 206, 207).

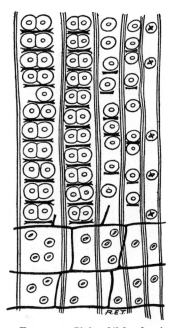

FIG. 203.—*Ginkgo biloba:* longitudinal section of mature wood showing pitting and "Bars of Sanio."— After JEFFREY.[301]

With so much variation in the leaves, species based upon leaf characters alone are open to more or less suspicion.

The dichotomous venation of the leaf is very regular. In the petiole there are two strands, each, by repeated forking, forming the venation of its side of the leaf (Fig. 208). It may be that the more vigorous growth of seedlings and long shoots may be responsible for the bilobed character of their leaves, while the leaves of the slow growing spurs are seldom bilobed.

The veins occasionally have a few centripetal tracheids, and thus have an indistinct mesarch structure. A single strand enters the cotyledons, distinctly mesarch below, but becoming exarch higher up.

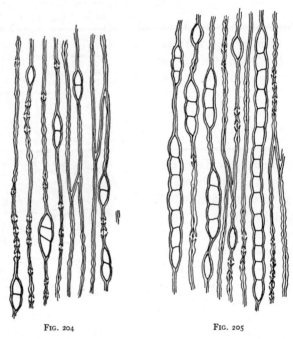

FIG. 204   FIG. 205

FIG. 204.—*Ginkgo biloba:* longitudinal tangential section of long shoot, showing medullary rays, one to three cells in longitudinal extent; ×180.

FIG. 205.—*Ginkgo biloba:* longitudinal tangential section spur shoot, showing medullary rays, one to fifteen cells in longitudinal extent; ×180.

The mucilage cavities in the leaves are elongated, 1–5mm. in length, and are nearly as conspicuous as the veins themselves. They take the same direction as the veins, and are usually spaced about half-way between adjacent veins. Many cells contain a large crystal of calcium oxalate, and tannin cells are abundant.

The two strands in the petiole are endarch, with spiral protoxylem elements. At a distance of several cells from the protophloem there is a sheath of thick-walled cells, and, just within it on the protoxylem side, there are often some thick-walled suberized tracheids (fig. 209).

The tissue is rather uniform throughout the leaf, there being no well marked palisade in the leaves of the spur shoots. The leaves on

FIG. 206.—*Ginkgo biloba:* tracings of leaves from a single tree at the University of Chicago. The leaves in the upper part of the figure are from long shoots; and the ten lower leaves are from spur shoots; one-third natural size.

the long shoots, especially the larger leaves, have a well-marked palisade. The stomata are on the abaxial surface and are slightly sunken (fig. 210).

The root.—The root has a diarch cylinder, except when there are three cotyledons, in which case it is triarch.

Fig. 207.—*Ginkgo biloba:* tracings of three leaves from a young tree about two meters in height; one-third natural size.

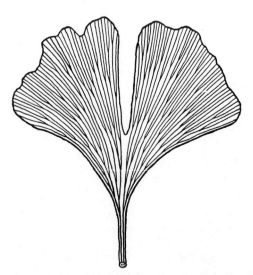

Fig. 208.—*Ginkgo biloba:* leaf from long shoot. There are two strands in the petiole, each, by repeated dichotomies forming the venation of its side of the leaf blade; natural size.

A short distance back from the root tip, the outer layers of cells are suberized, and just within the suberized layers, tannin is very abundant. Starch, as in most roots, is very abundant.

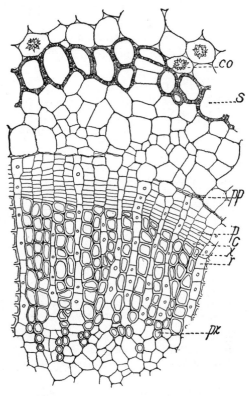

FIG. 209.—*Ginkgo biloba:* part of one of the two strands in the petiole of the leaf; *co*, calcium oxalate crystals; *s*, sheath; *pp*, protophloem; *p*, phloem; *c*, cambium; *x*, xylem; *r*, rays; *px*, protoxylem; ×180.

Within a millimeter of the tip, the endodermis can be distinguished, and the next layer of cells outside it have characteristic ring thickenings.

The mature root looks much like the mature stem, with annual rings and with similar bordered pits.

The reproductive structures of *Ginkgo* are the most primitive in living seed plants, except the Cycadales.

The male strobilus.—The male strobilus is strikingly like that of the extinct *Baiera*, the principal difference being that *Baiera* has as many as six microsporangia on a sporophyll, while *Ginkgo* almost always has only two. The number two, however, is not entirely

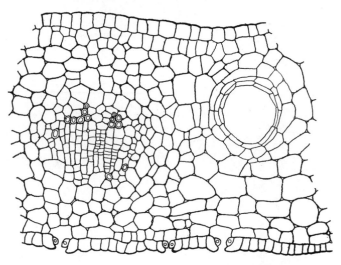

FIG. 210.—*Ginkgo biloba:* section of a young leaf cut at a right angle to the vein. The spiral protoxylem has lignified but the walls of the rest of the xylem have scarcely begun to thicken. A large mucilage cavity is shown at the right; ×180.

rigid, for material grown in the United States often shows three or four sporangia, and SPRECHER[576] cites a case with seven.

The slender sporophyll is surmounted by a hump and bears two pendant microsporangia (figs. 211, 212). The stalk has two small collateral endarch bundles.

The development of the microsporangium follows the usual eusporangiate type, an archesporial cell giving rise to a primary wall cell and a primary sporogenous cell, the latter giving rise to the sporogenous tissue and, later, to the spores.

Miss ANNA STARR[578] investigated the hump at the top of the sporophyll and found that its large mucilage cavity developed like a microsporangium (fig. 213). COULTER and LAND[152] had found that in *Torreya* resin ducts are formed from three of an original seven sporangia, so that the sporophyll is really peltate, like that of *Taxus*. In *Ginkgo* the mucilage cavity in the hump shows the type of de-

FIG. 211.—*Ginkgo biloba:* long shoot with spur shoots bearing male strobili and young leaves; about natural size. —After COULTER.[153]

FIG. 212.—*Ginkgo biloba:* single male strobilus, showing sporophylls, each bearing two sporangia; ×3.5. —After COULTER.[153]

velopment which they found in *Torreya*. Since *Baiera* has regularly more than two sporangia on a sporophyll, and *Ginkgo* occasionally has more than two, the mucilage cavity might represent lost sporangia. Against this theory, it can be urged that *Baiera*, with all its sporangia, still has a hump, and that *Ginkgo*, in the rare cases with more than two sporangia, has the hump just as well developed as when there are only two. Further, the mucilage cavities in the leaf, in early stages, look like those in the hump.

Fujii,[199] who has made an extensive study of abnormalities in *Ginkgo*, found microsporangia growing on foliage leaves. They were usually near the base of the leaf blade.

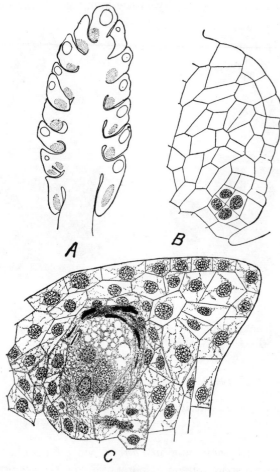

FIG. 213.—*Ginkgo biloba: A*, topography of strobilus, showing sporogenous tissue (dotted) and mucilage cavity in the hump (outlined); *B*, early stage in development of microsporangium, showing two of the primary wall cells and two of the primary sporogenous cells; *C*, the hump, with its mucilage cavity; *A*, September 2, ×20; *B*, beginning of sporogenous tissue, ×485; *C*, ×485.—After Dr. Anna M. Starr.[578]

In the northern part of the United States the male strobili can be recognized early in July as small papillae in the axils of bracts. Before winter stops their growth, the sporogenous tissue is well developed, and may reach the mother-cell stage. Reduction of chromosomes takes place as soon as growth is resumed in the spring. Eight and sixteen are the x and $2x$ numbers.

The female strobilus.—The ovules are borne, often in great numbers, on spur shoots (fig. 214). This branch shows an unusually large number of peduncles bearing two full-sized ovules. Usually one of

FIG. 214.—*Ginkgo biloba:* long shoot with spur shoots bearing ovules. Many of the peduncles bear two fully developed ovules.

the two ovules aborts early. As may be seen at the extreme left, the long shoot, with its spurs, has come from an earlier spur. It will be noted that the leaves are merely rounded, with none of the bilobed character.

The bilobed condition is probably due to a vigorous early growth of the two earliest veins, the leaf traces, which would cause the lobing by growing faster than the parenchyma of the leaf blade. The leaves on the spurs are very immature during the early development of the strobili. It may be that the diversion of food materials to the rapidly developing strobili may cause the leaves to grow slowly and evenly at this early period, during which the contour of the leaf is being determined. When spurs do not bear reproductive organs, the leaves are often lobed.

The young ovules break through the bud scales and pollination occurs late in April or early in May, while the leaves are still immature (fig. 215).

In northern Ohio the bud of the spur begins to swell about April 1. By dissecting away the outer brown bud scales and the inner

FIG. 215.—*Ginkgo biloba:* spur shoots with ovules and young leaves, shortly after pollination. In the photo at the right, the leaves have been cut away. The collar is conspicuous at this stage; ×1.5.—After COULTER.[153]

greenish scales, one can see the pale, cream-colored ovules and the very young greenish foliage leaves. At this time the single integument has appeared, but has not begun to cover the nucellus. By May 1, sections show the megaspore mother-cell surrounded by the spongy tissue characteristic of gymnosperms (fig. 216). On the same tree, at the same time, some of the mother-cells have divided, giving rise to linear tetrads. Sometimes the mother-cell gives rise to a row of three cells, one of the first two cells produced by the mother-cell having failed to divide. In such a case, only two megaspores are produced; and in any case only one megaspore functions. Occasionally, there are two megaspore mother-cells, one above the other, with one or more parenchyma cells between. Miss CAROTHERS counted 8 as the x number of chromosomes. SPRECHER did not determine the exact number, but estimated that it was not less than 7 or more than 10.

By the end of April, a pollen chamber has been formed by the breaking down of cells at the apex of the nucellus. Some of the

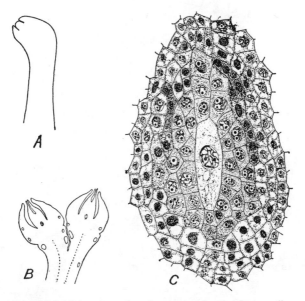

FIG. 216.—*Ginkgo biloba:* A, section of young ovule, showing nucellus and integument, April 1; B, section of pair of ovules; C, megaspore mother-cell surrounded by spongy tissue, May 1. A, ×15; B, ×12; C, ×325.—After CAROTHERS.[90]

broken down material is mucilaginous and is exuded, appearing just outside the micropyle as the pollination drop. Pollen, caught in this drop, is drawn down into the pollen chamber and is sealed in by the drying of the drop. The further development of the pollen chamber and other parts of the ovule is doubtless stimulated by the presence and development of the pollen.

The ovules increase rapidly in size, maintaining a mottled pea-green color. One of the two ovules on each peduncle usually aborts; but when conditions are favorable, it is not at all uncommon for both ovules to develop into good seeds (fig. 214).

A striking feature of the ovule is the collar. It is conspicuous throughout the development of the ovule, but is proportionately larger during the earlier stages (fig. 215). Fujii found many ovules

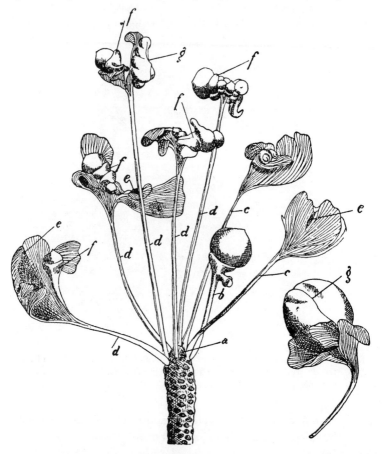

Fig. 217.—*Ginkgo biloba:* abnormal development of ovulate structures; *a,* bud; *b,* nearly normal strobilus; *c,* leaf with irregular thickenings; *d,* leaves bearing ovules; *e,* ovule; *f,* thickening at base of ovule; *g,* longitudinal striation along fleshy part of seed.— After Fujii.[199]

borne on more or less modified foliage leaves (fig. 217). These exceptional cases led to the conclusion that the collar is a modified leaf-sporophyll bearing an ovule. The fact that the peduncle has four vascular bundles, while the petiole of a leaf has only two, strongly supports the interpretation that the peduncle is a stem, bearing two sporophylls, the collars, each bearing an ovule (fig. 218). When a peduncle bears three ovules, there are six bundles; and when there are several ovules, the peduncle has double that number of bundles, so that a transverse section has a zone of wood like that in a stem.

In general, the development of the ovule resembles that of a cycad (figs. 219 and 220). There is a prominent nucellus with a large pollen chamber, surmounted by a beak which becomes brown and hard. The single integument, with the lower part of the ovule, becomes differentiated into three layers, the outer fleshy layer, and inner fleshy layer, with a stony layer between them. The develop-

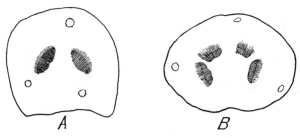

FIG. 218.—*Ginkgo biloba: A*, transverse section of petiole of leaf, showing two vascular bundles; *B*, similar section of peduncle, showing four bundles; ×17.

ment of the inner fleshy layer differs from that of a cycad, for its cells are very thin walled and watery until the ovule reaches a considerable size. It then develops as in a cycad, finally becoming a thin, dry, papery brownish membrane. The outer fleshy layer remains fresh, greenish, and juicy until the frost comes in autumn. The ovules then fall to the ground, the fleshy layer becomes wrinkled, but still remains watery, and has a characteristic odor which is unpleasant to most people. The ovules are poisonous to some people, causing sores on the hands or other parts which may be touched.

The vascular supply of the ovule is very scanty. Two strands enter the inner fleshy layer, and, without any branching, extend to the free part of the nucellus. The entire outer vascular system, so prominent in the outer fleshy layer of the cycad ovule, is entirely lacking. In the rare cases in which the ovule is triangular in transverse section, there are three bundles in the inner fleshy layer.

In the very abnormal cases in which several ovules are borne on a branching axis, only one ovule terminates each branch, and its peduncle has only two bundles, still further supporting the theory that the collar is a modified leaf blade-sporophyll, bearing an ovule (fig. 221).

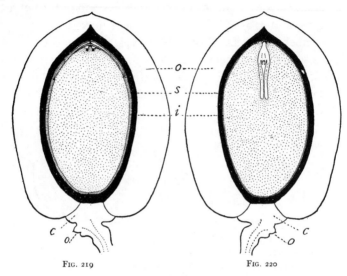

FIG. 219.—*Ginkgo biloba:* longitudinal section of an ovule shortly after pollination; *o*, outer fleshy layer of integument; *s*, stony layer of integument; *i*, inner fleshy layer of integument; *c*, collar; *o* (lower), abortive ovule. The inner fleshy layer and nucellus are shaded with lines; ×2.—From Coulter and Chamberlain, *Morphology of Gymnosperms*[154] (University of Chicago Press).

FIG. 220.—*Ginkgo biloba:* longitudinal section of ovule, after the stony layer has become hard and the inner fleshy layer has become dry and papery; ×2.—From Coulter and Chamberlain, *Morphology of Gymnosperms*[154] (University of Chicago Press).

THE GAMETOPHYTES

The gametophytes, especially the male, bear some resemblance to those of the cycads, but have such definite characteristics that the Ginkgoales and Cycadales could be identified by their gametophytes.

The male gametophyte.—The microspore is the first cell of the male gametophyte. As in the cycads, it germinates while still enclosed in the microsporangium. At the first mitosis, two very unequal cells are formed, the smaller one, a prothallial cell. The inner, larger cell divides again, producing another prothallial cell, and a larger cell which is the antheridial initial. The first prothallial cell soon aborts, but the second is persistent. The antheridial initial divides, producing a generative cell, in contact with the second pro-

FIG. 221.—*Ginkgo biloba:* axis with seven ovules, each borne singly on a peduncle, not in pairs. Each peduncle has two bundles instead of the four which appear when the peduncle bears two ovules.—After SPRECHER.[576]

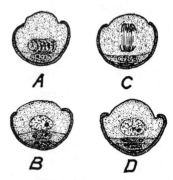

FIG. 222.—*Ginkgo biloba:* early development of the male gametophyte; *A*, first prothallial cell and inner cell; *B*, second prothallial cell and inner cell dividing to form the generative cell and tube cell; *C*, mitosis in antheridium initial; *D*, first prothallial cell (aborting), second prothallial cell, generative cell, and tube cell—the shedding stage. The exine is shaded with lines. It does not cover the top of the pollen grain. The intine is represented only by a line. It alone covers the top of the pollen grain; ×770.—From CHAMBERLAIN, *Methods in Plant Histology*[127] (University of Chicago Press).

thallial cell, and an inner cell, the tube cell, which does not divide again. In this four-celled condition the pollen is shed (fig. 222). If female trees are within 200 meters, some pollen will reach the pollination drops and there will be some seed. If there are female trees within 100 meters, pollination is likely to be so abundant that most of the ovules will be pollinated.

The exine does not cover the entire pollen grain, being lacking at the top, which is covered only by the intine. Upon reaching the pollen chamber, the intine protrudes and becomes anchored in the tissue of the nucellus, where it acts as a haustorium, the original function of a pollen tube. As in the cycads, the pollen grain end of the tube advances toward the female gametophyte, breaking down and absorbing the tissue before it, so that the pollen chamber is enlarged until it reaches entirely through the nucellus, and nothing remains between the pollen tubes and the female gametophyte.

HIRASE[253] traced the development of the pollen tube from its earliest stages up to the mature sperms (fig. 223). After reaching the pollen chamber, the generative cell divides, producing a stalk cell and body cell. HIRASE's figures show the nuclei, but not differentiated cells. The blepharoplasts appear only in the body cell, where they increase in size but apparently take no part in the division, unless they may function in the orientation of the nuclear figure. In each of the two sperms formed by the division of the body cell, the blepharoplast becomes attached to the nucleus, a small portion of which seems to be attracted so that it forms a beak. The blepharoplast is then drawn out into a spiral band, which develops hundreds of cilia. With the exception of the sperms of cycads, these are the largest swimming sperms which have ever been recorded, about 80 microns in length, as estimated from HIRASE's figures. The sperms are more elongated than in the cycads, and the spiral, ciliated band, with fewer turns, is more confined to the apical region. *Ginkgo* and the cycads are the only known living seed plants which have retained the swimming sperm of their very remote ancestry.

The female gametophyte.—The megaspore is the first cell of the female gametophyte. Although four megaspores are usually formed from the megaspore mother-cell, only the lower one develops. The four spores are formed about the first of May, the time of pollination, so that the development of the pollen tube and the development of the female gametophyte start together.

The megaspore enlarges rapidly, its elongated shape changing to nearly spherical. A period of free nuclear division follows, like that in the cycads, with the protoplasm, containing the nuclei, pressed in a thin sheet against the megaspore membrane by the turgidity of the fluid in the large central vacuole. After hundreds of free nuclei have been formed, wall formation begins and progresses from the periph-

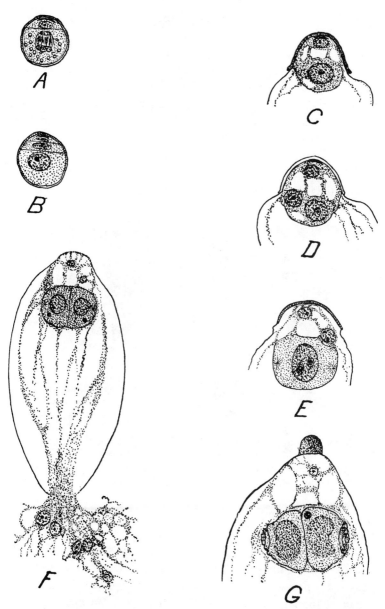

FIG. 223.—*Ginkgo biloba*: *A*, pollen grain showing the first prothallial cell, aborting; second prothallial cell; and the mitosis which will form the generative cell and tube cell, April 24; *B*, later stage, same date; *C*, still later stage, in the pollen chamber, July 10; *D*, the large nucleus in *C* has divided, July 13; *E*, body cell with blepharoplasts, July 27; *F*, two young sperms, September 12; *G*, two sperms just ready to be discharged from the pollen tube, Sept. 12; *A*, *B*, *C*, *D*, *E*, ×600; *F*, ×144; *G*, ×372.—After HIRASE.[253]

ery toward the center. The gametophyte soon becomes elliptical, in both longitudinal and transverse directions. In later stages it takes on a pale-green color, due to the development of chlorophyll, because the stony layer of the seed is rather thin and the outer fleshy layer is so translucent that there is enough light for the production of chlorophyll.

The megaspore enlarges rapidly, its elongated shape changing to nearly spherical as the period of free nuclear

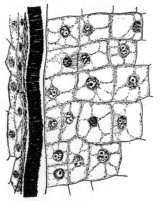

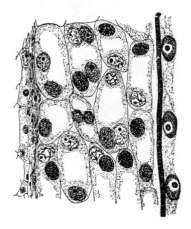

FIG. 224.—*Ginkgo biloba:* free nuclei in the thin layer of protoplasm lying against the megaspore membrane, June 5; ×650.—After CAROTHERS.[90]

FIG. 225.—*Ginkgo biloba:* detail of peripheral portion of female gametophyte, July 19. The megaspore membrane is more than four times as thick as on June 5. The membrane about the female gametophyte, entirely independent of the megaspore membrane, has been formed; ×650.—After CAROTHERS.[90]

division begins. The first mitoses of the free nuclear stage are simultaneous, but at the fifth mitosis there are figures in metaphase and telophase, and at the sixth, there will be some nuclei which do not divide. The free nuclear period continues from the second week in May to the first week in July, the number of free nuclei usually reaching more than 256 before any walls begin to be formed (fig. 224).

Toward the close of the free nuclear period a delicate membrane forms on the outer surface of the thin layer of protoplasm. It is entirely distinct from the megaspore membrane, just as the walls of microspores are distinct from the wall of the microspore mother-cell.

Cell walls now begin to be formed perpendicular to this membrane, and with their outer edges attached to it (fig. 225). As wall formation progresses, the inner side of the innermost cell has no wall; but when the period of wall formation comes to a close a wall is formed on this inner side, so that each of the inner cells has its own wall. (Fig. 226). Consequently, the female gametophyte can be split apart along this central region.

During the early growth of the female gametophyte the spongy tissue surrounding it encroaches upon the tissues outside it; but,

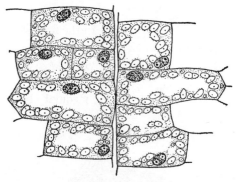

FIG. 226.—*Ginkgo biloba:* vertical section of part of female gametophyte at line of closure, showing independent end walls of opposite cells (August 21); ×325.—After CAROTHERS.[90]

later, it is itself absorbed by the growing gametophyte and is reduced to a mass of collapsed and deeply staining cells. Most of the upper part of the nucellus is also absorbed.

Archegonium initials appear long before the wall formation in the gametophyte has reached the center. By the middle of June the two-celled neck and the central cell have been formed, and the central cell is enlarging rapidly. Usually there are only two archegonia, lying in such a plane that longitudinal sections of both can be secured by cutting longitudinally and parallel with the flatter face of the gametophyte. Occasionally there are three archegonia. In such cases, the gametophyte and stony layer are triangular in transverse section, and there are three bundles in the inner fleshy layer of the ovule.

The mitosis for the formation of the ventral canal cell and the egg takes place in the second week in September. A definite cell wall is formed. Consequently, the development is quite different from that in the cycads, for in none of them is a wall formed at this mitosis, the two nuclei lying free in a common mass of protoplasm. As far as this feature is concerned, *Ginkgo* is more primitive than the cycads.

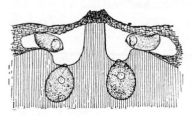

FIG. 227.—*Ginkgo biloba:* upper part of female gametophyte, showing two archegonia and the crevice-like archegonial chamber, also the tent-pole prolongation of the gametophyte supporting the nucellus. The swollen ends of two pollen tubes are shown, just ready to discharge the sperms (September 9); ×24.—After HIRASE.[253]

In the final stages of the development of the female gametophyte *Ginkgo* differs from the cycads. Instead of the cup-shaped archegonial chamber of the cy-

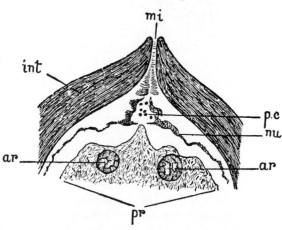

FIG. 228.—*Cycadinocarpus angustodunensis:* upper part of ovule, showing striking resemblance to *Ginkgo*; *mi*, micropyle; *int*, integument; *ar*, archegonia; *pc*, pollen chamber with pollen grains; *nu*, nucellus; *pr*, female gametophyte.—After RENAULT.[465]

cads, *Ginkgo* has a circular crevice, surrounding a mass of solid tissue upon which the nucellus rests, like a tent on a pole (fig. 227).

In general topography, *Ginkgo*, at this stage, bears a striking resemblance to *Cycadinocarpus angustodunensis*, a paleozoic seed assigned to the Cordaitales (fig. 228).

FERTILIZATION

In the cycads, at the time when the pollen tubes discharge their sperms, the archegonial chamber is moist but contains no free liquid. There is no liquid in the archegonial chamber except that discharged from the pollen tubes. This feature has been observed by so many in so many cycads that it can be regarded as a well-established fact.

In *Ginkgo*, HIRASE[253] reported free droplets of juice in the archegonial chamber, sometimes filling it completely. Personally, I have never been able to make observations upon living material at this stage; but material at the formation of the ventral canal cell, and, later, at the fusion of the egg and sperm nuclei, does not indicate anything different from the well-known cycad condition. It is very desirable that both living material and sections of well-prepared material at this stage should be investigated.

The egg and sperm nuclei unite near the center of the egg. IKENO[281] observed that in rare cases the wall between the ventral canal cell and the egg breaks down and the ventral canal nucleus fuses with that of the egg, a behavior which has been observed in several of the Coniferales.

EMBRYOGENY

After fertilization there is a period of simultaneous free nuclear division, as in the female gametophyte. The development, however, is very different, for here the nuclei are evenly distributed throughout the dense protoplasm of the egg; while, in the gametophyte, they are kept in a thin peripheral layer of protoplasm by the large central vacuole. There are usually eight free nuclear divisions, giving rise to 256 free nuclei. The number may be somewhat smaller through the failure of one or more of the nuclei to divide (fig. 229).

Walls are then formed simultaneously throughout the embryo, forming cells of approximately the same size. Very little further division takes place in the micropylar region, but there is a vigorous development at the opposite end, and not much between. Consequently, there are three not very well-marked regions. The cells at the micropylar end elongate considerably, those in the middle enlarge somewhat, while those at the base, through repeated division, become small and numerous (fig. 230). Although there are three

regions, there is no organized suspensor. The further development of
the basal region is rapid, and soon there is a differentiation into stem,
root, and cotyledons (fig. 231 *A*, *B*). During their earlier develop-

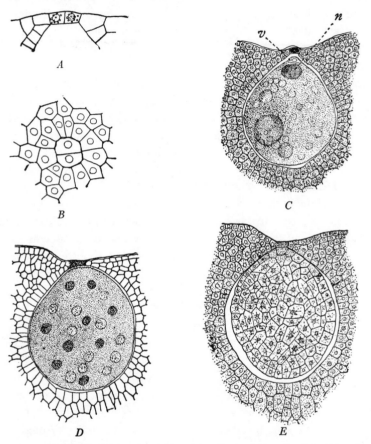

FIG. 229.—*Ginkgo biloba:* archegonium and embryo; *A*, top of archegonium, showing the two neck cells; *B*, transverse section of the two neck cells; *C*, archegonium just
after the formation of the ventral canal cell (*v*); *n*, nucleus of eggs; *D*, free nuclear stage
of the embryo; *E*, the embryo has become cellular throughout; *A* and *B*, ×160; *C*, *D*,
and *E*, ×66.—After STRASBURGER.[596]

ment, one of the cotyledons is longer than the other and is notched
at the tip, while the shorter one is deeply cleft, recalling the bilobed
character of the foliage leaf. At maturity, the cotyledons are of
nearly equal length. Mucilage canals are abundant in the stem and

large mucilage cavities are abundant in the cotyledons. The mature embryo usually has five leaves, the first two of which are decussate with the cotyledons, while succeeding leaves in the embryo and seedling are irregular in their arrangement (fig. 231 C, D).

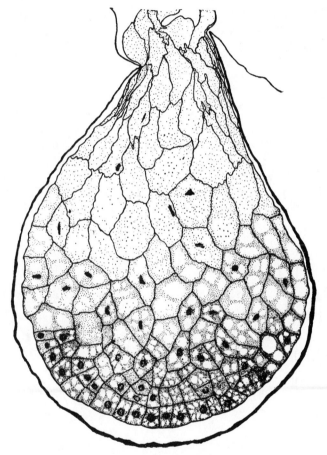

FIG. 230.—*Ginkgo biloba:* embryo at stage in which three regions are recognizable. The stem and root will be organized from the small-celled tissue; × 160.—After LYON.[375]

Seeds germinate readily, the terminal part of the cotyledons remaining inside and enlarging considerably. They gradually absorb all of the female gametophyte and pass it on to the growing seedling. There is a strong tap root, and the leaves are deeply lobed (fig. 232).

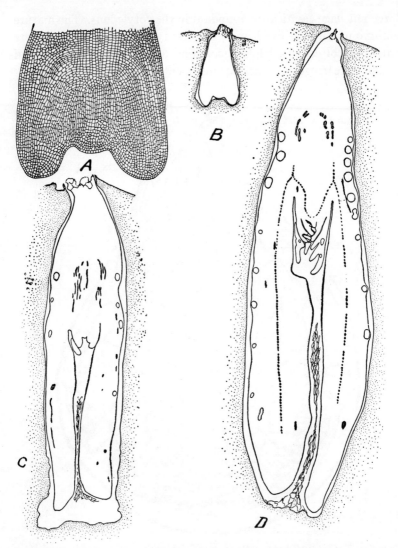

FIG. 231.—*Ginkgo biloba:* A, embryo in upper part of female gametophyte, ×40; B, topography of same embryo, ×10; C, embryo at about the stage shown in fig. 220, ×15; D, nearly mature embryo, ×10.—From COULTER and CHAMBERLAIN, *Morphology of Gymnosperms*[154] (University of Chicago Press).

Where weather conditions are about the same as in Chicago and northern Ohio, scarcely any seedlings grown in the open survive the first winter. They should be kept in the greenhouse the first winter, put out in the spring after frosts are over but while the weather is still cool, and then taken in after the first light frost in autumn. By putting them out earlier and earlier in the spring, and taking them in later and later in the autumn, for four or five years, they become hardened so that many will survive the winters. Even where there is some snow and ice, but not such severe cold as in the Chicago region, a considerable proportion of the seedlings survive without any such precautions.

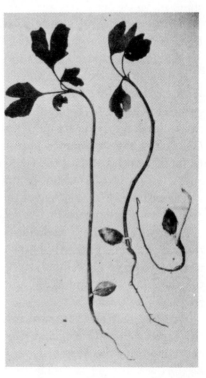

PHYLOGENY

How far back into geological times the Ginkgoales extend depends upon the interpretation of leaves which may or may not belong to this group. It is certain that as far back as the Lower Permian it was abundant and widely distributed. *Baiera*, some of the species of which can scarcely be excluded from the genus, *Ginkgo*, was abundant in the Lower Permian. In the Carboniferous, only leaves have been found, but they seem to belong to Ginkgoales rather than to Cordaitales. All of the order, except one species of *Ginkgo*, have been extinct since the Upper Jurassic, and many think that even the one species is extinct, except as it is kept alive by cultivation.

Fig. 232.—*Ginkgo biloba:* seedlings, bearing a general resemblance to those of cycads, or of *Quercus*.—From Coulter and Chamberlain, *Morphology of Gymnosperms*[154] (University of Chicago Press).

It would seem that the Ginkgoales have come from the Cordaitales, or that both groups have come from some common ancestor.

The swimming sperm is a Pteridophyte character, which has been lost by all living seed plants except the cycads and *Ginkgo*. However, some of the Coniferales seem to have lost the swimming habit rather recently, geologically speaking. If Ginkgoales came from Cordaitales, the Cordaitales must have had swimming sperms; for such a character, once lost, could not be regained.

It was once thought that the Cycadales came from the Bennettitales, but such a derivation is regarded as impossible; and now both groups are generally believed to owe their origin to the Cycadofilicales. Similarly, it seems quite possible that both Cordaitales and Ginkgoales have a common ancestry. If reproductive organs could be found associated with the Ginkgoales-like leaves of the Carboniferous, the problem would be simplified.

The extremely fernlike leaf of the Ginkgoales would favor a direct origin from some heterosporous member of the Filicales.

An origin from the Cycadofilicales seems to be supported only by the leaf gap. The profusely branching habit, the extensive development of wood, with a comparatively small amount of pith and cortex together with the simple leaf, indicate a Coniferophyte rather than a Cycadophyte alliance.

With the increasing interest in paleobotany in America and the Orient, as well as in England and Europe, and with new fields for collecting being discovered, it is reasonable to hope that material will be discovered which will help to solve the difficult problems of relationships and the evolution of those structures upon which theories of relationship are based.

CHAPTER XI

CONIFEROPHYTES—CONIFERALES

The description of all the previous groups has been a description of phyla which have had their origin, rise, culmination, and decline in far away geological eras, with the cycads and *Ginkgo* as their only surviving remnants.

In the Coniferales we have a group which, although many of its members have become extinct, is still the dominant forest-maker of the world. The previous groups have belonged almost exclusively to warm climates. The Coniferales extend from the arctic to the antarctic circle, with a good representation in the tropics, and reaching their greatest display where the winters are so severe that the branches droop with snow and ice.

The immense dinosaurs of the Triassic and Jurassic reached their maximum size, and, at its culmination, became extinct. There have been trees, some of them very large, ever since the Devonian; but none of them even approached the size of some of the gigantic conifers of today. Probably, without protection, the *Sequoias*, especially *Sequoia gigantea*, would be on the way to extinction. Gigantism, in both animals and plants, leads to extinction.

In the Northern Hemisphere, members of the Abietaceae form immense forests. Formerly, *Pinus strobus*, the white pine, was a dominant lumber tree, but the forests have been cut so ruthlessly, without adequate provision for reforesting, that this lumber has become too expensive for most of its previous uses. *Pseudotsuga taxifolia*, the Douglas fir, is the principal lumber tree of western North America. The Long-Bell Lumber Company cut 2,000,000 feet of lumber a day, but such efficient reforesting is under way that there is no danger of any scarcity in the future. In Canada, 400 acres of forest are cut every week to supply paper for one newspaper, the *Chicago Tribune*.

No other place in the world has such an interesting display of conifers as the western part of the United States.

Pseudotsuga taxifolia is often 190 feet high and 6 feet in diameter, with some trees 200 feet high and 10 feet in diameter (fig. 233). A tree 8 feet in diameter will be about 400 years old.

Pseudotsuga macrocarpa, although of little interest as a lumber tree, has a very large cone and a very characteristic spreading of the branches. In Southern California it is associated with extremely large specimens of *Yucca whipplei* (fig. 234).

Pinus ponderosa, the western yellow pine, reaches a height of 61 meters and an age of 500 years.

Pinus lambertiana, the sugar pine, is still larger, sometimes 60 meters tall and 2 meters in diameter. One immense tree near Calaveras Grove, in California, is 66 meters tall and nearly 4 meters in diameter, probably 600 years old, and the largest pine in the world (fig. 235).

Abies magnifica, a magnificent fir, deserves its name. It reaches 66 meters in height and an age of 700 years (fig. 236).

Fig. 233.—*Pseudotsuga taxifolia:* "Topping a fir." Tops are cut off about 30 meters from the ground, and cables are attached so that logs can be carried high in the air, thus saving young trees. This is in the forest of the Long-Bell Lumber Company, south of Seattle, Washington.

The most remarkable of all the conifers is *Sequoia*, named from an Indian chief, who invented a phonetic alphabet and taught his tribe to read and write (fig. 237). There are two living species, *S. sempervirens*, mostly north of San Francisco and near the coast, and *S. gigantea*,

FIG. 234.—*Pseudotsuga macrocarpa: P. macrocarpa*, the tree at the left, with *Yucca whipplei* at right. San Antonio Canyon, near Los Angeles, California.

Fig. 235.—*Pinus lambertiana:* the sugar pine (second tree from left), in the Mariposa Grove of Big Trees, California.

FIG. 236.—*Abies magnifica:* Yosemite, California

mostly south of San Francisco, at a higher elevation on the western slopes of the Sierra Mountains. *S. sempervirens* (fig. 238) grows in dense stands, with average large trees 100 meters high and 5 meters in diameter, and 1,000 years old. *S. gigantea* is in scattered groups connected by straggling specimens. It is not so tall, the larger trees rarely reaching 100 meters in height, but the diameter ranges from 4 to 11 meters, and some are known to be 4,000 years old. Many of these trees have their own names. The General Sherman tree would make 50,000 feet of lumber; but, fortunately, *S. gigantea* does not make good lumber, and so is not in such danger as *S. sempervirens*, which is an excellent lumber tree and would probably become extinct if it were not for the extensive reservations.

Perhaps the most remarkable tree in the world is *Taxodium mucronatum*, the "Big Tree of Tule," near Oaxaca, in southern Mexico. It is 16 meters in diameter, and does not seem to have a single dead twig (fig. 239).

In the Eastern Hemisphere, *Agathis australis*, the Kauri, of New Zealand, may be the most interesting tree (fig. 240). Like *Sequoia*, it might be in danger of extinction were it not for extensive reservations; for the lumber is excellent, looking like that of *Pinus strobus* but much harder and taking a finer polish. The tree often reaches 50 meters in height and 2 meters in diameter, with a beautiful cylindrical trunk which may measure 26 meters up to the first branch. The largest trees have a diameter of 3 meters where the branching begins.

Cryptomeria japonica is not so large, but reaches 60 meters in height and is a beautiful tree. The lumber is excellent and the tree is popular for streets and parks. Reforestation is so efficient in Japan that there is no danger from lumbering.

Some of the smaller conifers are interesting. *Larix lyallii*, the Alpine larch, 13 meters high and .6 meter in diameter, is known to have reached an age of 700 years. *Picea engelmannii*, the Engelmann spruce, often grows in rocky, wind-swept places, and, here and there, stunted specimens, not more than 15 centimeters in diameter, may be 200 years old. Still more extreme dwarfing has been noted on Vancouver Island. A tree of *Picea sitchensis*, less than 30 cm. in height and only 19 mm. in diameter, was 86 years old; and another

FIG. 237.—*Sequoia gigantea:* "General Grant"—"Nation's Christmas Tree"—General Grant Park, California.

FIG. 238.—*Sequoia semp.:* circles of young trees coming from old stumps. Such a circle might grow together and simulate one immense tree.

specimen, 30 cm. in height and 25 mm. in diameter, was 98 years old, so that the width of an average growth-ring was only 132 microns, or about seven growth-rings to the millimeter. In this region there is just as extreme dwarfing of *Tsuga heterophylla* and *Thuja plicata*

Fig. 239.—*Taxodium mucronatum:* the "Big Tree of Tule," about 15 miles south of Oaxaca, Mexico.

(*gigantea*). These dwarf trees have much the same appearance as the famous Japanese dwarf conifers. One of these trees, in a single year in a favorable location, produces as wide a zone of wood as the dwarf produces in 50, or in nearly 100, years. *Thuja plicata* has been known to reach a diameter of nearly 4 meters. On the neighboring San Juan Island, in Puget Sound, *Pteris aquilina* reaches a height of 3 meters, with a rhizome about 15 mm. in diameter; but in rocky, wind-swept places the leaf is reduced to 15 cm. However, these dwarf ferns may have rhizomes 25 mm. in diameter. That the dwarfed condition is not due entirely to wind and weather is shown by the fact that the Japanese keep *Pinus thunbergia* in large vases for a couple of hundred years, although the species, in nature, is a large tree.

Fig. 240.—*Agathis australis:* the "Kauri" of New Zealand. From a photograph by JONES and COLEMAN.

TAXONOMY

In such a large assemblage, with so many living representatives, it is convenient, for the sake of ready reference, to have its various genera distributed into groups along lines as nearly genetic as possible. The morphologist is not likely to know as much about technical taxonomy as he should, and, perhaps, for that reason, is not deeply interested in tribes, sub-tribes, sub-genera, sub-species, varieties, and forms. So we shall simply use the name "family" for a group of genera which seem to belong together.

The list below does not include all the described genera. The discovery of a really new genus is important; but a new genus made by making two from one already known, is not so interesting.

The following list is based upon EICHLER'S[185] account in *Die natürlichen Pflanzenfamilien* (1889), but we have used the family names. The number of species, indicated in parentheses, is taken from ENGLER in *Pflanzenfamilien*. In the later Mesozoic the number of species was much larger; in some genera, like *Pinus*, at least two or three times as large. The geographic distribution is much more detailed in ENGLER's[188] account.

CONIFERALES

The principal features of the six families, listed below, are as follows:

In the *Abietaceae*, the leaves and sporophylls are developed spirally; the bract and ovuliferous scale are distinct; pollen grains are winged; and leaves are of the needle type.

The *Taxodiaceae* are also spiral, but the bract and ovuliferous scale are almost completely united, and the pollen is wingless.

In the *Cupressaceae*, the arrangement is cyclic and the strobili, in most species, ripen fleshy.

The *Araucariaceae* have the spiral arrangement; the bract and ovuliferous scale are so thoroughly united that there is some doubt whether the structure is double. The ovules are solitary and the microsporangia hang from a peltate sporophyll.

The *Podocarpaceae* have winged pollen and belong mostly to the Southern Hemisphere.

The *Taxaceae* have wingless pollen and belong mostly to the Northern Hemisphere.

I. ABIETACEAE

1. *Pinus* (80–90), N. Hemisphere. S. Hemisphere only at Sunday Islands.
2. *Cedrus* (4), Mediterranean region, W. Himalaya.
3. *Larix* (10), N. Hemisphere.
4. *Pseudolarix* (1), China.
5. *Picea* (40), China, Japan, N. America, Central Asia, Europe.
6. *Tsuga* (14), Asia from Himalaya to Japan and N. America.
7. *Pseudotsuga* (7), Pacific, N. America and East Asia.
8. *Keeteleria* (3), China.
9. *Abies* (40), Middle and S. Europe, Central and temperate Asia, N. America.

II. TAXODIACEAE

10. *Sciadopitys* (1), Japan.
11. *Sequoia* (2), California.

12. *Cunninghamia* (2), China, Formosa.
13. *Taiwania* (1), Formosa.
14. *Arthrotaxis* (3), Tasmania.
15. *Cryptomeria* (2), China, Japan.
16. *Taxodium* (3), S.E. United States and Mexico.
17. *Glyptostrobus* (1), S.E. China.

III. CUPRESSACEAE

18. *Actinostrobus* (2), West Australia.
19. *Callitris* (20), Australia, New Caledonia, Tasmania.
20. *Widdringtonia* (5), S. Africa.
21. *Fitzroya* (1), Tasmania.
22. *Thujopsis* (1), Japan.
23. *Libocedrus* (9), California, Chili, China, New Zealand, New Caledonia, New Guinea, Molucca.
24. *Thuja* (6), East Asia and North America.
25. *Cupressus* (12), W. North America and Asia to E. Mediterranean region.
26. *Chamaecyparis* (6), North America, Japan, Formosa.
27. *Juniperus* (60), Alaska to Central America, West Indies, Europe, N. Africa, Asia.

IV. ARAUCARIACEAE

28. *Agathis* (20), New Zealand, Australia, Fiji, New Caledonia, New Hebrides, Philippines, Indian Archipelago, Malay Peninsula, Cochinchina.
29. *Araucaria* (12), New Guinea, Chili, S.W. Argentina, Brazil, E. Australia, Norfolk Island.

V. PODOCARPACEAE

30. *Podocarpus* (70), New Zealand, Australia, India, E. Africa, Indian Archipelago, W. Indies, Central America, South America.
31. *Dacrydium* (20), New Zealand, Australian Islands, Chili.
32. *Microcachrys* (1), Tasmania.
33. *Pherosphaera* (2), Tasmania.
34. *Saxagothea* (1), S. Chili.
35. *Phyllocladus* (6). New Zealand, Tasmania, Borneo, New Guinea.

VI. TAXACEAE

36. *Taxus* (1), England, Europe, Asia Minor, Himalaya, Japan, Philippines, Celebes, U.S. America, Mexico.
37. *Torreya* (5), Japan, China, California, Florida.
38. *Cephalotaxus* (5), Tropical Himalaya, S. and middle China, Japan.
39. *Acmopyle* (1), New Caledonia.

EICHLER[185] begins with the Araucariaceae. His sequence of genera is as follows:

I.   1. *Agathis*, 2. *Araucaria*.
II.   3. *Pinus*, 4. *Cedrus*, 5. *Larix*, 6. *Pseudolarix*, 7. *Picea*, 8. *Tsuga*, 9. *Abies*.
III. 10. *Sciadopitys*, 11. *Cunninghamia*, 12. *Arthrotaxis*, 13. *Sequoia*, 14. *Cryptomeria*, 15. *Taxodium*, 16. *Glyptostrobus*.
IV.   17. *Actinostrobus*, 18. *Callitris*, 19. *Fitzroya*, 20. *Thujopsis*, 21. *Libocedrus*, 22. *Thuja*, 23. *Cupressus*, 24. *Chamaecyperis*, 25. *Juniperus*.
V.   26. *Saxagothea*, 27. *Microcachrys*, 28. *Cephalotaxus*, 39. *Dacrydium*.
VI.   30. *Phyllocladus*, 31. *Ginkgo*, 32. *Cephalotaxus*, 33. *Torreya*, 34. *Taxus*.

Pseudotsuga, Keeteleria, Taiwania, Widdringtonia, Pherosphaera, Acmopyle, and *Polypodiopsis,* have been added since EICHLER's account, partly by discovery and partly by splitting other genera. It is interesting to note the position assigned to *Ginkgo.*

PILGER,[452] in the 1926 edition of *Die natürlichen Pflanzenfamilien,* has more genera, arranged in a different order:

I.   TAXACEAE. *Torreya, Taxus, Austrotaxus.*
II.   PODOCARPACEAE. *Pherosphaera, Microcachrys, Saxogothea. Dacrydium, Acmopyle, Podocarpus, Phyllocladus.*
III. ARAUCARIACEAE. *Araucaria, Agathis.*
IV.   CEPHALOTAXACEAE. *Cephalotaxus, Amenotaxus.*
V.   PINACEAE. *Abies, Keeteleria, Pseudotsuga, Tsuga, Picea, Pseudolarix, Larix, Cedrus, Pinus.*
VI.   TAXODIACEAE. *Sciadopitys, Sequoia, Taxodium, Glyptostrobus, Cryptomeria, Arthrotaxis, Taiwania, Cunninghamia.*
VII. CUPRESSACEAE. *Actinostrobus, Callitris, Tetraclinis, Callitropsis, Widdringtonia, Fitzroya, Diselma, Thujopsis, Libocedrus, Fokienia, Cupressus, Chamaecyparis, Arceuthos, Juniperus.*

PILGER's work is primarily taxonomic, but the geographic distribution is treated very thoroughly, and morphology is well presented. The bibliography is very complete.

BUCHHOLZ[81] has recently rearranged the genera and families. For several years he has been making an extensive examination of the order and no previous investigator has ever studied such a wide range of material prepared for morphological study, especially for a study of the embryogeny.

Every student of the group has realized that there are two groups which can be called families or suborders or something else. One group includes the Abietaceae, Taxodiaceae, Cupressaceae, and Araucariaceae; and the other contains the rest, the Podocarpaceae and Taxaceae. To the first group BUCHHOLZ gave the subordinal name *"Phanerostrobilares,"* because there is obviously an ovulate cone; to the other he gave the name *"Aphanostrobilares,"* because there is not such an obvious cone. The second name is not so appropriate, because some of its genera have obvious strobili, and even cones. Both of the names are too long for laboratory use, and in some of the Aphanostrobilares there is a good strobilus, even a cone. To obviate both of these objections, the name "Pinaceae," for the first group, is objectionable, because it is also used to cover only the Abietaceae; and Taxaceae is just as objectionable for the second group, because it is so often used to cover both taxads and podocarps. Using the ending *ares*, approved by the international congress as the official ending for suborders, BUCHHOLZ now proposes the name *"Pinares,"* to cover Abietaceae, Taxodiaceae, Cupressaceae, and Araucariaceae, with whatever else may be made by splitting any of these; and *"Taxares"* to cover Podocarpaceae and Taxaceae, with any which may be made by a similar splitting. These names, which are short, useful, and free from any ambiguity, should come into general use. We shall use them throughout this work.

The grouping into families and the sequence of families and genera will depend upon each investigator. If he is an anatomist, anatomy will determine the treatment. If strobili are considered more important, they will determine the grouping and sequence. If the gametophytes are emphasized, there will be still another arrangement.

But whatever the arrangement may be, it must not be imagined that any family is derived from the one mentioned before it; or that a highly developed organ has been derived from the less highly developed organ of another genus. Both may have been derived from a still earlier type, one having advanced farther than the other.

The families, in all of the lists, seem to be groups of more or less closely related genera. Geologically, some have been traced farther back than others, and so, in at least one way, can qualify as ancestors.

According to ENGLER, in 1926,[188] there were 40 genera, with about 400 species, in the Coniferales. ENGLER'S previous account, in 1889, listed 34 genera, with about 350 species. Some of the additional genera and species are due to discovery and part to the splitting of those already known.

Writers have made as many as 70 species in the genus *Taxus;* ENGLER makes only one. Although we prefer ENGLER'S account, it would seem that forms as different from *Taxus baccata* as the *T. canadensis*, of the eastern United States, and *T. brevifolia*, of the western United States, should be recognized as good species.

From the first list it will be noted that *Pinus, Podocarpus,* and *Juniperus* are the largest genera, and that they also have wide geographic distribution. Nine of the 39 genera are monotypic and restricted in distribution, while four more are almost monotypic, each having only 2 species.

GEOGRAPHIC DISTRIBUTION

Whatever uncertainty and difference of opinion there may be in grouping genera into families and in arranging the genera in a family, there can be no difference of opinion in regard to geographic distribution. The record may be incomplete, but there can be no other uncertainty.

In the cycads, not a single one of the nine genera is common to the Eastern and Western hemispheres. All of the western genera are north of the Equator, except *Zamia*, which extends from Florida to Chili; and all of the eastern genera are south of the Equator, except *Cycas*, which extends from Australia to Japan.

In the Coniferales many genera are common to the Eastern and Western hemispheres, but the proportion of genera crossing the Equator is no greater than in the cycads. In the cycads more than half of the genera are south of the Equator; in the conifers, more than half are north.

The Podocarpaceae, Taxodiaceae, and Cupressaceae have genera in both Northern and Southern hemispheres. All of the Abietaceae, except a species of *Pinus* in the Sunday Islands, are north of the Equator. The Araucariaceae and most of the Podocarpaceae belong to the Southern Hemisphere.

The richest regions in genera and species are in western North America and in extra-tropical eastern and central Asia. There are not many conifers in tropical and southern Africa.

In the immense forests, where there is the greatest display of individuals, the number of genera and species is not correspondingly great.

Pinus, with its 90 species, is the dominant genus of the Northern Hemisphere; while *Podocarpus*, with 70 species, is just as dominant in the Southern Hemisphere.

Pseudotsuga taxifolia is the dominant lumber conifer of North America, various species of *Pinus* coming next. *Araucaria braziliana* holds a similar place in South America. *Cryptomeria japonica* is the principal lumber conifer of Japan; *Araucaria bidwilli* is an important lumber conifer of northeastern Australia; and *Dacrydium cupressinum* and *Agathis australis* are the principal lumber trees of New Zealand. Various species of *Pinus* are the conifer lumber trees of Europe; and the exotic *Araucaria bidwilli* and *Pseudotsuga taxifolia* seem likely to become the conifer lumber trees of South Africa. Seeds of *Pseudotsuga taxifolia* are being exported in great quantities for reforesting in various countries of both the Northern and Southern hemispheres.

The great mass of conifers, both living and extinct, belong to extra-tropical northern regions; and in geological times, the northern extension was even greater than at present.

In the Miocene, *Pinus*, *Taxodium*, *Sequoia*, and *Glyptostrobus* flourished in Greenland, with *Picea* and *Tsuga* also represented. At the same time, Spitzbergen had *Pinus*, *Juniperus*, and *Libocedrus*; and Iceland had *Pinus*, *Picea*, and *Sequoia*. *Araucaria* has been identified in the Rothliegende of France. *Pinus* and *Widdringtonia* are known from the Jurassic onward.

Araucarioxylon arizonicum, of the famous petrified forest of Arizona, goes back to the Triassic; but some question whether it belongs to the Araucariaceae. However, there is no doubt that Arizona, at that time, had a tree with wood very much like that of *Araucaria* (fig. 241).

Although many conifers, in the wild state, are now very much restricted in their distribution, they flourish when planted in far distant places. *Cupressus macrocarpa*, a very endemic species of a small area in southern California, grows just as well in New Zealand; the Australian *Araucaria bidwilli* is used for reforestation in South Africa; *Pseudotsuga taxifolia*, of the western United States, is used for reforestation in Japan, Australia, and South Africa; the Japanese *Sciadopitys verticillata* flourishes in the New York Botanical Garden; the Asiatic *Cedrus deodara* grows just as well in England and France; the Chilean *Araucaria imbricata* and the Australian *Araucaria bidwilli* are popular exotics in California; and many other cases could be mentioned.

FIG. 241.—*Araucarioxylon arizonicum:* silicified trunk in the petrified forest near Holbrook, Arizona. The formation is Triassic, about 200,000,000 years old.

THE LIFE-HISTORY

A complete life-history has not been worked out in any of the genera of this large order. More is known about *Pinus* than about any other genus. Miss FERGUSON'S[194, 195, 196] extensive study of the reproductive phases of several species, the study of the embryogeny by BUCHHOLZ, together with the investigation of the anatomy by JEFFREY and his students, and by THOMSON, have made our knowledge of this genus fairly complete. Still, it will not be safe to generalize until a comparative study of more species has been made, especially the southern and southernmost species, and species of the western Pacific and Asiatic regions.

In other genera, investigators have been more concerned with reproductive structures, especially the gametophytes and early embryogeny. Anatomists have studied, almost exclusively, the adult structures, with scant attention to the origin and development of the vascular system. The valuable results secured by vertebrate paleontologists, working almost entirely with bones, have led anatomists to assume that the woody structures of plants are equally reliable in tracing phylogeny. A study of ecological anatomy shows that woody structures are quite susceptible to changes in conditions; while phylogenetic anatomy indicates that some features of the vascular system keep their characters in spite of changed environment. These remarks are intended to apply not to sudden ephemeral changes in environment, but to such changes as bring about extinction or modification of a species, genus, or order.

THE SPOROPHYTE—VEGETATIVE

The Coniferales are characteristically trees with evergreen leaves, very few, like some species of *Juniperus*, being small enough and diffuse enough to be ranked as shrubs. There are no herbaceous forms.

The stem.—The usual growth of the stem is strongly spiral, resulting in the typically pyramidal form of the tree. But diffuse branching is also common, the strong apical growth being lost, so that it is impossible to determine what is the main axis and what may be branches, as in *Pinus torreyana, Taxodium mucronatum, Cupressus macrocarpa,* and *Juniperus monosperma* (figs. 242, and 239).

In *Pinus sabiniana* the stem is often, perhaps usually, dichotomously branched (fig. 243). It is not hard to find trees of other genera in which there is dichotomy, as in Pteridophytes. A single dichotomy is very widespread in the order. I have personally observed it in more than 20 genera.

Many of the conifers are extremely endemic. Probably the greatest extreme in endemism in the entire gymnosperm phylum can be seen along the western coast of California, from the Monterey-Carmel region southward. In the Monterey-Carmel region, four endemic species can be found in an hour's walking, *Cupressus macrocarpa, C. goweniana, Pinus radiata,* and *P. muricata* (fig. 244).

Cupressus macrocarpa grows down to the water's edge, with *Pinus radiata* coming in a hundred meters farther back; so that the *Cupressus* is confined, principally, to a strip about 100 meters wide. The *Pinus* cannot grow where it is drenched by the breaking waves; but, farther back, it crowds out the *Cupressus*. *Pinus torreyana*, with its principal display a little north of San Diego, is also very restricted in its distribution (fig. 245). *Cupressus pygmaea*, along the same California coast, is equally restricted.

FIG. 242.—*Juniperus monosperma:* adult plants of bushy habit, near Tucson, Arizona.

There are other conifers almost as closely restricted in their geographic distribution. Some of these extremely endemic forms, especially *Cupressus macrocarpa*, have a world-wide distribution as exotics.

In some conifers, like *Cedrus*, *Larix*, *Pseudolarix*, and *Pinus*, there are long shoots and spur shoots, like those of *Ginkgo*, but the leaves on the spurs are fascicled. In the first three of the four genera, the leaves are numerous and spirally arranged, and fall off in 1–5 years, leaving the spur attached to the long shoot. In *Pinus*, leaves

FIG. 243.—*Pinus sabiniana:* the "Digger Pine," between Fresno and Grant Park, California.

are fewer—one to eight—their arrangement is cyclic, and the spur, with its leaves, falls off in the second to the twentieth year.

In its first year's growth the long shoot of *Larix* bears simple leaves which fall off at the end of the first season. In the second season, buds from the axils of the simple leaves develop into spurs bearing fascicled leaves.

In *Phyllocladus*, the spur, or dwarf shoot, which is borne in the axil of a leaf, becomes flattened, and functions as a leaf, while the

Fig. 244.—*Cupressus macrocarpa:* Monterey, California

very deciduous real leaf drops off. In *Pinus* and *Sciadopitys* leaves are borne only on dwarf shoots, except in seedlings. In the rest, leaves are borne on both kinds of shoots.

With the great mass of the order in temperate regions, and with most of the rest in warmer regions with rainy and dry seasons, the annual rings are well developed. The character of the wood depends, to a considerable extent, upon the relative amounts of spring and summer wood, the early, large-celled spring wood being softer, while the small-celled later wood is harder. Where the early and late parts of the year's growth are nearly equal, and the transition between them rather abrupt, as in *Pseudotsuga taxifolia*, the lumber is very valuable, because the large amount of late wood gives extreme strength, while the early wood prevents brittleness. Where the amount of spring wood is relatively large, as in *Pinus strobus*, the timber is light and not so strong.

The growth-ring in a year with abundant rainfall will be larger than in a dry year. Sometimes there are dry periods of several years, and, consequently, trees over great areas show the small rings; and subsequent, wet or moderate conditions are similarly recorded.

Fig. 245.—*Pinus torreyana:* at Torrey Pines, California, with the Pacific Ocean in the background.

By cutting living trees in such localities, one can count back and determine the dates of various wet and dry periods. It is claimed that the dates on which the timbers for some of the prehistoric buildings in New Mexico were cut can be determined with certainty; and the claim seems well founded. A log of *Pseudotsuga taxifolia*, 586 years old, was felled in 1260 A.D. In this way it was determined that the Pueblo Bonito, in northwestern New Mexico, was under construction as early as the ninth century A.D. The differences in annual rings are not hard to recognize (fig. 246).

In a Sphagnum bog *Tsuga canadense* grows very slowly, with very narrow rings of small, thick-walled cells; but, when a bog is drained,

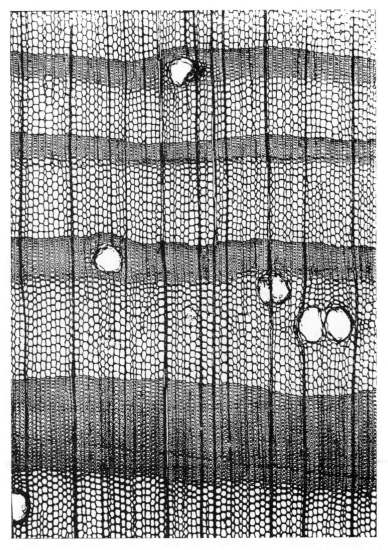

Fig. 246.—*Pinus palustris:* transverse section of stem, showing easily recognizable differences in the annual rings. From a photomicrograph by Dr. Simon Kirsch.

growth immediately becomes very vigorous, so that the rings are many times wider than under bog conditions (fig. 247).

Histology.—The woody cylinder of all the conifers is, typically, an endarch siphonostele; but there are many traces of the ancient mesarch condition which characterized their remote Pteridophyte ancestors. Centripetal wood is more prevalent in the Taxaceae and

FIG. 247.—*Tsuga canadense:* transverse section of stem. The small rings were grown under bog conditions; the larger ones, after the bog was drained.

Podocarpaceae than in the other families, so that, in this respect, they are more primitive. It is claimed that *Cephalotaxus* has a mesarch cylinder; it is certain that the bundles of the cotyledons are mesarch. In *Taxus* and *Torreya* the strand is mesarch at the base of the cotyledons, but changes to exarch higher up. The bundles in the phylloclads of *Phyllocladus* are mesarch. HILL and DE FRAINE[251] examined the position of the protoxylem in all the families of the conifers, paying special attention to the "rotation" of the protoxylem from mesarch to exarch. It will be remembered that, in the cycads, bundles which are endarch in the stem become exarch in the leaves. Cotyledons and cone axes are regarded as conservative structures, and consequently more likely to retain ancient characters. STILES[581] finds some centripetal xylem in the axis of the male cone of *Saxogothea*. Cotyledons, cone axes, and young seedlings would probably yield many cases of mesarch structure.

In the other four families no distinct mesarch character is evident, although there may be traces of it in *Cupressus* and *Juniperus* and in the ovuliferous scales of *Araucaria*. BUCHHOLZ[82] has recently made a very careful examination of the cotyledons of *Cedrus*, but found no centripetal xylem, a conclusion in accordance with the findings of HILL and DE FRAINE for other members of the Abietaceae. Of course, if transfusion tissue is interpreted as xylem, the needles of *Pinus* and many others would have mesarch bundles.

The protoxylem, as in all vascular plants except the angiosperms, consists entirely of tracheids, there being no continuous vessels formed by the breaking down of the end walls of adjacent cells. The first cells of the strand to become lignified may be annular, but the succeeding ones have the spiral marking.

The secondary wood consists of tracheids traversed by medullary rays. A detail of the structure of the secondary wood of a typical conifer is shown in fig. 248.

In this figure the large, comparatively thin-walled tracheids of the spring wood are shown at the right; and the smaller, thicker-walled cells of the later wood are shown at the left. In the upper half of the longitudinal radial section there is part of a medullary ray. The lower two rows of cells of this ray are called *ray tracheids*. They are more or less lignified, and have small, bordered pits; while the rows of cells above have cellulose walls and large, simple pits. The pits of the spring wood are much larger than those of the later, thick-walled cells.

Medullary rays and ray tracheids.—A striking feature of fig. 248 is the medullary ray, as shown in the longitudinal radial section. The upper border of the ray is not shown, but it would be similar to the lower. The upper three rows of cells have large, simple pits, while the two rows below, the ray tracheids, have small, bordered pits. They are characteristic of the Abietaceae, and it has been claimed that they are confined to this family, and that even here they do not occur in *Abies* and *Pseudolarix*. However, they have

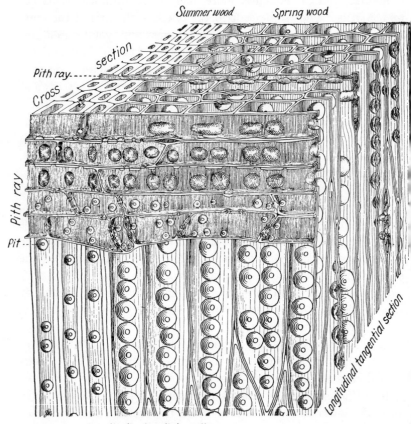

FIG. 248.—*Pinus strobus:* cube of secondary wood, showing transverse, longitudinal radial, and longitudinal tangential sections, and pith ray; at the right, the larger, thinner-walled cells of the spring wood; at the left, the larger, thicker-walled cells of the summer wood; ×400.—From COULTER and CHAMBERLAIN, *Morphology of Gymnosperms*[154] (University of Chicago Press).

been found in wound tissue of *Abies amabilis* and *A. concolor*, and they occur, sporadically, in a few species of Taxodiaceae and Cupressaceae. PENHALLOW[448] thinks the rare cases mark the beginning of a condition which later became prominent; while JEFFREY,[300] basing his conclusion upon their appearance in wound tissue of *Cunninghamia sinensis*, thinks the rare cases are atavistic.

Ray tracheids have the position of ordinary cells of the ray, together with much of the structure of tracheids. Some think they are modified cells of the ray, while others claim that they are modified tracheids. THOMPSON[625] has presented the principal evidence in

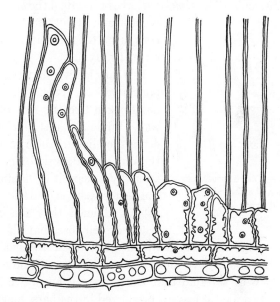

FIG. 249.—*Pinus resinosa:* a series of tracheids in a wounded region, showing transformation to ray tracheids.—After THOMPSON.[625]

favor of the latter view. In the adult stem of *Pinus resinosa*, a series of tracheids from a wounded region showed various gradations between ordinary tracheids and the usual ray tracheids; and in the cone axis of *Pinus strobus*, which is not supposed to have any ray tracheids, the end of an ordinary tracheid is sometimes bent along a ray (figs. 249, 250).

Besides these narrow rays, usually only one cell wide, there are rays several cells in width, broad enough to contain a resin canal. Similar rays, in the cycads, contain a mucilage canal, and, below it, a leaf trace, variously connected with the lower part of the rays. In the conifers, leaf traces are similarly connected with the bottom and sides of the broad fusiform ray.

Bars of Sanio.—Many botanists believe that the "bars" or "rims" of SANIO are reliable criteria in determining affinities. SANIO,[485] as long ago as 1873, found thin spots in the young cellulose walls of tracheids of *Pinus sylvestris,* and around the thin spots, a thickened border. The thin spots he called *Primordialtüpfeln* and the thickened borders, *Umrissen.* The *Umrissen* have been called the *bars* of SANIO.

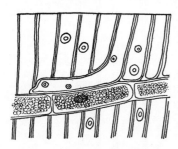

GROOM and RUSHTON[227] called them *rims,* a better translation of SANIO's term (fig. 251).

It is now known that the marginal portion of the primordial pit does not thicken like the rest of the cell wall. While the rest thickens by a deposit of lignin, the rim begins to thicken by a deposit of pectin and, later, by a deposit of lignin, so that the pectose part is overlaid by lignin. It was claimed that the bars con- sisted of cellulose, but the presence

FIG. 250.—*Pinus strobus:* longi- tudinal section of a cone axis, show- ing a tracheid bent along a ray.— After THOMPSON.[625]

of pectose seems established by chemical tests. In their reaction to stains the bars behave more like pectin than cellulose, staining so intensely with safranin that the stain can be drawn from the lignified parts and still leave a bright red in the bars, making them look like superficial structures.

In passing from the pith to the mature wood, the rims become more separated from the pits and there is a tendency to fuse, so that the structure looks more like a bar than a rim. The bar appearance is even more pronounced when there are two pits side by side.

Miss GERRY found, in 1910[207] the bars or rims of SANIO in all families of conifers except the Araucariaceae, and concluded that the presence of bars in coniferous wood indicated Abietacean affini- ties, while their absence indicated Araucariacean affinities. But later, in 1912, JEFFREY,[300] found bars in the cone axis of four species of *Araucaria* and concluded that their presence in such a conserva- tive region indicated an ancestry in which bars were normally present in the main body of the wood. Consequently, the Araucariaceae could not have come from the Cordaitales, and any theory of the origin of the Coniferales would have to make the Abietaceae the most primitive group. THOMSON[638] (1913) found a bar in Araucaria-cean wood and believed the bars are present, in rudimentary form, in all the family.

A cytological study of the origin and development of the bordered pit and the bars and rims of SANIO would be interesting. The technique which has been developed in studying the structure of proto-plasm and chromatin could be modified, if necessary, for a study of these structures. Dr. GRACE BARKLEY'S[32] work on the origin of spiral thickenings in the protoxylem of *Trichosanthes anguina* was a step in solving the relation of protoplasm to the spiral band. Anatomists, who have the foundation for the problem, lack the technique; while cytologists, who have the technique, lack the foundation for such problems, and, besides, they can think of nothing but chromosomes.

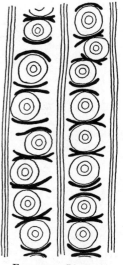

FIG. 251.—*Pinus strobus:* bars and rims of SANIO, showing separate and fused conditions; ×375.

In the Taxaceae the tracheids have a ter-tiary thickening of the cell wall, in the form of a spiral band, which looks somewhat like the spiral thickening in protoxylem, except that it is very commonly double. A similar thickening is also found in *Pseudotsuga*. The spiral is very conspicuous in *Taxus* (fig. 252), and gives the wood an elasticity which has long made it popular with archers. The yew was especially famous for bows before the appearance of the rifle. The western *Taxus brevifolia* has even thicker spirals than the fa-mous *Taxus baccata*, and archers are beginning to claim that it has greater "cast."

Tyloses are rare in conifers. CHRYSLER[134] found them only in *Pinus*, and there only in the root and in the axis of the female stro-bilus. He examined the roots of 32 species in 13 genera, and cone axes of 23 species in 8 genera.

The phloem.—Phloem has not received as much attention as the xylem. Paleobotanists have neglected it because it is usually poorly preserved or entirely lacking; and anatomists dealing with living material have not considered it as important as the xylem.

The general movement of crude food materials is up through the xylem; and the general movement of elaborated food materials is

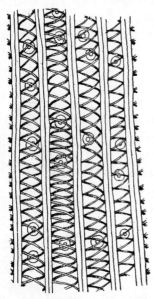

FIG. 252.—*Taxus brevifolia:* longitudinal section showing the tertiary spiral thickening. In the tracheid at the right, there is a single spiral; in the others, there are two spiral bands. The material is from San Juan Island, in Puget Sound; ×433.

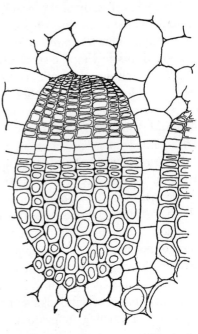

FIG. 253.—*Picea nigra:* vascular strand of a one-year stem, showing rows of phloem continuous with rows of xylem. The section was cut from a Christmas tree. It is evident that the warmth of the house had started cambial activity. The outer cells of the phloem have begun to disorganize; ×750.

downward, through the phloem. Phloem also serves as a storage region.

The phloem, like the xylem, is formed by the cambium. A cambium cell divides and one of the two resulting cells—let us say the inner one—becomes a xylem cell. The other cell is now the cambium cell and at its next division, the outer cell becomes a phloem cell, and the process is repeated. However, there is no such regular alternation, and the embryonic region may be more than one cell thick, as shown by mitotic figures. At the beginning, there must be only one cambium cell for each row of cells, as seen in transverse section; be-

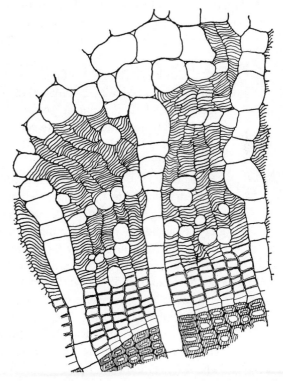

FIG. 254.—*Picea nigra:* transverse section of seven-year-old stem, showing xylem, cambium, and phloem. The phloem, except that of the last year, is crushed, and the cells have lost all their contents; ×433.

cause each row of xylem cells is continuous with a row of phloem cells (fig. 253).

After the first year, the cells of the phloem lose their contents and become variously crushed and crowded (fig. 254). Later, they disappear entirely, weathering off, together with the original cortex, so that the comparative amounts of xylem and phloem, as shown in fig. 253, are maintained only for a short time.

The principal feature of the phloem is the sieve tube. While the tubes are usually in rows, there is no breaking down of transverse walls to form continuous tubes, like the xylem vessels of angiosperms. The transverse walls are as thick, or even thicker, than the lateral, and just as permanent. The sieve tubes taper at both ends, but not so sharply as the xylem tracheids, and often the ends of the tubes are merely rounded. Their most characteristic feature is the sieve area, or sieve plate (fig. 255). The plates occur irregularly throughout the entire length of the tube, but are confined to the radial walls. In a well-stained preparation the plates look somewhat like nuclei, so that the sieve tube looks like a multinucleate cell.

JEFFREY,[301] in his *Anatomy of Woody Plants*, gives an excellent illustration of the phloem of *Pinus* (fig. 256). In this figure the cells of the phloem containing protoplasm—indicated by the dotting—belong to one year's growth. The older, dead cells, becoming crushed and distorted, have lost all their contents. In the living sieve cells the strands of the sieve plates—looking like protoplasmic connections —furnish an extensive communication between contiguous cells. After the first year, as the cells die and lose their protoplasmic contents, a callus forms over the sieve plates. The callus is shown in black in the illustration. Four large parenchyma cells are shown, two in the living phloem and two in the dead.

FIG. 255.—*Pinus:* longitudinal section of cells of the phloem, showing numerous sieve areas, or sieve plates; ×433.

They contain abundant protoplasm and some starch. Two types of rays are shown. The cells of the ray at the left contain no starch, and die with the phloem; while the cells of the one on the right contain starch and are long-lived.

In the course of evolution, the plates become more and more confined to the ends of the cells, and finally, in their highest development in some of the angiosperms, the tapering character is entirely lost, the end wall is transverse, and the sieve character is confined to the end wall.

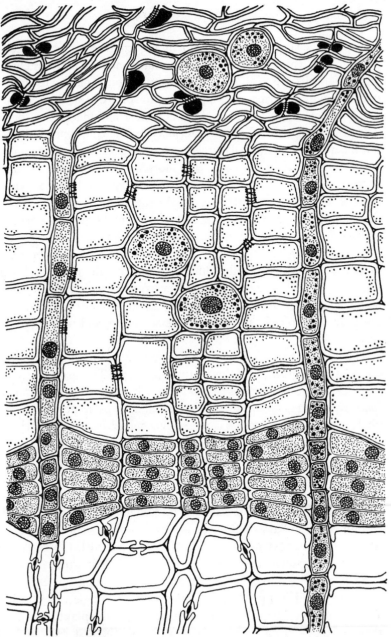

Fig. 256.—*Pinus:* transverse section of phloem of the first year and older phloem. Below the cambium (cells densely dotted) are a few cells of secondary xylem. There are two medullary rays, the one on the right with cells containing starch, and the other with no starch. There are four large cells, shown with nuclei and starch, two in the living phloem and two in the dead. The rest of the dotted cells are living sieve tubes; the cells above them, which have lost their contents, are sieve tubes of the preceding year. The lines looking like protoplasmic connections indicate the sieve plates. In the dead phloem, they are covered by the callus, shown in black.—After JEFFREY.[301]

Besides the sieve tubes, the phloem may contain companion cells, parenchyma, thick-walled tracheids, and stone cells; but tracheids and stone cells are rare in Coniferales, and companion cells do not occur in gymnosperms unless, perhaps, in some of the Gnetales.

The cortex.—The term "cortex" is almost as indefinite as bark. The primary cortex is limited externally by the epidermis, but does not include it; centripetally, its innermost layer of cells is the endodermis. In this sense the cortex is a morphological tissue, as definite as xylem or phloem; but there is a secondary development which soon obscures the primary cortex. As the stem grows, the cortex does not keep pace with the stelar structures, and so becomes stretched and cracked, and the outer portions peel off or scale off. The embryonic layer forming the secondary "cortex" becomes deeper and deeper, until it is finally formed by the phloem. When this stage has been reached, there is no structure which can be called homologous with either the primary or secondary cortex. It is, from the beginning to old age, a protective structure, and may be called *bark.*

The structure of the bark in adult trees is so characteristic that many can be identified by this feature (fig. 257). This group includes *Libocedrus* and two species of *Pinus;* but if *Abies magnifica* and *A. concolor*, which grow in the vicinity, could have been included in the photograph, all five species could be recognized from their bark.

In early stages the cells of the cortex contain chlorophyll, and do considerable photosynthetic work. In many genera there are resin canals, and tannin is abundant. There are other substances in the bark, some of them giving a characteristic odor, so that forest rangers claim that some species can be recognized by the odor. It is certain that the bark of *Sequoia sempervirens* has such strong antiseptic qualities that in poultry houses, bedded with the shredded bark of this species, the fowls escape some of their worst diseases.

Resin canals.—Cells, canals, or cavities containing turpentine or resin are found in all the Coniferales with the single exception of *Taxus*. In some, they are abundant throughout the plant; in others, they are absent from the wood, except that of the first year; and, in others, they are entirely absent from any wood, but occur in the cortex.

FIG. 257.—*Libocedrus* and *Pinus:* bark of a group of large trees in the Mariposa Grove of Big Trees, near Yosemite Valley, California. Of the five trees, the one in the middle is *Pinus ponderosa;* on each side of it, *Pinus lambertiana;* the two outside trees are *Libocedrus decurrens*.

They make their greatest display in the Abietaceae, and, within this family, in *Pinus, Picea, Larix,* and *Pseudotsuga,* where they form an anastomosing system in the wood and cortex of both root and shoot. In the rest of the family—*Abies, Pseudolarix, Cedrus,* and *Tsuga*—they are absent from the secondary wood of both root and shoot. However, in these four genera, the canals are sometimes found in the wood of the axis of the female cone, and they can be produced in the secondary wood in response to wounding.

In the Cupressaceae there are, normally, no resin canals in the wood, except that in *Sequoia gigantea* canals appear in the wood of the first year, and in the wood of the peduncle, axis, and scales of the female cone, and also in the leaf traces of vigorous leaves. In *Sequoia sempervirens* canals are absent from all these parts; but JEFFREY[290] found that, as the result of injury, resin ducts appear in the wood of both root and shoot. He concludes that *S. sempervirens* is a more recent type than *S. gigantea* and that the wounding has made *S. sempervirens* revert—as far as resin ducts are concerned—to the earlier condition of *S. gigantea.*

Resin cells—not ducts or canals—are a constant feature of the wood of Taxodiaceae and Cupressaceae, especially in the later part of the annual ring; but there are canals in the cortex.

In the Araucariaceae there are resin canals in the medullary rays, cortex, and leaves, and resin is laid down in tracheids bordering the medullary rays. The abundant resin of *Agathis australis* is the basis of a high grade of varnish. Some of the resin is obtained from living trees, but most of it is mined on the sites of ancient forests where the tree no longer exists.

In the Podocarpaceae there are no resin canals in the wood or cortex; but there are canals in the leaves, and parenchyma cells containing resin are widely distributed.

The Taxaceae present the least display of resin in the six families. *Cephalotaxus* has resin canals in the pith and cortex, with resin-like contents in some of the parenchyma cells of the wood. In *Torreya* there is a large resin canal in the leaf, and parenchyma cells in the wood contain resin. *Taxus* has no resin canals at all; but resin cells are reported for the roots of *Taxus cuspidata* and *Austrotaxus.*

From the foregoing it is evident that a series can be arranged from a great display of resin canals, through a lesser display to a condition in which there are none at all. Sometimes such a series can be read as one of increasing complexity, or of a continuous simplification. JEFFREY's experiments, causing the canals to appear in regions from which they are normally absent, as a response to wounding, indicate that the series should be read from the complex to the simple. His claim that wounding causes a reversion to a more ancient condition seems well founded. The evidence from fossils, as far as it goes, is in favor of JEFFREY's theory.

The leaf.—The leaves of Coniferales, in comparison with those of the Cycadophytes, are very small, even smaller than those of the Cordaitales. There are no compound leaves in the order. The small simple leaf has led some to look to the lycopods for the origin of the group; but, in spite of the small size of the leaf, the leaf gaps are present and well developed throughout. As far as this feature is concerned, the Coniferales belong definitely to the Pteropsida rather than to the Lycopsida. It has been said that the Coniferales are palingenetically megaphyllous, but coenogenetically microphyllous; which means that their remote ancestors had large leaves which, in the course of evolution, have become reduced to small leaves.

The arrangement of the leaves is spiral, except in the Cupressaceae where it is cyclic, and in *Microcachrys*, which also has the cyclic arrangement.

The dominant leaf of the order is so small, so slender and rigid, and so sharp-pointed that it is commonly called a "needle leaf" (fig. 258). But there are many conifers, belonging mostly to the Southern Hemisphere, which have broad leaves, not at all needle-like. These belong, mostly, to *Podocarpus* and the Araucariaceae (fig. 259). The leaves of *Podocarpus wallichianus* reach a length of 12.5 cm. and a width of 3.5 cm. In some species of *Araucaria* the leaves are broader and nearly as long.

In the large leaved forms, there is no differentiation into long shoots and spur shoots, all leaves being borne upon long shoots. Some forms with needle leaves have only long shoots, like *Abies*, *Picea*, *Tsuga*, *Juniperus*, etc., while others, like *Pinus*, *Cedrus*, *Larix*, and *Pseudolarix*, have both long and spur shoots.

In *Larix*, in the first year's growth of stem or branch, there are no

FIG. 258.—*Abies grandis:* needle leaves, showing a mosaic arrangement; about one-half natural size.—From CHAMBERLAIN, *Elements of Plant Science* (McGraw-Hill Book Co.).[125]

spur shoots, and needle leaves are borne singly on long shoots (fig. 260). In *Pinus*, in the seedling, needles are borne singly on the shoot; but, in later stages, only scale leaves are borne on the long shoot, all foliage leaves being borne on spurs (fig. 261; see also fig. 265).

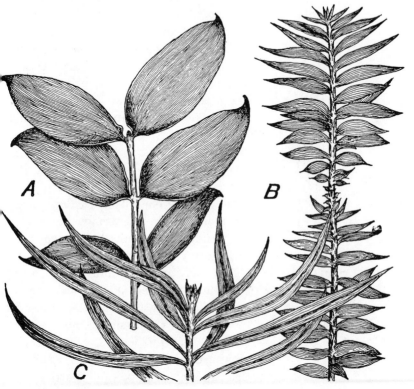

FIG. 259.—Leaves of gymnosperms: large leaves; *A, Agathis robusta; B, Araucaria bidwilli;* the small leaves, between the two groups of larger leaves, are the persistent leaves (hardly to be called bud scales) which protected the bud; *C, Podocarpus coriacea;* all about one-half natural size.

The needle leaves of *Pinus palustris* are the longest leaves in living Coniferophytes, reaching a length of 40 cm. The number of leaves on a spur is a valuable taxonomic character. *Pinus monophylla* has only one leaf on a spur, but two and three are the most usual numbers in the genus. *Pinus quadrifolia* has four; *P. strobus* and a few others have five. Occasionally, there may be as many as eight leaves on a spur.

In *Larix*, *Pseudolarix*, and *Cedrus*, the number of leaves on a spur is much larger, usually thirty to fifty, or even more; but the leaves are never so long as in *Pinus*, seldom reaching more than 25 to 40 mm. in length.

FIG. 260.—*Larix laricina:* tip of branch showing first year's growth with leaves borne directly on the long shoot; and, below, three spur shoots with numerous leaves; natural size.

The spur comes from the axil of a scale leaf on the long shoot, and bears several thin, membranaceous scale leaves, closely wrapped around the spur, before it produces the needle leaves (fig. 262). The needles are always lateral, the terminal meristem persisting for a longer or shorter time after the usual number of needles has been formed. In *Pinus*, where the spur itself is deciduous, the growing point produces only one set of needles, but in forms like *Larix*, where only the needles are deciduous, the apical meristem produces many sets of needles, and, as in *Ginkgo*, may grow out into a long shoot. Sometimes, even in *Pinus*, the apical meristem, after producing the two-, three-, or five-needle leaves, again becomes active, and the spur proliferates, a long shoot growing from the tip of the spur. Proliferation can sometimes be caused artificially. If parts beyond the spur be removed, nutrition which would have gone to the removed parts then goes to the spurs, and, if the terminal meristem of the spur has not died, proliferation is likely to occur.

Besides the needle leaves and broader leaves, many conifers have small, flat, appressed leaves, as in *Thuja*, *Libocedrus*, some species of *Juniperus*, and others (fig. 263). Another modification is seen in the Japanese *Sciadopitys verticillata*, in which two long-needle leaves, borne on a spur shoot, are united by their edges throughout their entire length. In *Phyllocladus*, the spur shoot, coming from the axil of a bract, becomes flattened into a leaflike branch—phylloclad —which functions as a leaf (fig. 264).

In the seedlings, of all these cases with modified leaves, the first leaves are of the familiar needle type (figs. 265 and 266). Young shoots, coming from wounds, also have needle leaves. Occasionally, individuals of a species which has appressed leaves revert more or less completely to the primitive type with needle leaves. Such forms, called *Retinospora*, retain rather persistently the needle leaf. *Juniperus*, which has some species with needle leaves and some with appressed leaves, has given rise to many horticultural forms. In beds of seedlings the horticulturist watches for desirable variants, and propagates them by grafting or by cuttings.

It is evident that, as far as living conifers are concerned, with the possible exception of broad-leaved forms, the needle leaf, borne on a long shoot, is the most primitive type of foliage, from which concrescent leaves, leaves borne on spurs, fused leaves, and phylloclads are later derivatives.

Nearly all conifers are evergreen, *Larix* and *Taxodium* being the only deciduous American genera. *Taxodium distichum* is always deciduous, and I was told that in northern Mexico *T. mucronatum* is deciduous. However, the "Big Tree of

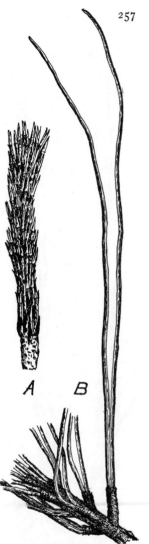

Fig. 261.—*Pinus laricio: A*, young long shoot with numerous spur shoots showing the pairs of needle leaves just breaking through scale leaves; *B*, mature long shoot with several spurs, each bearing two needle leaves. Below the lowest spur with two complete needle leaves are two scars left when the spurs, with their leaves, had fallen off; both natural size.

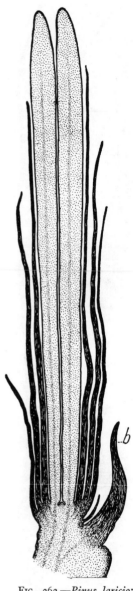

Fig. 262.—*Pinus laricio:* spur shoot from the axil of a bract (*b*), with scale leaves and two needles and the growing point between them; ×12.

Tule," in southern Mexico, is evergreen. This tree is generally regarded as *Taxodium mucronatum*, although some prefer to call it *T. distichum* var. *mucronatum*.

In *Pinus strobus* and *P. palustris* the leaves fall the second year, but in most species they live longer: in *P. sylvestris*, 3 years; *Pinus cembra*, 4–7 years; and in *P. aristata* and *P. balfouriana* they persist for even 12–14 years. In *Picea excelsa* and *Abies alba* the leaves live from 6 to 9 years and, sometimes even 10–12 years. In some of the Araucariaceae the leaves may not fall until the branch which bears them breaks off.

The evergreen leaf and the beautiful habit have made the conifers very popular as decorative plants on lawns, in city parks, and around farm houses in the country. Unfortunately, the dirt, dust, smoke, and perhaps gases of a large city are fatal to plants with leaves which must function more than one year. Thirty years ago, in Washington Park, Chicago, *Pinus laricio*, *P. sylvestris*, *Picea engelmannii*, *Picea excelsa*, and various other conifers were prominent decorative features; but, as the city developed southward and Cottage Grove Avenue lost the features which gave it its name, the conifers died. South of the city, a region of steel mills, stone-crushing plants, and sulphuric acid factories, a region formerly covered with a luxuriant growth of *Pinus banksiana*, the pine keeps retreating several miles in advance of the progress of civilization. Plants with leaves which must function more than one year do not prosper under such intense civilization, and even deciduous plants shed their leaves a little earlier in the autumn.

Histology of the leaf.—The structure of the conifer leaf is xerophytic, in many cases exceedingly so. The needle of *Pinus* is typical of the forms with needles on spur shoots (fig. 267, 268). There is a thick layer of cutin, the epidermal cells are small and thick walled and the hypodermal cells, one to three layers deep, are also thick walled. The stomata are deeply sunken. Surrounding the bundle area is a conspicuous endodermal sheath of large, thick-walled cells, marked with the prominent Casparian strips which are so often found in endodermal cells. Within the sheath there are two bundles in *Pinus laricio* and one in *P. strobus;* and, in both, there is abundant transfusion tissue.

Since many of the cells of the transfusion tissue are more or less lignified and have bordered pits, some believed that this tissue is a reduced xylem portion of the bundle, an interpretation which would make the bundle mesarch. This feature is very well shown in *Sciadopitys verticellata*, where most of the cells beyond the

Fig. 263.—*Thuja occidentalis:* end of branch showing appressed leaves; natural size. See also fig. 266.

protoxylem could be interpreted as centripetal xylem (fig. 269, *C*).

Although the leaf of *Sciadopitys* consists of two needles, fused along the posterior margins, the internal structure shows no evidence of a fusion, the tissue being quite uniform. In the concrescent leaves of *Thuja*, and others of this type, the fusion is not so complete. The leaves adhere strongly, but it is usually possible to recognize the epidermis along the lines of contact. There are many large air spaces in the leaf of *Sciadopitys*, and numerous sclerotic cells, with sharp, projecting prongs, like those so conspicuous in the dicot, *Nymphea*.

FIG. 264.—*Phyllocladus rhomboidalis:* part of a small branch showing leaflike phylloclads.—From a photograph by LAND, in COULTER and CHAMBERLAIN, *Morphology of Gymnosperms*[154] (University of Chicago Press).

A more bizarre stomatal region than that of *Sciadopitys* could not be found in the entire order. The stomata are confined to a broad groove on the abaxial face of the leaf (fig. 269 *B*). The epidermal cells of this region have long, heavily cutinized projections, which become shorter and shorter beyond the region of stomata, until, at a few cells beyond the last stoma, there is no projection and no more cutinization than on the rest of the surface.

The small, rigid leaves of *Cryptomeria* have a single bundle and a single resin canal (fig. 270). The walls of the epidermal and hypodermal cells are very thick, while the walls of the mesophyll cells are thin, with none of the crenate lobing so characteristic of the pines.

Large, broad leaves like those of most of the Araucariaceae and of many species of *Podocarpus*, often look like the leaves of dicotyls, and they often have a strong palisade at the adaxial surface, with a looser tissue below (fig. 271). The veins, however, while appearing to be more or less "parallel," are likely to show the dichotomy so characteristic of the "parallel" veins of the cycads.

Fig. 265.—Juvenile leaves: *Pinus laricio,* early simple leaves and later spur shoots, each bearing a pair of needle leaves.—From CHAMBERLAIN, *Elementary Plant Science* (McGraw-Hill Book Co.).[125]

The epidermis, and especially the stomata, have recently been investigated in great detail by FLORIN,[198] who has made a critical comparison of these features in living and in fossil forms. This study not only adds to the value of the epidermis and stomata as criteria in the phylogeny of fossil plants, but indicates that these structures might well be utilized in determining relationships of living forms.

In the gymnosperms of the Carboniferous, in both the Cycadophyte and Coniferophyte lines, the double-leaf trace was a familiar feature. In the living Abietaceae the trace is double, but in the Cupressaceae it is single. Some botanists doubt whether the double-leaf trace is a primitive feature, because the traces in the cotyledons of such characteristic forms as *Pinus* and *Abies* are single. In fact, the traces of the cotyledons are single in all of the Taxodiaceae and Cupressaceae, except, occasionally, in *Cupressus torulosa*. They are double in Araucariaceae. In all cases the cotyledonary strands connect with the poles of the root.

The root and hypocotyl.—Many conifers, like *Pinus sylvestris* and *P. maritima*, are anchored by a powerful tap root; but in some pines,

like *P. montana*, and in several other genera, the primary root soon aborts, and practically the only anchoring is by lateral roots. Those which have no strong tap root, especially those of the *Picea excelsa* type, are more easily blown down; but in many the lateral roots are wide spreading, and often extend obliquely downward, thus affording considerable stability.

Besides the long roots of both the tap and lateral type, there are short roots, which are small and often profusely branched. These roots, which do not attain any great age, often failing to reach the secondary wood stage, are the principal absorbing organs of the plant. The profusely branched roots frequently contain mycorhiza, but there are no ectotrophic mycorhizas in the Araucariaceae,

FIG. 266.—*Thuja occidentalis:* two cotyledons, juvenile leaves, and later appressed leaves; natural size.

although cells of the cortex are often filled with mycorhizas of the endophytic type. In the Podocarpaceae there are root tubercles,[575] resembling those of the Leguminosae, and such roots have root hairs, though in some genera similar roots have no root hairs. It has been claimed that there are no root hairs on coniferous roots; but the observations were very superficial, for root hairs are almost invariably present near the tip (fig. 272). It is a partial excuse for the mistake that the root hairs are confined to a very small region at the tip and break off so easily that they are lost unless the washing is very carefully done. In the series from which fig. 272 was drawn the region of root hairs was not more than 1 millimeter in vertical extent.

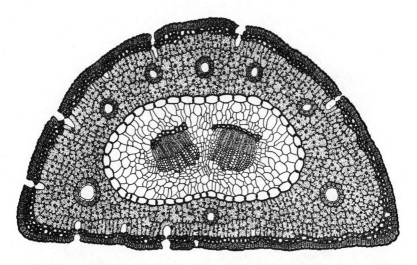

Fig. 267.—*Pinus laricio:* transverse section of a needle, showing the sheath inclosing two bundles and the transfusion tissue. Outside the sheath is the tissue of crenately lobed cells and numerous resin ducts. The heavily cutinized epidermal cells have thick walls, and the hypodermal cells, one to three layers in thickness, are also thick walled. The stomata are deeply sunken; ×93.

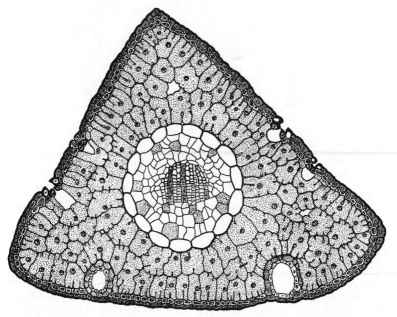

Fig. 268.—*Pinus strobus:* transverse section of needle with a single bundle; ×155

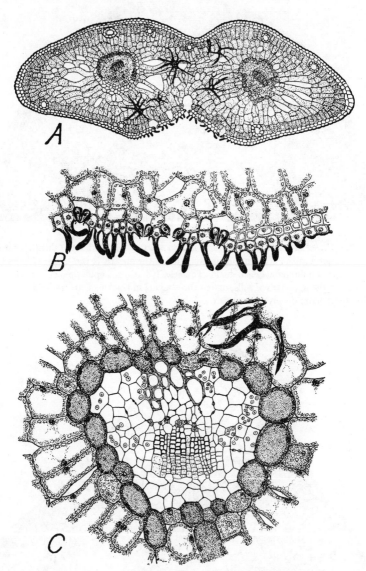

FIG. 269.—*Sciadopitys verticillata: A*, transverse section of the two fused leaves. Stomata only on a small portion of the lower side. There are many air spaces and large sclerotic cells with projecting spines; *B*, part of the stomatal region; the epidermal cells have large, strongly cutinized projections; *C*, a bundle, showing cells with bordered pits, many of them on the protoxylem side of the bundle; *A*, ×37; *B* and *C*, ×175.

Taxodium, when growing in its favorite swampy habitat, has peculiar vertical outgrowths from the roots, called "cypress knees," extending upward so far that they are seldom covered by the water (fig. 273). The base of the trunk, in swampy habitats, is often im-

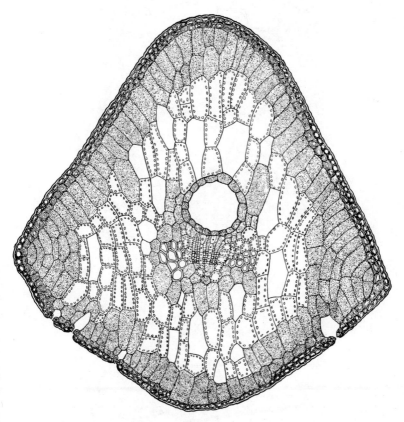

FIG. 270.—*Cryptomeria japonica:* transverse section of leaf, showing a single bundle and single resin duct. The cells in which plastids are indicated are intensely green. A thinner section would have shown more numerous air spaces; ×155.

mensely swollen, and may be thickly covered with short, fleshy, adventitious roots (figs. 274, 275). When dry, the adventitious roots and the "cypress knees" are very light, with xylem tracheids as thin as in the wood of *Ochroma*, the famous "balsa" wood.

The young root of *Pinus*, as it is found in a ripe seed, has about the same structure as in the rest of the conifers and will serve as a type for the group (fig. 276).

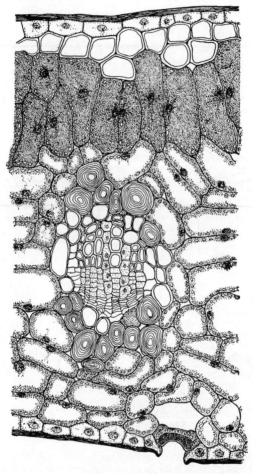

FIG. 271.—*Agathis robusta:* transverse section of leaf showing strong palisade with looser tissue below; the bundle is nearly surrounded by very thick-walled cells. In a transverse section, most of the stomata are cut longitudinally; ×312.

There is no dermatogen. A meristematic group of initials with large nuclei (the nuclei of the group are indicated in fig. 276) gives rise to plerome, periblem, and root cap. It can be seen that rows of cells are continuous from this group to root cap, periblem, and plerome. Of course, the root cap comes from the lower layer of meristematic cells, and so it is said to come from the periblem. This single layer of cells seems to form a mantle over the tip of the plerome, and, laterally,

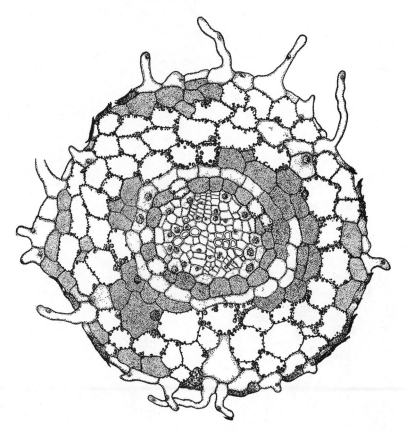

FIG. 272.—*Pinus banksiana:* transverse section of young root, showing root hairs. The root is diarch and secondary growth is beginning; ×130.

in the longitudinal section, it is continuous with the periblem. That it gives rise to periblem and root cap seems to be a safe conclusion, but whether some periclinal mitosis may not add a cell to the group above is not so certain. Cells immediately above this single layer

FIG. 273.—*Taxodium distichum:* "cypress knees," near Tallahassee, Florida.—From a negative by Dr. HERMANN KURZ.

FIG. 274.—*Taxodium imbricarium:* showing broad trunk bases; near Tallahassee, Florida.—From a negative by Dr. HERMANN KURZ.[333]

are either plerome or give rise to it. However, just how definite the differentiation into periblem and plerome may be within the meristematic group is not so easy to determine. There is certainly no such marked differentiation as in the *Capsella* type among dicotyls.

It was once claimed that there is no true epidermis in Pteridophytes except at the root cap, because it was only at this point that

FIG. 275.—*Taxodium imbricarium:* extreme swelling of the lower part of the trunk. The swollen part of the tree at the right is covered with adventitious roots. After KURZ.[333]

there was a segment of the apical cell giving rise to the special layer. As a matter of fact, the layer which was called periblem was still an embryonic layer which had not yet become differentiated into periblem and dermatogen. No doubt, conifers have an epidermis. Whether it is better to say that the epidermis comes from the periblem, or that an embryonic region is late in differentiating into periblem and dermatogen, may be a problem which different people will decide differently. At any rate, the group of initials, as one sees

it in embryo after embryo, is about as it is shown in the figure.
Practically all authorities say that the root cap comes from the periblem, and it is obvious that there is no differentiated dermatogen or
calyptrogen at the tip of the root.

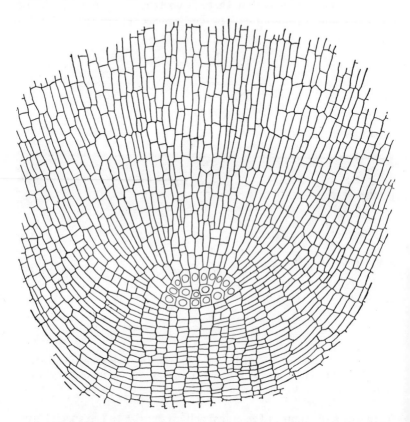

Fig. 276.—Root tip of *Pinus edulis:* longitudinal section of the root end of an embryo
in a ripe seed, showing a meristematic group of initials (the nuclei are indicated), the
plerome, periblem, and root cap; ×125.

In the root of the seedling, two protoxylem points are prevalent
throughout the whole group; but in the dominant genus, *Pinus,*
more than two protoxylem points are the rule (fig. 272). *Pinus
sylvestris* and *P. banksiana* have diarch roots; in *P. laricio* and many

others the roots are triarch; in and *Pinus edulis*, tetrarch. In adventitious roots of *Taxodium imbricarium*, the pentarch condition is common; but even in the same cluster of roots, some are likely to be tetrach, some, triarch, and many, diarch.

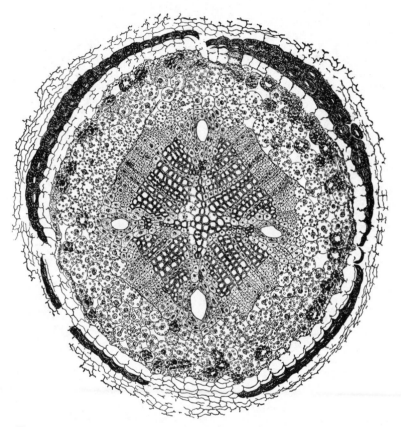

FIG. 277.—*Pinus edulis:* transverse section of a young root after secondary growth has become established. The outer part is scaling off in plates. There is a resin duct opposite each of the four protoxylem points. The crushed protophloem is still visible, and outside it are cells rich in starch, and just beneath the scaling off layers are numerous resin cells; ×118.

The protoxylem points, always exarch, appear early, and there are indications of secondary development before the metaxylem differentiates. As the regions differentiate, it is evident that there is an extensive, many-layered pericycle and a definite, one-layered endodermis (fig. 272). Often there is a resin duct opposite each pro-

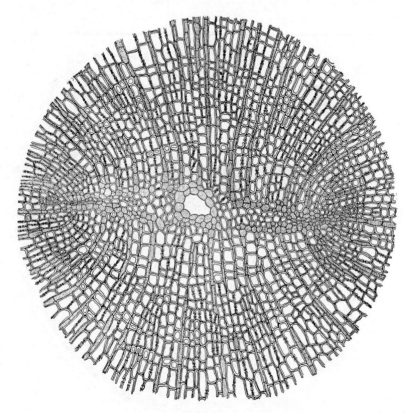

FIG. 278.—*Abies balsamea:* transverse section of root, showing diarch primary xylem with a resin duct in the metaxylem. The rays in the secondary wood show the symmetrical growth curves; ×100.

toxylem point; but sometimes there is a resin duct in the metaxylem, as in *Abies* (fig. 278).

The later stages in the structure of the root are much like those in the stem, except that the tracheids are sometimes longer and broader, and the growth-rings usually not so wide.

The origin of the root will be considered under the heading "Embryogeny."

The hypocotyl.—In the young seedling the hypocotyl is the most prominent and most extensive part of the plant. In its lower part the structure is much like that of the root, with phloem groups al-

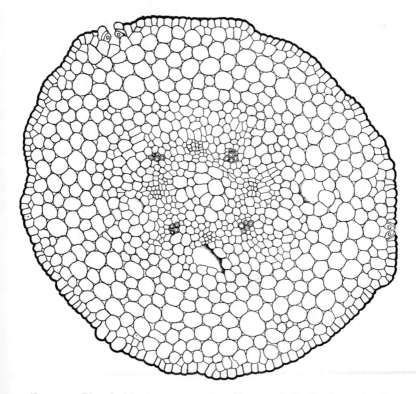

FIG. 279.—*Pinus laricio:* transverse section of hypocotyl, showing four protoxylem points, with four alternating groups of phloem. There are also two resin ducts, not well differentiated at this stage. Two stomata are shown in the epidermis; ×160.

ternating with the exarch bundles in typical radial arrangement (fig. 279). But there is no scaling off at the outside, and stomata are present, although not so abundant as in the leaves and young stem. Higher up in the hypocotyl the bundles begin to rotate, making a half-turn, so that near the cotyledons a transverse section shows an endarch protoxylem. There is no centripetal xylem at any time, the change from an exarch to an endarch position of the protoxylem being due entirely to rotation.

The stomata on the hypocotyl of *Pinus edulis* seem to be a little different from those on other parts of the plant; and those on the cotyledons and leaves are so different from each other that, taken separately, they might seem to belong to different species, or even different genera. The hypocotyl of conifers would seem to be a good place for a thorough study of comparative anatomy.

CHAPTER XII

CONIFEROPHYTES—CONIFERALES—*Continued*

THE SPOROPHYTE—REPRODUCTIVE

The cone is the most characteristic feature of the order and the one to which it owes its name. The staminate strobili are conelike throughout, but the Taxares (Taxads and Podocarps) have sometimes been described as conifers without cones because the female strobili do not look like the familiar cones of the other families.

The separation of the sexes shows all conditions from bisporangiate strobili to monoecism and to a complete separation in typical dioecism. The monoecious condition is dominant. Bisporangiate strobili occur only as occasional abnormalities.

The Abietaceae and Taxodiaceae are uniformly monoecious. In the Cupressaceae, *Fitzroya*, *Diselma*, and *Arceuthos* are dioecious, and *Juniperus communis*, usually dioecious, occasionally bears both male and female strobili on the same plant; but, in such cases, either the male or the female is dominant, recalling the condition in *Cannabis sativa* and some other angiosperms, which are evidently in transition from monoecism to complete dioecism. The other genera of Cupressaceae are monoecious. The Araucariaceae are dominantly dioecious, but *Agathis australis* and *Araucaria bidwilli* are monoecious. The Taxaceae are dioecious, except in occasional individual cases. In the Podocarpaceae the dominant genus, *Podocarpus*, is dioecious, although there have been reports—not very convincing—of occasional monoecism. Some species of *Phyllocladus* and *Dacrydium* are monoecious.

The survey shows that the great majority of the genera are monoecious, a much smaller number having attained the dioecious condition. In the plant kingdom, from the algae to the highest dicotyls, the course of evolution shows a progressive separation of the sexes, with such intermediates and mixtures that the dioecious condition is evidently the goal. As far as this single feature is concerned, the

FIG. 280.—*Pinus contorta:* tip of lateral branch showing staminate cones just ready to shed their pollen; an ovulate cone ready for pollination at the tip of the branch; ovulate cone a year older, a little farther down; and, near the bottom, an ovulate cone two years older. Puget Sound Biological Station, Friday Harbor, Washington; June 20, 1929.

dioecious species are later developments than the monoecious; or, rather, they have progressed farther along this line of evolution; but dioecism may be associated with very primitive features. Consequently, one could hardly claim that a monoecious family, as a whole, is more primitive than a dioecious family. It is simply more primitive in this one respect.

Monoecism, the prevalent condition in the order, is well illustrated in *Pinus*, the dominant genus of the Northern Hemisphere (fig. 280). This figure shows staminate cones a day or two before shedding their pollen, and ovulate cones of three successive seasons; at the top, a couple of cones just ready for pollination; lower down, an ovulate cone which was pollinated the previous year and which would show young embryos; and near the bottom, an ovulate cone which was pollinated two years earlier than the one at the top, and has shed its seeds. The ovules in *Pinus contorta* are pollinated in June, the eggs are fertilized the next June, the embryos complete their development during the summer, and the ripe seeds are shed the following summer. In some pines, like *Pinus radiata*, the cones remain tightly closed for years and shed the seeds only when there is a fire or an unusually hot, dry season. Pines with hard cones usually shed their seeds the third season, like *Pinus contorta*, *P. banksiana*, and many others.

BISPORANGIATE STROBILI

Bisporangiate strobili are always described as teratological. In the evolution of sex there is a constant tendency to wider and wider separation, so that the theoretical series would be bisporangiate strobili, monosporangiate strobili with both sexes on the same plant (monoecism), and, finally, monosporangiate strobili on different plants (dioecism).

In the Cycadophytes bisporangiate strobili are common and normal in the Bennettitales, but are unknown in Cycadales, all of which are not only monosporangiate, but are strictly dioecious. In the Coniferophytes nothing is known of conditions which preceded the Cordaitales, and even in the Cordaitales themselves it can only be said that there no bisporangiate strobili have been found. Ginkgoales are monosporangiate and dioecious.

But in the Coniferales bisporangiate strobili occur in many of the genera, and in some they occur so frequently that most botanists who study plants in the field have seen these interesting cones in one form or another.

Bisporangiate strobili are most abundant in the Abietaceae, but have been found in all the families except the Taxaceae. The most frequently reported examples are in *Picea excelsa, Abies alba, Pinus laricio*, and *P. maritima;* but they have been found in other species of *Pinus* and *Picea*, and also in *Pseudotsuga taxifolia, Sequoia sempervirens, Juniperus communis*, and others. Such cones occur often in cultivated specimens of *Picea excelsa*, where the ovulate sporophylls are at the top, with the staminate below (fig. 281). In *Picea* the cone axis is long, fleshy, weak, and turgid. The staminate sporophylls bear one or two more or less globular sporangia, containing some apparently good pollen, some dead and shriveled, and some in which development seems to have been arrested at various stages (fig. 282). The bracts at the base of the ovulate part bear neither microsporangia nor megasporangia.

FIG. 281.—*Picea excelsa:* bisporangiate strobili. Below are staminate sporophylls, each bearing one or two sporangia; above are the ovuliferous structures, most of the scales bearing two ovules which seem to be normal. At the base of the ovulate part are a few bracts which have neither ovules nor stamens; natural size.

GOEBEL[212] found hundreds of bisporangiate strobili on a single tree of *Pinus maritima* (fig. 283). They bear microsporangia below, megasporangia at the top and, between the two, have sporophylls with microsporangia on the abaxial side, and rudimentary ovuliferous scales in the axils.

A tree of *Pinus thunbergia* in the Botanical Garden at Tokyo, Japan, bears cones with microsporophylls and megasporophylls intermixed from the bottom to the top.

STRASBURGER[600] observed, in *Pinus laricio*, branches with staminate cones at the base and ovulate cones at the top, while the part of the branch between bore both kinds of cones and also bisporangiate cones. The latter had staminate sporophylls at the base, ovulate sporophylls at the top, with sporophylls (bracts) between bearing neither kind of sporangia.

In most bisporangiate cones the ovulate sporophylls are at the top with the staminate below; but cases have been reported in which the arrangement was just the opposite.

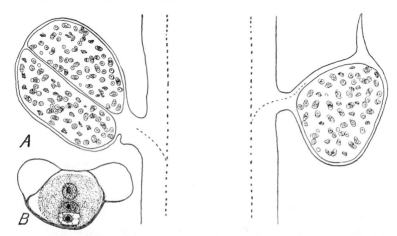

FIG. 282.—*Picea excelsa: A*, sections of microsporangia from lower part of a strobilus like those shown in fig. 281; *B*, section of a pollen grain which seems to be normal. The material was merely wrapped in paper and sent from a considerable distance; hence the shrunken protoplasm. *A*, ×20; *B*, ×300.

An abnormal cone of *Pinus* sp. was once sent to our laboratory as a curiosity. On one side, from the bottom to the top, it looked like a normal cone; while the other side bore spur shoots with two somewhat stunted needles.

Pines have been noted in which some of the ovulate structures of the cone were replaced by spurs with two needles.

Admixtures of male and female characters occur even in dioecious angiosperms. In *Salix petiolaris*[101] the staminate sporophyll may be tipped with a stigma, and carpels, bearing ovules near their bases, may bear microsporangia higher up; and still higher up, may be tipped with good stigmas.

What causes the changes in sex characters has not been determined for either gymnosperms or angiosperms. These peculiarities have been noted more frequently in exotic individuals; but whether the conditions are more likely to occur in such cases, or such cases are more likely to be noticed, might be questionable. It has been claimed that abnormalities occur more frequently in nursery material: it is certain that they would be more likely to be noticed.

Comparatively little histological work has been done in this field, nearly all the accounts dealing with mature cones. It would not be impossible, or even very difficult, to collect a series in various stages of development, for a tree which produces teratological cones produces them year after year.

In the most frequent teratological cases the arrangement of staminate and ovulate sporophylls on the cone axis resembles a frequent arrangement of staminate and ovulate strobili on a tree; for the ovulate cones are higher up, with the staminate lower down, as in *Abies*. In *Pinus* it is very rare to see a staminate cone at the top of a tree or tip of a branch, while this is the usual place for ovulate cones. In seasons in which scarcely any cones are produced, two or three ovulate cones can usually be found at the top of the vertical shoot at the extreme top of the tree. In *Saxagothea* the ovulate cone is terminal on a short branch, which bears staminate cones farther back in the axils of its leaves. In general, the ovulate cones are more numerous at the top of the tree or at the ends of the branches, with staminate cones farther down or farther back on the branch, suggesting the arrangement in the bisporangiate angiosperm flower.

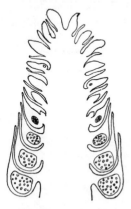

FIG. 283.—*Pinus maritima:* bisporangiate strobilus. The lowest three sporophylls on each side bear microsporangia; the next sporophyll above, on each side, has a microsporangium in the lower part and a rudimentary ovuliferous scale in the axil; above these are ordinary ovuliferous structures.—After GOEBEL.[212]

THE STAMINATE STROBILUS

Throughout the entire order, the staminate strobilus is simple, the sporophylls being borne directly upon the cone axis. There are no bracts; consequently, the staminate strobilus is a flower, not an inflorescence. The ancient discussion as to whether the ovulate strobilus is a flower or an inflorescence will be considered later.

The cones vary greatly in size. The cone of *Juniperus communis*, 2 mm. in length, with nearly mature pollen, but before the rapid lengthening which allows the pollen to be shed freely, is very small; while the cone of *Araucaria bidwilli*, 10 cm. in length, is extremely large. It is claimed that this cone reaches a length of 20 cm. Dr. GEORGE GRAVES of Fresno, California, where there are scores of fine large trees of this Australian species, has collected a few cones 12.5 cm. in length, but has never seen any approaching the reputed 20 cm. In *Araucaria rulei* it is reported that cones reach a length of 24 cm. In *Araucaria cunninghami* the cones have a greater diameter and reach a length of 7 cm. before the rapid lengthening begins. They occur in immense numbers and produce a prodigious amount of pollen (fig. 286). It would not be exaggerating to estimate the output of a single cone at 10,000,000 pollen grains.

The origin of sporophylls from the meristem is dominantly spiral, the Cupressaceae being the only family which shows the cyclic arrangement throughout. The arrangement of sporophylls, however, is so geometrically regular that they often seem to be in vertical rows, as they would be if the arrangement were cyclic (figs. 284 and 285).

FIG. 284.—*Pinus contorta:* shoot with a large number of axillary staminate cones. The axis of the shoot is prolonged beyond the cones, and, at the base, shows pairs of needles nearly covered by bracts; higher up, the needles are entirely covered by the bracts. Although the sporophylls appear to be in vertical rows, their arrangement on the cone is strictly spiral; natural size.

The sporophylls, like the cones, vary greatly in size (fig. 287). The figure shows typical sporophylls of ten genera. Some of the pines have smaller sporophylls than *Pinus laricio;* and it is possible that some species of *Araucaria* may have larger sporophylls than *A. cunninghami;* but the figure, with all the sporophylls drawn to the same scale and magnified 8 diameters, shows the general range of size and appearance.

The leafy character is quite pronounced in *Araucaria cunninghami* and *Picea excelsa*, and in *Dacrydium elatum* it is scarcely distinguishable from the foliage leaf; while in many it is more reduced, and in some there is no more resemblance to the original leafy blade than in the cycad, *Zamia*.

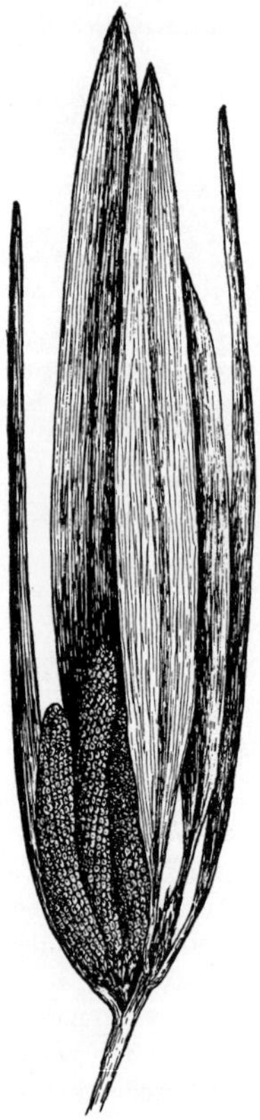

The sporangia are borne on the abaxial face of the sporophyll. However, HAGERUP[228] claims that in *Dacrydium elatum*, a central Sumatran conifer, the sporangia are on the "upper" surface. He says that the ovules also are on the upper face of the sporophyll, and he regards both male and female sporophylls as homologous with those of Lycopodiales.

The dominant number of sporangia is two, but many conifers have more (fig. 287). The figure shows several genera with two sporangia, and several with more. The number is 2 in all of Abietaceae; 2–5 in the Taxodiaceae; 2–6 in the Cupressaceae; and many more in the Araucariaceae. *Araucaria cunninghamia* has 13 and they are very large. *Agathis australis*, the New Zealand Kauri, has 5–15 sporangia on a sporophyll; and in *A. bornensis* the number of sporangia often reaches 15. Some of the Araucarian sporangia reach a length of 7 mm., and a length of 4–6 mm. is not at all rare.

FIG. 285.—*Podocarpus* with three male cones.

In *Taxus* the sporophylls, each bearing, usually, 6 sporangia, but sometimes as many as 8, are peltate, with the sporangia hanging down, as in *Equisetum* (fig. 288). In *Torreya* the condition is similar, but there are only four sporangia borne on one half of the nearly peltate top. COULTER and LAND[152] found, in the sterile half of the top, resin canals which might represent the missing sporangia. In early stages the resin canals look very much like young sporangia.

In the Podocarpaceae there are two sporangia. The sporophylls are generally small, but are often very numerous, in long, slender cones.

Fig. 286.—*Araucaria cunninghami:* a spray of staminate strobili, at Rockhampton, Queensland, Australia; about one-half natural size. The strobili are from 5 to 8 centimeters in length.

The dehiscence is longitudinal, as in *Pinus*, in the greater number of cases, but often transverse, as in *Abies*. In some cases it is oblique, as in *Picea*.

Microsporogenesis.—The development of the microsporangium and its microspores is the usual development of a eusporangiate sporangium, and, in the earlier stages, does not differ much from that of *Selaginella*, or even from that of a eusporangiate homosporous form, like *Lycopodium*. There is a hypodermal cell, or layer of cells, which may be called the archesporium. A periclinal division in the

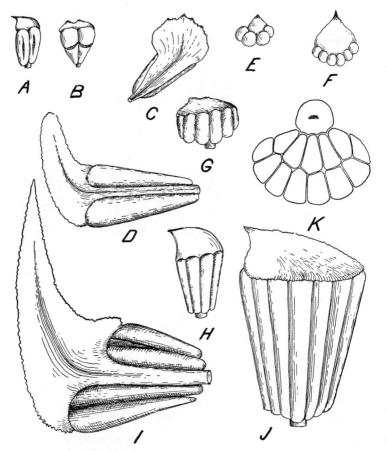

Fig. 287.—Male sporophylls of conifers: *A, Pinus laricio; B, Abies grandis; C, Picea alba; D, Cedrus libani; E, Juniperus communis; F, Cryptomeria japonica; G, Cupressus macrocarpa; H, Agathis australis; I, J,* and *K, Araucaria cunninghami; I,* view from upper surface; *J,* view from lower surface; *K,* transverse section showing 13 sporangia in two rows; all ×8.

archesporium gives rise to two cells or two series of cells, the outer forming the parietal, or wall, layers, and the inner giving rise to the sporogenous tissue.

It has been shown in so many cases that the tapetum, as far as it is derived from either of these series, consists of modified wall cells, that any claim of a sporogenous origin would have to be strongly supported. Of course, much of the tapetum does not come from either of these sources, but is differentiated from whatever cells happen to be in contact with the sporogenous cells.

The development of the sporangium in most conifers is very slow, the young cone becoming recognizable in the spring, the archesporium appearing in early summer, and the development of sporogenous tissue continuing until the autumn weather becomes too cold, even for a conifer. During the earlier stages of development the cones are entirely covered by scale leaves (fig. 289). The actual dates could not be given, even for a single species, except in some special locality; for, the date for a special stage, like the appearance of

FIG. 288.—*Taxus baccata:* *A*, staminate shoot with numerous strobili; *B*, single staminate strobilus; *C*, ovulate shoot with two ovules; *A* and *C*, natural size; *B* ×2.

the archesporium, for the appearance of the microspore mother cell, for the reduction of chromosomes, and for the shedding of pollen, will vary with the latitude, the elevation, and, in some cases, with the proximity of warm or cold ocean currents. Many conifers are very successful exotics. The times of shedding pollen of *Cupressus macrocarpa* at Monterey, California, and at Auckland, New Zealand, differ by six months. Since this naturally endemic conifer thrives from the latitude of Monterey to that of Auckland, the pollen is doubtless shed at various times, and other stages would vary correspondingly. However, in any particular locality, the same stages will appear at about the same time, year after year.

In the Chicago region, some conifers pass the winter in the microspore–mother-cell stage (fig. 290). This was easily determined by comparing late autumn, mid-winter, and early spring conditions. In *Juniperus virginiana*, in the same locality, the mother cells divide,

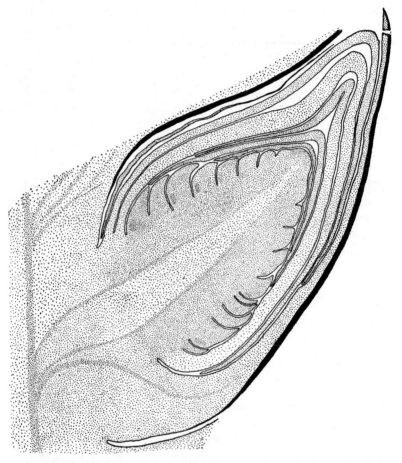

FIG. 289.—*Pinus banksiana:* young staminate cone with sporangia in early sporog-enous stages at the bottom; at the top, archesporial cells have not yet appeared; near Chicago (September 10, 1931); ×45.

the exine and intine of the microspores are developed, and the pollen is nearly ready for shedding when winter arrives; but in *Juniperus communis*, growing close to the other species, the winter is passed in the mother-cell stage.

The reduction of chromosomes.—The time at which reduction occurs varies with the species and the locality, and may differ a few
days in different years. In the Chicago region, in *Pinus laricio*, reduction occurs the first week in May. Dr. MARGARET FERGUSON,[196]

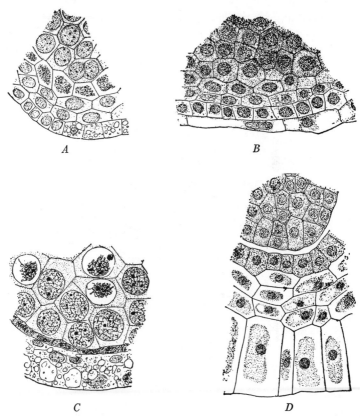

FIG. 290.—*A, Pinus laricio,* microsporangium on October 1; *B*, the same on January 3; *C*, the same on April 4; *D, Taxus canadensis* on October 1, showing microspore-
mother-cell stage.—After CHAMBERLAIN.[102]

whose work on *Pinus* is the most complete account of the life-history
of any genus of the conifers, gives about the same date for reduction
in *Pinus laricio* (*austriaca*), *P. rigida*, and *P. strobus*. Her collections were made in the vicinity of Wellesley, Massachusetts. HOF-
MEISTER,[258] in Germany, found that in *Picea* and *Abies* the pollen

mother-cell stage is reached by the end of November. So they pass the winter in the pollen mother-cell stage.

In all of these localities the autumn and winter conditions are approximately the same. In warmer climates the dates would doubtless be different. We have seen a species of *Pinus* near Jalapa, in Mexico, shedding its pollen in September. It would be interesting to know the life-history of such a species, with dates for the various

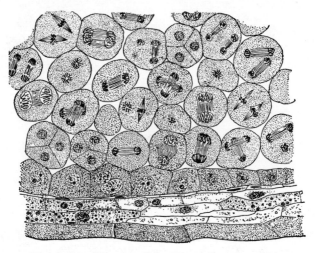

Fig. 291.—*Pinus laricio:* reduction of chromosomes in pollen mother-cells, showing stages from the telophase of the first reduction division to young microspores;[154] Chicago (May 3); ×500.

stages. In *Araucaria bidwilli*, at Fresno, California, where there are many large, luxuriant specimens, reduction takes place the last week in March.

In an angiosperm like *Lilium*, with elongated anthers, a longitudinal section at the reduction period shows simultaneous mitosis; but stages at the top, middle, and bottom may be quite different. In *Pinus*, a section of the sporangium, in any direction, shows as wide a range of stages as are found from the top to the bottom of an anther of *Lilium* (fig. 291). In an extremely long microsporangium, like that of *Araucaria*, stages at the top and bottom would probably be different.

The number of chromosomes have been counted in several genera.

If any numbers can be said to be dominant, they are 12 and 24 for the x and $2x$ phases of the life-history. At least 8 species of *Pinus*, 5 species of *Larix*, and 2 species of *Podocarpus* have these numbers. GOODSPEED[214] found 12 and 24 in *Sequoia gigantea;* but LAWSON[344] found 16 and 32 in *S. sempervirens*. In *Abies balsamea*[275] the numbers are 16 and 32; in *Sciadopitys verticillata*,[349] in *Cephalotaxus drupacea*,[346] 10 and 20; and in *Taxus baccata*,[604] 8 and 16. The lowest numbers, 6 and 12, are reported by SAXTON[491] for *Callitris cupressoides*.

THE OVULATE STROBILUS

Throughout, we have been using the terms "strobilus" and "cone" almost synonymously. All cones are strobili; but not all strobili are cones. The heading, *the ovulate strobilus*, is more appropriate than *the ovulate cone*, because it includes the podocarps and taxads, some of whose ovulate structures cannot be called cones, although we do not hesitate to call them strobili. The spore-producing structure of *Lycopodium lucidulum* is a strobilus, but not a cone. However, it represents a more primitive condition from which the typical cone of *Lycopodium clavatum* could have been developed, with forms like *L. inundatum* as intermediates. The term "cone" is shorter, and throughout this work we have used it often, but only when either term, "cone" or "strobilus," could be employed; and we have used the more comprehensive term, "strobilus," when the term "cone," would have been appropriate.

In striking contrast with the simple staminate strobilus, the ovulate strobilus of the Coniferales is compound. The ovule-bearing structures are not borne directly upon the cone axis, as in the staminate cone, but in most cases are borne upon a much-discussed structure associated with a bract. This bract is borne directly upon the main axis, and is homologous with the male sporophyll. As in the staminate cone, the parts are formed in spiral succession, except in the Cupressaceae and a few scattered genera in other families.

Except in the Taxaceae and some of the Podocarpaceae, the ovulate strobili are cones, varying in size and appearance from the typical cones of *Pinus* to the small berry-like cones of Juniperus and plumlike ovules of *Torreya* (figs. 292–96).

Pinus and *Araucaria* have the largest cones. The longest ovulate cone in conifers is that of *Pinus lambertiana*. SUDWORTH'S illustration was made from a cone $23\frac{1}{2}$ inches (nearly 60 cm.) in length, and

FIG. 292.—*Pinus radiata:* (Monterey Pine), a very endemic California species; ovulate cone, natural size.—After SUDWORTH.[606]

cones from 40 to 50 cm. in length are not at all rare. These immense cones, hanging down from the extreme tips of the branches, can be seen at a distance of a quarter of a mile, and give the tree a characteristic appearance (fig. 235). The cone of *Pinus coulteri*, reaching a length of 23–35 cm., has a greater diameter, and its average weight is probably greater than that of *P. lambertiana*. Another western pine, *Pinus sabiniana*, has a cone from 16 to 26 cm. in length, nearly globular in form, and very heavy. In *Araucaria bidwilli* the cone reaches a diameter of 30 cm. Since the cones in this family are nearly spherical, this cone may be heavier than any of the longer cones of

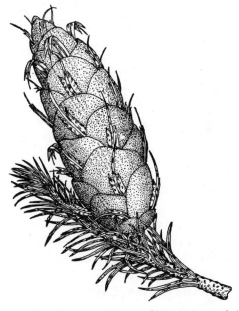

FIG. 293.—*Pseudotsuga taxifolia:* ovulate cone; natural size

Pinus. In other species of *Araucaria* and in *Agathis* the cones are smaller, the cones of the immense *Agathis australis*, the Kauri of New Zealand, being only 6 cm. in diameter. In *Sequoia gigantea*, the largest of all trees, the cones are only from 4–6 cm. in length; and in *S. sempervivens*, the tallest of conifers, reaching a height of 115 meters, the cones are even smaller, seldom more than 1.5 cm. in length. The cones of *Tsuga canadensis* and *Larix laricina* are also about 1.5 cm. in length.

The berry-like cones of *Juniperus* are still smaller, that of *J. communis* having a diameter of 6–8 mm. In *Taxus* the seed, including the aril, is from 9 to 13 mm. in diameter.

Between the extremes there are cones of all sizes; of the more or less elongated type, like *Pinus*, of the more or less globular type, like

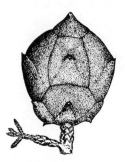

Cupressus; and of the berry-like type, as in *Juniperus;* and, besides, there are the ovulate structures, generally small, of the taxads and some of the podocarps, which are responsible for the appellation, "conifers without cones."

Structure of the ovulate strobilus.—In the Abietaceae the ovulate structures are more or less elongated cones; in the Taxodiaceae the cones range from the elongated type, as in *Sciadopitys* and *Sequoia*, to the spherical type, as in *Taxodium;* in the Cupressaceae and Araucariaceae the spherical type dominates; in the Podocarpaceae such strobili as are called cones are slightly elongated, as in *Microcachrys* and *Saxagothea;* while such structures as those of *Podocarpus*, *Dacrydium*, and all of the Taxaceae, make the designation "conifers without cones" seem ap-

Fig. 294.—*Cupressus macrocarpa:* ovulate cone; natural size.

Fig. 295.—*Juniperus communis:* berry-like ovulate cones; natural size.

Fig. 296.— *Torreya taxifolia:* plumlike ovule.

propriate. However, even in these cases, we believe the ovuliferous structures can be interpreted as very much reduced cones.

If one could interpret the ovulate cone of *Pinus*, the rest of the order would not make much trouble. It seems safe to interpret the so-called "bract" as the homologue of the sporophyll of the staminate cone; but the structure which bears the ovule is not so easy to interpret. The appearance of the much discussed and variously interpreted structure is shown in fig. 297.

At this stage the cone bears striking resemblance to the cone of Lycopodium, the debatable structure resembling the young sporangium of the lycopod. But, in a conifer, this structure is certainly not an ovule. Generally, it seems to be axillary; but occasionally it seems to be borne on the face of the sporophyll. What is its homology?

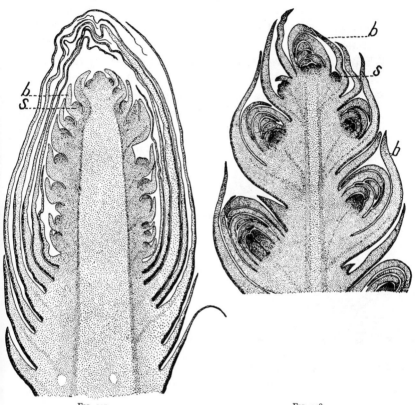

FIG. 297.—*Pinus banksiana:* young ovulate cone still inclosed within the protecting bud scales: *b*, the bract, or sporophyll; *s*, the structure which bears the ovule; ×20.

FIG. 298.—*Pinus banksiana:* longitudinal section of young vegetative shoot, showing bracts (*b*) and spurs (*s*). The spur (*s*) on the right has not yet begun to develop scale leaves; the one opposite, on the left, is developing scale leaves; all of the spurs below show not only scale leaves, but the two needles. The drawing is somewhat diagrammatic, since so many spurs would not be shown in median view in a single thin section; ×20.

As one traces the evolution of the sporophyte from forms like *Riccia,* where nearly all of the sporophyte consists of spores, there is strong support for the theory that tracing the evolution is tracing an increasing amount of sterilization of sporogenous tissue. At the lycopod level the amount of sporogenous tissue is not only greatly restricted, but it appears much later in the individual life-history than in *Riccia*. In the conifers the comparative amount of sporogenous tissue is still more restricted, and it appears still later in the individual life-history.

Whatever may have been the origin of sporogenous tissue in the liverworts, or, even earlier, in the algae, the spore-bearing structures, from the lycopods up, are modifications of vegetative structures. In

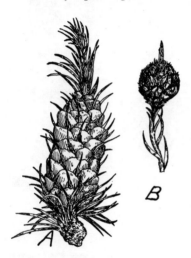

Lycopodium lucidulum the sporophylls are like the vegetative leaves, and practically all the leaves are sporophylls; in *L. inundatum* the spore-bearing leaves are somewhat modified, are confined to the upper part of the shoot, and are grouped into a loose strobilus. In lycopods of the *L. clavatum* type the sporophylls are quite different from the vegetative leaves, and are grouped into a compact cone.

The cones of conifers, both ovulate and staminate, frequently proliferate, changing from the reproductive to the vegetative phase (fig. 299). The proliferating branch may again bear cones. If an ovu-

FIG. 299.—Proliferating cones: *A, Larix heterophylla; B, Cryptomeria japonica;* natural size.

late cone, like that of *Pinus*, is a modified shoot, the modification has been extreme (fig. 298). At the top of the figure, the young spur (*s*) looks much like the debatable structure (*s*) in fig. 297. Histologically, the young spur shoot and the debatable ovuliferous structure look alike (fig. 300). The figure, although drawn from a young ovulate cone, might pass for a young vegetative spur in the axil of its bract; but, later, the young spur produces scale leaves, and finally a pair of needle leaves, while, in the young cone, the axillary structure produces no scale leaves, but bears two ovules on the face directed toward the axis of the cone.

The structure has been called an ovuliferous scale, a flattened branch in the axil of the bract; it has been called an open carpel, a placenta, a ligule, the blended integuments of two ovules; it has been called a leaf of an axillary shoot, the first two leaves of an axillary shoot fused by their margins; and if any possible structures have been omitted from this list, it may be assumed that someone has applied them to the ovule-bearing structure. WORSDELL,[707] in 1900, collected and discussed the literature, and practically nothing has been added since.

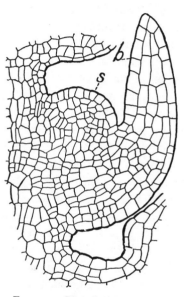

In all of the investigations and philosophizing great stress has been laid upon abnormal cones, where various intergrades between reproductive and vegetative structures have been found. Nearly all of these abnormal cones have been studied only in the mature condition. Since trees which produce abnormal cones produce them year after year, material of young stages could be collected, and it would be interesting to make a comparative study of the development of such cones throughout the order, comparing especially the cones of forms with and without spur shoots; and comparing those with bract

FIG. 300.—*Pinus banksiana:* part of young ovulate cone, showing bract (*b*), with the "ovuliferous scale" (*s*), in its axis; ×350.

and ovuliferous scale free, as in Abietaceae and Podocarpaceae, with those which have the bract and ovuliferous scale "fused," as in Taxodiaceae and Cupressaceae. On account of the peculiar relations of the ovuliferous structures, a study of young proliferating cones in Araucariaceae should be particularly interesting. A comparative study of young stages in the ovuliferous structures of the Taxares—Podocarpaceae and Taxaceae—would also be valuable, since it might reveal the presence of lost structures, the absence of which started the designation of "conifers without cones."

For many botanists, any structure in the axil of a leaf must be a shoot, and so a leaf in the axil of another leaf is an impossibility. Consequently the ovuliferous scale could not be a leaf, unless some shoot could be so reduced as to become present only theoretically.

In a transverse section through the bract and ovuliferous scale, the bundles of scale and bract show a reversed orientation, the xylem of the bundles facing each other, with the phloem outside; and this is true, whether the bract and scale are free from each other or "fused" into one structure. But the bundles of the bract connect below with the vascular bundles of the cone axis, while the bundle of the ovuliferous scale connects above; consequently, with this connection, the orientation is not at all peculiar, but only what should be anticipated. From a study of the bundles, VAN TIEGHEM[649] drew the conclusion that the ovuliferous scale is a leaf on a suppressed branch, a conclusion which was later strengthened by the bundle situation in the "double" leaves of *Sciadopitys*.

Some claim that the cones of Araucariaceae are quite different from those of the preceding families. The cone of *Araucaria* looks as if it had a bract and scale, fused as in the Cupressaceae; and Dr. HANNAH AASE,[1] from a study of the vascular anatomy, is inclined to believe that the structure is compound. THOMSON,[638] also studying the anatomy, concludes that there is only a simple sporophyll, so that the cone is simple, like the staminate cone. In the other genus, *Agathis*, there is no such appearance of bract and scale. Taxonomists separate the two genera on the presence (*Araucaria*) or absence (*Agathis*) of a "ligule." The ligule of *Araucaria* has the position of an ovuliferous scale, and looks like one (fig. 301).

At present, we prefer to use the term "ovuliferous scale." Until some decisive proof of some theory is produced, we shall continue to believe that the bract of the ovuliferous cone is the homologue of the sporophyll of the staminate cone, and shall guess that the ovuliferous scale—at least in forms with bract and scale—is a modified shoot which, with or without leaves, bears the ovules.

Unless some entirely new theory, different from all of these, can be proved, the ovulate cone is compound, and, therefore, is not a flower, but an inflorescence.

The megasporangium.—All of the megasporangia, commonly called "ovules," of the conifers are borne in strobili, which are defi-

nitely organized as cones, except in the taxads and some of the podocarps, where it is possible that a cone is present, but so reduced or
modified that botanists fail to recognize it.

There is a single integument. Only by interpreting the epimatium,
the aril, or the ovuliferous scale as an integument, can there be two
integuments. We should interpret the epimatium as an ovuliferous
scale. The nucellus is free from the ovule, at least in early stages of
development. Where the two structures are not free from each other,
there is said to be a union or fusion. Probably there is not a single
case of fusion in the order, but, rather, the same phenomenon appears

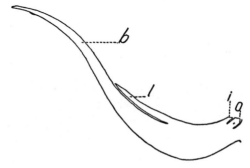

FIG. 301.—*Araucaria bidwilli:* the ovuliferous structures: *b*, bract; *l*, the "ligule";
o, young ovule in the spore–mother-cell stage; *i*, integument; ×7.

which gives rise to perigyny and epigyny in angiosperms. A growth
below the free portions carries them up, and, throughout this region
of common growth, the nucellus and integument are said to be
united. In this sense, there is considerable union in the Abietaceae,
where nucellus, above the level of the megaspore, is free from the integument. In the Taxodiaceae there is some union at the base. In
the Cupressaceae the two are free, or are more or less united at the
base. In the Araucariaceae the nucellus and integument are very
free, in *Agathis australis* the ovule even being stipitate. In *Taxus* the
nucellus and integument are free, even in later stages; but in *Torreya*,
chalazal growth is so extensive that, in later stages, only a small part
of the nucellus is free.

Ovules are orthotropous, as in *Taxus*; or anatropous, as in *Podocarpus*; or may have intermediate positions. Approximately half of

the genera have more or less anatropous ovules, while, in the other
half, they are more or less orthotropous.

The free condition is regarded as primitive, and the more or less
"united" condition as more advanced. It must be remembered that
both conditions existed in the early gymnosperms of the Carboniferous. In *Trigonocarpus* the nucellus was entirely free from the integument, while, in the best-known of all paleozoic seeds, *Lyginopteris*
(*Lagenostoma*), the "union" was almost complete.

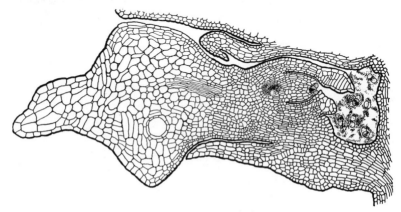

Fig. 302.—*Pinus banksiana:* bract; ovuliferous scale; and ovule. The bract and scale,
in such a condition, are said to be free from each other; ×25.

Nowhere in the order is there any extensive vascular system in the
ovule, like that of the cycads. In most cases, there are no bundles at
all in the integument, or in the aril, where this structure is present.
In *Microcachrys* and *Saxagothea* there are bundles at the base of the
integument, and, in *Podocarpus*, bundles sometimes extend almost
to the top of the integument.

While there is not such a differentiation of the integument into
strongly marked regions, as in the cycads, three regions are often
distinguishable, a middle layer which becomes hard, with a fleshy
layer on each side. The outer layer may remain fleshy for a longer or
shorter time, while the inner, fleshy layer always becomes dry and
membranous.

The megasporangium, throughout the order, is eusporangiate and
massive, and shows great diversity in its appearance (figs. 302–6).

The relation of the ovule to associated structures can be seen more easily than it can be interpreted. In fig. 303 C, in this case, LAW-

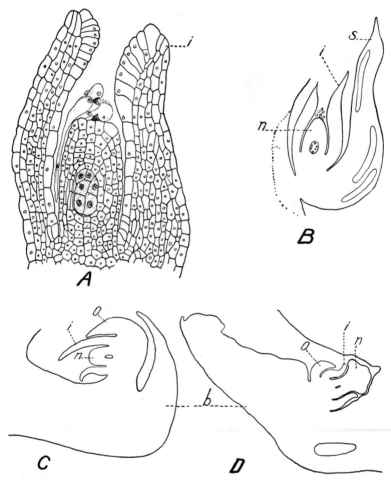

FIG. 303.—Ovules of conifers: A, *Sequoia sempervirens; B, Pherosphaera; s, sporophyll; C, Microcachrys; D, Saxagothea conspicua; b*, bract; *o*, ovuliferous scale; *i*, integument; *n*, nucellus; A, ×95; B, ×33; C, ×66; D, ×25.—A,[344] B,[351] and C,[350] after LAWSON; D, after NOREN.[419]

SON[350] claims that the ovule is borne on the face of a sporophyll. The structure which we have marked *b*, he regards as the sporophyll, while the one which we have designated as the ovuliferous scale (*o*), he regards as a second integument. In *Pherosphaera*[351] (fig. 303 *B*) LAWSON says the single erect ovule is borne on the sporophyll, close to the axis of the cone. There does not seem to be any structure

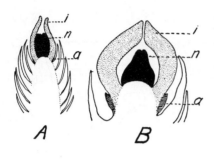

which could be called an ovuliferous scale. In *Saxagothea*[419] (fig. 303 *D*), the ovuliferous scale is comparatively small, and the nucellus protrudes from the micropyle and is more or less glandular, like a stigma. In *Microcachrys*,[350] also, the ovuliferous scale, in early stages, is rather small (fig. 303 *C*).

Dacrydium elatum, a Sumatran species recently described by HAGERUP, seems to bear the ovule on the adaxial face of a sporophyll, which is the homologue of the male sporophyll (fig. 305). HAGERUP[228] claims that both microsporangia and megasporangia are borne on the upper (adaxial) face of sporophylls, just as sporangia are borne in lycopods. The "cone" consists of only two sporophylls, and, between them, the sterile tip of the branch which sometimes proliferates. The fact that

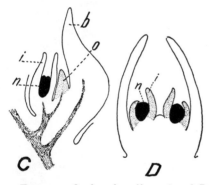

FIG. 304.—Ovules of conifers: *A* and *B*, *Taxus baccata*—*A*, at time of pollination and *B*, somewhat later: *i*, integument; *n*, nucellus; *a*, aril; ×15. *C*, *Cryptomeria japonica: b*, bract; *o*, ovuliferous scale; *i*, integument; *n*, nucellus; ×22. *D*, *Thuja occidentalis: i*, integument; *n*, nucellus; ×35.—All after HAGERUP.[228]

HAGERUP describes and figures an "epimatium" may mean that there is something representing the ovuliferous scale. A detailed study of the development would be interesting.

When ovules are terminal on the axis, as in *Taxus*, there is no sporophyll or ovuliferous scale to confuse the interpretation (fig. 304 *A*, *B*). However, in this case, there is an aril, which many regard as an integument. It can be distinguished at the time of pollination, and, in late stages, becomes red and fleshy, giving the seed its berry-like appearance.

In the Podocarpaceae the epimatium is a striking feature of the ovule (fig. 306). It starts like an integument and looks like one. Below it, is the receptacle, which becomes very large and fleshy. The aril of *Taxus* and the outer fleshy covering in *Torreya* start in the same way. In *Gnetum* a delayed integument also starts in this way. Some regard all of these structures as tegumentary

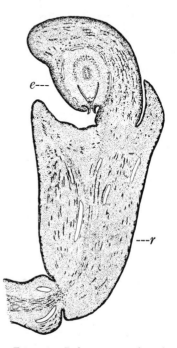

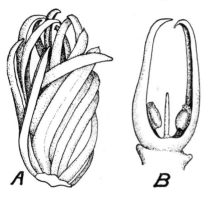

Fig. 305.—*Dacrydium elatum: A*, tip of twig with ovuliferous structures covered by leaves; *B*, the same with leaves dissected away, showing two leaves, each bearing an ovule on its inner (adaxial) face; ×6.— After Hagerup.[228]

Fig. 306.—*Podocarpus:* ovule and epimatium. The female gametophyte in an early free nuclear stage. *e*, epimatium; *r*, receptacle; ×10.

in their origin, but the epimatium may be homologous with the ovuliferous scale, rather than with the integument.

The megaspore.—In many cases the megaspore mother-cell becomes recognizable so late in the development of the ovule, and is so deeply placed, that it is impossible to determine just what the origin may have been (fig. 307 *E*). In a species like *Pinus*, where the megaspore mother-cell is so deeply placed, one can imagine a row of cells from a hypodermal cell down to the mother-cell. Wherever the origin can be traced, it is hypodermal. In *Taxus*, the archesporial cell, or cells, are hypodermal, and can be recognized very easily by the deep staining; and, later, the line of cells between the mother-cell and the periphery is very easily traced (fig. 307 *A,B*). In *Taxus* sev-

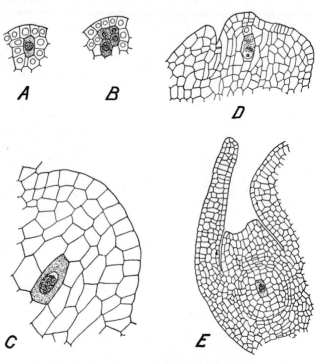

FIG. 307.—Archesporium and spore mother-cells of conifers: *A* and *B, Taxus baccata: A*, single archesporial cell; *B*, two archesporial cells have divided, giving rise to two tapetal cells and two primary sporogenous cells, which are also the megaspore mother-cells; *C, Keteleeria fortunei*, megaspore mother-cell; *D, Larix europea*, longitudinal section, young ovule showing megaspore mother-cell; *E, Pinus rigida*, deeply placed megaspore mother-cell; *A* and *B*, after DUPLER,[178] ×238; *C*, after HUTCHINSON,[276] *D*, after STRASBURGER,[600] ×141; *E*, after MARGARET FERGUSON,[196] ×46.

eral mother-cells may divide, and several megaspores may germinate, producing gametophytes which may reach an advanced free nuclear stage. In *Keteleeria*, a peculiar Chinese gymnosperm, which has been variously assigned to *Pinus, Abies*, and *Tsuga*, the mother-cell is sharply marked (fig. 307 *C*). Perhaps the earliest form in which the mother-cell was proved to be hypodermal in origin is *Tsuga* (fig. 307 *D*).

The cells surrounding the mother-cell soon become modified, and furnish nutrition to it as it increases rapidly in size (fig. 308). These cells constitute the "spongy" tissue, and furnish nutrition, not only

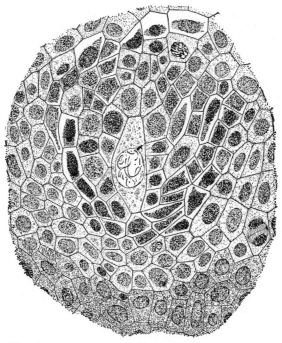

FIG. 308.—*Pinus laricio:* megaspore mother-cell with nucleus in prophase of reduction division. Surrounding it are modified cells, called the "spongy tissue," which furnish nutrition not only to the mother-cell, but to later stages; × 500.—From COULTER and CHAMBERLAIN, *Morphology of Gymnosperms*[154] (University of Chicago Press).

to the growing megaspore, but even through early stages of the female gametophyte. They are finally entirely absorbed.

Occasionally, the megaspore fails to develop. In such cases, the spongy tissue may become very active and its cells may look like megaspores, or like early cellular stages of a female gametophyte. This behavior is rather frequent in *Pinus contorta* (fig. 309).

When the mother-cell is developing normally, the tissue around it is densely packed with protoplasm, and stains deeply, appearing as in figs. 308 and 309 *A*. In fig. 309 *B*, the megaspore has aborted, and is probably represented by the black streak between the two groups of enlarged cells. Whether one or more of these enlarged cells, which, normally, would have been merely nutritive cells, might develop into a functional gametophyte was not determined. It would be worth while for someone, in contact with this western conifer, to work out its entire life-history.

The reduction division in microsporogenesis in angiosperms has been studied, described, and philosophized about, until

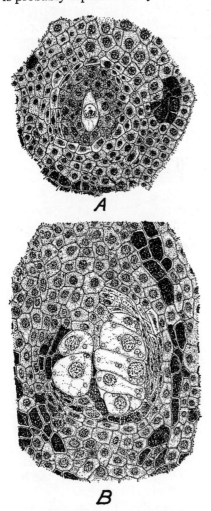

A

B

FIG. 309.—*Pinus contorta: A*, megaspore mother-cell developing normally, with spongy tissue around it; *B*, in this case, the mother-cell has aborted and the surrounding tissue is developing strongly, looking like a group of mother-cells; ×500.

FIG. 310.—*Pinus laricio:* megaspore mother-cell as it appears in the Chicago region, about June 1. The spongy tissue has the normal appearance.—From COULTER and CHAMBERLAIN, *Morphology of Gymnosperms*[154] (University of Chicago Press).

an appalling literature has accumulated; less is known about the reduction in megasporogenesis, because it is tedious to get the desired stages. In the gymnosperms not much is known, even about the reduction in microsporogenesis, and still less is known about reduction in megasporogenesis. Reduction certainly takes place, usually giving rise to a row of four megaspores, the lower one of which functions, while the other three abort (fig. 310). After the first reduction division, it often happens that only the lower cell divides, giving rise to two megaspores, only the lower one of which functions. The upper cell of the row of three is not a megaspore, because it still has the sporophyte number of chromosomes. So many cases of a row of three are reported that it would seem as if there might be a tendency toward the elimination of the division of the upper of the first two cells. With the reduction division, the sporophyte generation comes to a close. The megaspore is the first cell of the gametophyte generation.

CHAPTER XIII

CONIFEROPHYTES—CONIFERALES—*Continued*

THE MALE GAMETOPHYTE

The microspore is the first cell of the male gametophyte. All of the four microspores produced by a microspore mother-cell seem equally vigorous and capable of completing the entire life-history, and nearly all of them germinate and complete more or less of the life-history while still inclosed in the microsporangium. In some species of *Cupressus* and *Juniperus* the microspore is shed in the uninucleate condition; but, in such cases, a division occurs soon after reaching the nucellus, before the pollen tube begins to be formed. In these cases there are no prothallial cells, the first division giving rise to a generative cell and a tube nucleus. Consequently, the microspore is the antheridial initial.

In this more or less advanced stage of development, the microspores, or pollen grains, are shed. The whole order is wind-pollinated. In spite of occasional claims, it is very doubtful whether there is a single case of insect pollination in any gymnosperm. Pollen is shed in prodigious quantities. In pine forests, lumbermen speak of "sulphur showers." No doubt there are millions of pollen grains in a cone of *Araucaria bidwilli*, and BURLINGAME[84] estimated the output in *A. braziliensis* as high as a billion. In any case, the output is immense, and nearly all of the pollen grains die. Very few reach a nucellus, where they may continue their development and form pollen tubes.

The microspore always has two spore coats, exine and intine, which vary in their comparative thickness. Usually, the exine is thicker; but in some cases, like *Araucaria bidwilli*, the intine may be more than twice as thick as the exine. When the pollen is winged, the wings are formed from the exine. STRASBURGER[596] believed that the wings arose from a splitting of the exine. Dr. MARGARET FERGUSON[196] decided that they originate by a separation of the exine from the intine. A study of very thin sections of *Pinus* and *Abies*, sharply stained with safranin and light green, supports Dr. FERGU-SON's conclusion. Only about one-third of the genera have wings or bladders of any sort, the great majority having no such developments of the exine. When wings are present, there are generally two, as in *Pinus;* but *Microcachrys* has three, and sometimes four, or even five or six. Most species of *Podocarpus* have two large wings, but *P. dacrydioides* has three. *Pherosphaera* has very small pollen grains with three wings.

The male gametophyte is in various stages of development when the pollen is shed, but for any given species in any given locality the time of shedding will vary little, and the stage of development may not vary at all.

Very few species, like *Taxus canadensis* and *Cunninghamia sinensis*, shed the pollen in the uninucleate stage, and these will not have any prothallial cells. The first mitosis, after reaching the nucellus, will be the one which gives rise to the generative cell and tube cell. In species which have prothallial cells, these and the generative cell are formed before the pollen is shed.

Pinus is a familiar form with winged pollen and prothallial cells (fig. 311). The figure begins with the second reduction division (*A*), the tetrahedral arrangement of microspores is shown in *B*, and the beginning of the wings in *C*. The first mitosis of the young gametophyte is shown in *D–F*, in *F*, with the nucleus of the first prothallial cell already degenerating. *G* and *H* show the prophase and telophase of the second mitosis, and *I*, the two prothallial cells. These are usually overgrown by the vigorous intine before the third mitosis (*J*), which gives rise to the generative cell and tube cell, is completed. When the two prothallial cells and the generative cell (*K*) have been formed, the pollen is ready to be shed. In *Pinus* the succeeding stages are found after the pollen has reached the nucellus of the ovule (*L*).

This is a very prevalent course of development of the male gametophyte in conifers. Some differ in having no prothallial cells; some, in having a greater display of prothallial cells; others differ in the extent of development of the male gametophyte when the pollen

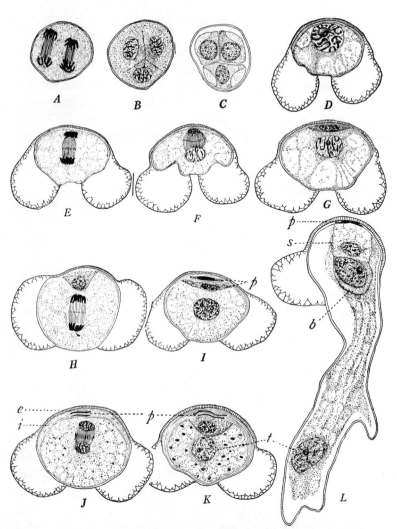

FIG. 311.—*Pinus laricio:* stages in the development of the male gametophyte; *A*, the second reduction division; *B*, tetrahedral arrangement of microspores; *C*, the wings are beginning to appear; *D*, prophase of first division in microspore; *E* and *F*, telophase of first division; in F, the nucleus of the first prothallial cell is already disorganizing; *G*, first prothallial cell and prophase of second division; *H*, telophase of second division; *I*, two prothallial cells; *J*, telophase of third division; the nucleus nearest the prothallial cell will belong to the generative cell and the other is the tube nucleus; *K*, the two prothallial cells, overlaid by the intine (*i*), the generative cell and the tube cell; this is the shedding stage; *L*, pollen tube, as found in nucellus, showing stalk and body cells: *p*, prothallial cells; *s*, stalk cell; *b*, body cell; *t*, tube nucleus; *e*, exine; *A* and *B*, May 3; *C*, May 10; *D–G*, May 20; *H–J*, May 25; *K*, June 15; *L*, May 1, nearly a year after the stage shown in *A*; ×600.—From COULTER and CHAMBERLAIN, *Morphology of Gymnosperms.*[154]

is shed; and others differ in the number of gametes or in the organization of gametes.

Prothallial cells are a constant feature of the Abietaceae; but in
most of the Taxodiaceae (*Sciadopitys, Cunninghamia, Sequoia,
Cryptomeria, Taxodium*), they are generally lacking. In many of
the Cupressaceae (*Callitria, Widdringtonia, Libocedrus, Thuja,
Cupressus, Chamaeceparus, Juniperus*), they are also lacking. There
are no prothallial cells in the Taxaceae. Wherever there are no prothallial cells, the microspore is the antheridial initial, as in angiosperms. In all of the Podocarpaceae, except *Pherosphaera*, there is a
vigorous development of prothallial cells. The greatest display of
these cells in the whole order is in the Araucariaceae, where the development of prothallial tissue is far greater than in any living
heterosporous pteridophyte (figs. 312, 313).

In *Araucaria*, and others with two or more prothallial cells, the
first two cells, and sometimes a third cell, are formed as in *Pinus*.
The large number of prothallial cells is due to the subsequent division of these two or three cells. More than two cells, formed as in
Pinus, are rare. When the first prothallial cell divides periclinally, it
looks as if three cells had been formed by the *Pinus* method. The
first division in the primary prothallial cells is nearly always anticlinal; and even when there are a dozen prothallial cells, there may
be no periclines. Where the number is large, sometimes as many
as forty, there will be both anticlines and periclines.

There can be no doubt that prothallial cells are vestigial. Originally they were green, independent plants, bearing the antheridia. In
some heterosporous pteridophyte ancestor, the prothallium (gametophyte) became included within the spore, became parasitic, and then
became reduced, and finally disappeared entirely. In angiosperms
there is no normal occurrence of a prothallial cell.

Throughout the order the generative cell divides, forming two
cells which are called the "stalk cell" and "body cell," the stalk cell
getting its name from its position in forms like *Pinus*, where it looks
like a stalk, bearing the body cell (fig. 311 *L*). In the Araucariaceae,
in *Dacrydium, Phyllocladus*, and *Podocarpus*, there is no stalk position, but the generative cell divides, forming two cells, one of which
aborts, while the other gives rise to gametes.

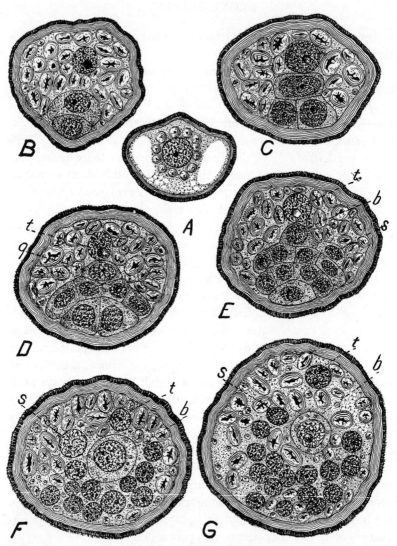

Fig. 312.—*Araucaria cunninghamii:* development of the male gametophyte; *A*, uninucleate microspore, with nucleus surrounded by starch grains; the exine and intine of about equal thickness; *B*, the first two prothallial cells; *C*, the first prothallial cell has divided anticlinally and the starch grains are very large; the intine is much thicker than the exine; *D*, two primary prothallial cells have divided and the generative cell (*g*) and tube cell (*t*) have been formed; *E*, the generative cell has divided into a stalk cell (*s*) and body cell (*b*); *F*, the body cell has enlarged, the walls of the prothallial cells have broken down, leaving the nuclei free; *s* is probably the nucleus of the stalk cell and *t*, the tube nucleus; *G*, the body cell is easily recognizable, *t* is the tube nucleus, and *s* may be the stalk nucleus; ×950.

Just what the stalk cell really is, no one has determined definitely. Where it does not have the stalk position, as in *Araucaria* and others, the stalk and body cells, at first, look alike, and probably

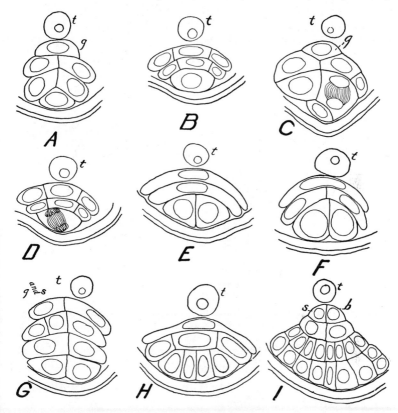

FIG. 313.—*Araucaria cunninghamii:* male gametophyte: in *A–C*, the first primary prothallial cell has not divided; in *D*, it is dividing periclinally; in *E–H*, it has divided anticlinally; *I*, shows an unusually large number of prothallial cells; *t*, tube nucleus; *g*, generative cell; *s*, stalk cell; *b*, body cell; ×900.

neither is predestined to become the "body cell" and produce the two gametes. In *Microcycas*, Dr. DOROTHY DOWNIE[173] found that the stalk cell divides repeatedly, each time cutting off a body cell, which later produces two gametes. In this case, the stalk cell is spermatogenous. In conifers, it may be, phylogenetically, a spermatogenous cell, like the body cell.

The microspore in conifers, as in cycads, has a very definite organization. The differentiation into apex and base is just as definite as the sporophyte differentiation into root and shoot. The behavior, as far as apex and base are concerned, is exactly the opposite of that in cycads and *Ginkgo*. In the cycads and *Ginkgo* the pollen tube functions principally as a haustorium—doubtless, the original function of a pollen tube—while the prothallial end of the tube, with the whole pollen grain, grows down into the nucellus, and this prothallial cell end of the tube is the one which ruptures and sheds the

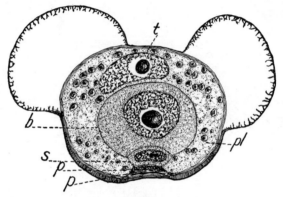

FIG. 314.—*Abies balsamea:* pollen grain at time of shedding; *b*, body cell; *s*, stalk cell; *p*, prothallial cell; *pl*, starch; *t*, tube nucleus; ×535.

gametes. In conifers, the prothallial cell end of the tube, with the entire pollen grain, remains where it alights upon the nucellus, and the tube grows down into the nucellus, serving as a haustorium, but also as a carrier of the gametes.

In the Araucariaceae, as shown in figs. 312 and 313, the generative cell divides and forms the stalk and body cell before the pollen is shed. This is also true of some others with extensive prothallial tissue, as in *Podocarpus*, *Dacrydium*, and *Phyllocladus*. This division occurs regularly in *Abies* and *Tsuga*; but here the stalk cell has a typical stalk position (fig. 314). In these two cases, one or both of the two prothallial cells may divide, so that there may be three or four prothallial cells. In the Abietaceae there is usually a considerable interval between the formation of the first and second prothallial cells, so that the rapidly thickening intine overgrows the first prothallial cell. Sometimes the interval between the formation of the second prothallial cell and the generative cell is long enough to have the second prothallial cell slightly overgrown by the intine. Where the generative cell divides before pollination, as in *Abies*, the body cell becomes very large. Pollen grains, in all the conifers, have a rich supply of starch.

The body cell does not divide until the pollen tube grows down into the nucellus. Its division, in nearly all cases, gives rise to only two gametes. The male gamete is a short-lived cell. Consequently one expects to find fertilization soon after this division.

Just at the time of pollination, in nearly all cases, a pollination drop appears on the tip of the ovule. It is colorless, and looks like a small drop of glycerine. The pollen, falling on this drop, is drawn down to the nucellus, where the growth of the pollen tube begins. In the Araucariaceae the pollen lodges on the ovuliferous scale, or on the ligule, or in the axil of the scale. In *Larix* and *Pseudotsuga* the pollen does not reach the tip of the nucellus, but finds a lateral position. There is a somewhat similar situation in *Arthrotaxis* and *Sequoia*. In such cases, the pollen tube grows somewhat laterally through the nucellus to reach the egg; while in most cases, as in *Pinus*, the growth is straight down, from the tip of the nucellus to the egg.

Dates of pollination and fertilization.—It is interesting to note the time at which various stages in the life-history may be found. While the time at which a certain stage, like pollination, takes place, may vary with latitude and other factors, the intervals between stages do not vary so much. Consequently, if the date of a certain stage is known, the dates for other stages can be predicted approximately.

In general, the interval between pollination and fertilization in gymnosperms is longer than in angiosperms, *Ephedra*, with an interval of 10 hours, being a notable exception. On the other hand, there are a few long intervals in angiosperms, the longest being in the oaks, where the interval is more than a year. Other members of the Fagaceae, and also of the Betulaceae and Juglandaceae, have long intervals. But, in general, in angiosperms the interval is to be reckoned in days or hours, rather than in the weeks or months of the gymnosperms.

In the latitude of Chicago, most pines are pollinated about the middle of June, and fertilization takes place a little more than a year later, during the last few days of the following June, or the first few days in July. In *Pinus strobus*, near Wellesley, Massachusetts, pollination takes place late in May or early in June, and fertilization a little more than a year later—about the middle of June.

HUTCHINSON[275] found that in *Abies balsamea* the interval between pollination and fertilization is only 4 or 5 weeks, and that for the greater part of this time the pollen remains unchanged on the tip of the nucellus. The pollen tube then develops very rapidly, reaching the egg and discharging the sperms in 2 or 3 days. Fertilization occurred June 25 in Ontario, Canada.

In *Pseudotsuga taxifolia* the interval is also very short, pollination taking place early in April, followed by fertilization early in June.

In *Tsuga canadensis* pollination takes place about the middle of May and fertilization about the first of July; so the interval is about six weeks.

In *Picea excelsa* the interval is shorter, with pollination in the middle of May and fertilization the middle of June.

In *Cedrus deodara* pollination occurs late in September, and fertilization about the end of the following May—an interval of 8 months.

Several observations have been made in the Taxodiaceae:

Sciadopitys is pollinated late in April (Kew) and fertilization occurs about the end of June of the following year—an interval of about 14 months.

Sequoia sempervirens is pollinated early in January and fertilization takes place late in June—an interval of about 6 months.

Taxodium distichum is pollinated the middle of March and fertilized the middle of June—an interval of 3 months.

In *Cryptomeria japonica* pollination begins in March, and the pollen grains remain unchanged on the nucellus for 4 or 5 weeks; then the pollen tubes grow rapidly, and in 3 or 4 weeks reach the egg, about the first of June—an interval of about 3 months.

In *Arthrotaxis selaginoides* pollination takes place early in April, and fertilization about the first of July—also an interval of 3 months.

Cunninghamia sinensis is pollinated early in April, and fertilized early in July—another interval of about 3 months.

In the Cupressaceae there are also long and comparatively short periods:

In *Actinostrobus pyramidalis* the interval between pollination and fertilization is about 3 months—from the middle of July to the middle of October.

In *Tetraclinis articulata* pollination extends over an unusually long period, from April 20 to June 1. Fertilization follows from 3 to $3\frac{1}{2}$ months later.

In *Widdringtonia cupressoides* the interval is long, with pollination in January and fertilization 14 or 15 months later—in February or March of the next year.

In *Libocedrus decurrens*, pollinated in California early in April, fertilization occurs about 2 months later—the first week in June.

Juniperus communis, in southern Sweden, is pollinated about the middle of June and fertilization takes place more than a year later—the first week in July. Near Wellesley, Massachusetts, pollination occurs about May 11, and fertilization about June 20—also an interval of about $12\frac{1}{2}$ months. *Juniperus virginiana*, with which *J. communis* is often associated, has a comparatively short interval, with pollination about May 1, and fertilization about June 20 of the same year.

In the Araucariaceae, records are not very complete, with almost no reports from anything except exotic material.

In *Araucaria braziliensis* fertilization occurs about April 1—5 or 6 months after pollen falls on the cone. In *Araucaria cunninghamii* pollen is shed (Queensland, Australia) in December.

In *Agathis australis* pollination occurs in September and October, with fertilization a year later.

In the Podocarpaceae, Dr. JOHANNA KILDAHL[323] found the pollen of *Phyllocladus alpina* already shed on November 1; Dr. MARY YOUNG[714] found pollen just ready for shedding on November 13. Both studied New Zealand material.

In the Taxaceae records are scanty: In *Taxus baccata* pollination, at Zürich, takes place March 1–15. According to DUPLER,[175] the interval between pollination and fertilization is only 1 month, while in the Zürich material the interval was over 2 months. In *Torrey taxifolia*, pollen is shed late in March or early in April, and fertilization, in 1904 material, took place August 12.

In this rather extensive survey, there are slight differences in the dates given by different observers. Most of the dates are for material growing in its native habitat, but some are from exotic material. However, this factor is not likely to influence the times of pollination and fertilization as much as would the differences in latitude, altitude, and immediate surroundings. While these factors certainly influence the time of pollination, the interval between pollination and fertilization does not seem to be affected.

In conifers with a long period between pollination and fertilization, there is usually a rapid growth of the pollen tube immediately after pollination. The tube grows down about to the level of the free part of the nucellus, and then stops and winters in this condition, resuming its growth the next spring. In forms with two growth-periods, and in which the division into stalk and body cell does not take place before the pollen is shed, the division into stalk and body cell occurs during the first period. The division of the body cell to form the two sperms takes place shortly before fertilization, usually less than a week before the fusion of gametes. In several closely observed forms, the interval is about 5 days.

In almost everything there are exceptions. In *Abies balsamea* the body cell divides before the tube begins to form; but here the growth of the pollen tube through the nucellus to the egg does not take more than 2 days, and the time may be reckoned in hours. Consequently, the interval between the division of the body cell and fertilization is not so long as in cases where the division takes place late in the development of the pollen tube.

The sperms.—The sperms, or male gametes, of conifers show considerable differences in organization, but there are only two categories: the sperm is either a highly organized cell, or it has lost its cell wall, and, at the time of fertilization, its cytoplasm may have blended more or less with that of the pollen tube.

The most primitive form is, doubtless, the highly organized cell, as it is found in *Juniperus* and other members of the Cupressaceae, Taxodiaceae, Podocarpaceae, and Taxaceae (figs. 315, 316). These two figures show a sperm almost as highly organized as in the cycads and *Ginkgo*. Whether each sperm is formed inside a sperm mother-cell, as in the cycads, or arises from the division of the body cell, so

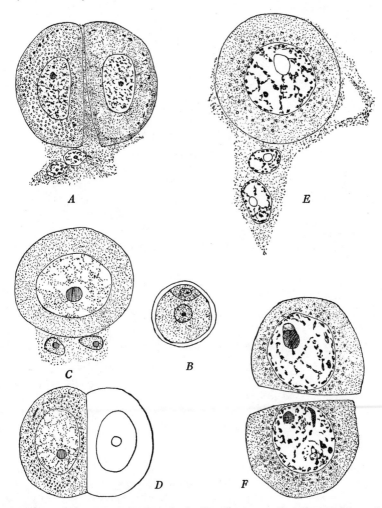

FIG. 315.—Body cells and sperms in the Taxodiaceae: *A, Taxodium distichum*, the two highly organized sperm cells, with the stalk and tube nuclei in advance; ×540; after COKER;[141] *B–D, Cunninghamia sinensis: B*, pollen grain with generative cell and tube cell (no prothallial cells); *C*, body cell and stalk and tube nuclei; ×430; after MIYAKE;[402] *E, F, Cryptomeria japonica: E*, body cell and stalk and tube cells; *F*, the two sperms; ×666; after LAWSON.[345]

that the outer wall of the body cell becomes part of the wall of the sperm cell, does not appear from these figures. At any rate, the sperm lacks only the cilia to make it motile, like the sperms of cycads and *Ginkgo*.

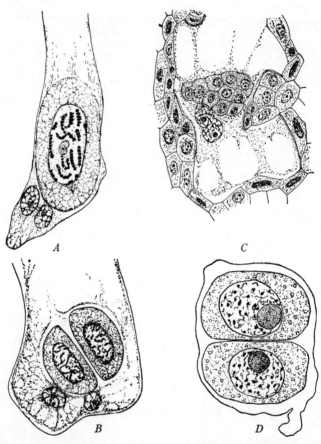

FIG. 316.—Pollen tube structures in the Cupressaceae: *A*, *B*, *Thuja occidentalis*: *A*, body cell, with stalk and tube nuclei; *B*, the two sperms; ×560; after LAND;[337] *C*, *Cupressus goweniana*; group of numerous male cells, with stalk and tube nuclei below; ×350; after JUEL;[307] *D*, *Libocedrus decurrens*; the two sperms; after LAWSON.[347]

In nearly all cases where the sperms are so highly organized, the sperms appear to be exactly alike in size and structure; but in *Taxus*, *Cephalotaxus*, and *Torreya*, there is great disparity in size. The mitotic figure in the body cell is so near. the periphery that one of the sperms is only a small lenticular cell which soon aborts (fig. 317).

The formation of sperms in pairs is thoroughly established in the liverworts, and probably goes farther back; but, from the liverworts to the sunflowers and orchids the pairing is constant. In the angio-sperms, each sperm has its own function, one fertilizing the egg and the other taking part in the triple fusion which initiates the second period in the development of the female ga-metophyte. In gymnosperms, in many cases, the two sperms differ in size, but whether they differ in chromatin content or in any other way, has not been determined, either in gymnosperms or in any other group. We suspect that a detailed investigation, with adequate technique, would reveal something interesting.

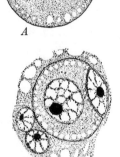

In *Cupressus goweniana*, and also in *C. ari-zonica*, there are several small sperms (fig. 316 C). In the latter species DOAK[166] found twelve fully developed sperms. Both of these investigators used exotic material. These two species recall the condition in *Micro-cycas*, which has a dozen or more sperms.

It is worth while to note that these highly organized sperms, doubtless primitive, are

FIG. 317.—*Taxus cana-densis: A*, body cell divid-ing to form two unequal sperms; *B*, the two sperms; the stalk and body nuclei are shown at the left; ×570; after DUPLER.[176]

associated with archegonia in which there is no wall between the ventral canal nucleus and that of the egg, a feature which is more advanced than that in *Ginkgo* and the Abietaceae, where there is a wall between these two nuclei. It is an instructive illustration of the fact that various lines of evolution do not keep pace with each other.

In the Abietaceae the sperms are very different. The wall of the body cell is thin, and when its nucleus divides, the daughter-nuclei are left free, with no wall between them. A wall begins to form at the equator of the spindle, but it soon breaks down. The wall of the body cell, although very thin, separates the cytoplasm surrounding the sperm nuclei from the general cytoplasm of the pollen tube, dur-

ing nearly all of the passage of the body cell down the tube (fig. 318).
As the tube is about to discharge the sperms, the wall of the body cell
seems to have disappeared entirely, so that the sperm nuclei are in a

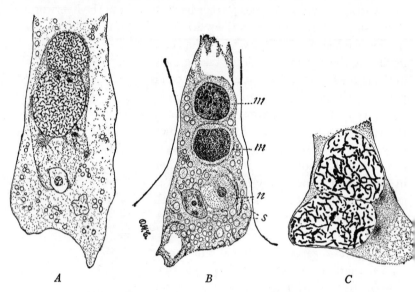

A   B   C

Fig. 318.—Pollen tubes of *Pinus: A, Pinus strobus*, two sperms, quite unequal; below the two sperms, the nucleus of the stalk cell and a little lower down, the tube nucleus; ×236; after Dr. Margaret Ferguson;[196] *B, P. laricio;* the two-sperm nuclei (*m*);
n, nucellus of stalk cell; the other nucleus is the tube nucleus; *s*, starch; ×500; after
Coulter;[147] *C, P. laricio;* the two-sperm nuclei with no wall of the body cell visible; at
the right of each nucleus, a dense mass which might represent a blepharoplast; ×500;
after Chamberlain.[104]

mass of cytoplasm which does not seem to be marked off at all from
the general cytoplasm of the pollen tube (fig. 318 *C*).

In such a condition, either as an organized cell or as a naked
nucleus, the sperms, together with the stalk and tube nuclei, are
discharged into the egg.

CHAPTER XIV

CONIFEROPHYTES—CONIFERALES—*Continued*

THE FEMALE GAMETOPHYTE

The megaspore is the first cell of the female gametophyte. The megaspore mother-cell, in the two divisions by which the four megaspores are produced and the number of chromosomes is reduced from the sporophyte number ($2x$) to the gametophyte (x) number, is usually so deeply placed in the nucellus, when it first becomes recognizable, that its origin looks indefinite. In all cases in which the origin can be recognized with certainty, the archesporial cell is hypodermal, and its first periclinal division gives rise to a tapetal cell and the megaspore mother-cell. An axial row of four megaspores has been observed in many cases (fig. 319).

It happens, frequently, that there is a row of only three cells. In such cases, the upper cell, resulting from the first division of the megaspore mother-cell, fails to divide, and does not reach the megaspore stage. The lower cell divides and produces two megaspores, the lower one of which continues to develop, while the other, together with the upper cell of the row of three, disorganizes. The failure of a division in the upper of the first two cells was noted in the cycads, *Stangeria*[342] and *Ceratozamia*;[645] but *Zamia*,[566] the

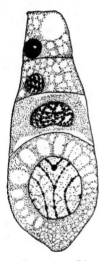

Fig. 319.—*Pinus laricio:* row of four megaspores, the lower one growing vigorously and the other three aborting; ×810.— After Dr. MARGARET FERGUSON.[196]

most advanced of all cycads, has a row of four. Since, in nearly all cases, only one megaspore germinates, it is natural that there should be a tendency to eliminate the useless spores.

The first indication of germination is an enlargement of the megaspore and its nucleus. After the first division of the megaspore mother-cell, the lower of the two resulting cells is likely to divide first. Although the division in the two cells is said to be simultaneous, and the two mitotic figures are seen at the same time, the lower figure is practically always a little more advanced, and its daughter-nuclei reach the resting condition, while those of the upper mitosis are still in the late telophase. Thus the lower two, and especially the lowest one, get into the resting, or, rather, the working, condition earlier than the upper pair. An excellent example is seen in LAND's drawing of *Ephedra*, in which the lowest megaspore is enlarging, the next above is beginning to disorganize, while the mitosis in the upper cell of the first "pair" is still in the late telophase (fig. 359 *A*). The reason for the more rapid development of the lowest cell is probably because the nutrition comes principally from beneath. In gymnosperms, almost invariably, and nearly as frequently in angiosperms, the lowest megaspore is the one which germinates and develops into the adult gametophyte.

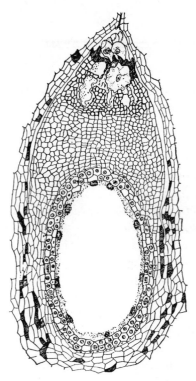

FIG. 320.—*Pinus strobus:* free nuclear stage in female gametophyte. The protoplasm, with its nuclei, is pressed outward by the large central vacuole. The gametophyte is surrounded by a jacket of spongy tissue; ×62.—After Dr. MARGARET FERGUSON.[196]

Free nuclear period.—In all conifers there is a period of free nuclear division before any cell walls are formed. Even as early as the close of the first division, a large vacuole may appear between the two daughter-nuclei. With succeeding divisions the outline of the megaspore increases immensely, and the central vacuole, filled with a transparent fluid, presses the protoplasm outward so that it forms a thin layer containing the free nuclei (fig. 320). Mitoses throughout the free nuclear period are simultaneous (fig. 359 B). Here again, a figure taken from LAND's splendid work on *Ephedra*, will also illustrate what takes place in conifers.

A free nuclear period is not confined to conifers, but is likely to occur in any plant where the cell is large in proportion to the nuclear figure. Where the cell is large and the nuclear divisions follow in rapid succession, one division follows another before a wall can be formed on the spindle. As the number of nuclei increases, and the interval between mitoses becomes more prolonged, walls make their appearance.

The extent of the free nuclear period depends upon the size and shape of the megaspore outline. If it is long and narrow, the period will be shorter; if more or less spherical, the period will be longer. So there may be only dozens of nuclei when walls begin to come in; or there may be hundreds. JÄGER[285] estimated the number in *Taxus baccata* at 256, and DUPLER[176] found the same number in *T. canadense*. COULTER and LAND[152] also found 256 in *Torreya taxifolia*, a number already reported for *Zamia* and *Ginkgo*. This must be regarded as a very low number for a gymnosperm.

Dr. MARGARET FERGUSON[196] finds a much larger number in *Pinus strobus*. She counted 2,000 when walls were coming in. Since these mitoses are simultaneous, that would mean 1,000 free nuclei. NOREN[418] estimated the number in *Juniperus communis* as about the same.

Period of wall formation.—There are two types of wall formation in the female gametophyte, one of which may be illustrated by *Pinus* and the other by *Taxus*.

In *Pinus*, at the final free nuclear division, walls perpendicular to the megaspore membrane are formed on the achromatic fibers which connect the nuclei. A wall is also formed on the side next the megaspore membrane; but the sixth side, toward the center of the megaspore cavity, remains open.[196, 345] As division continues, periclinal walls come in, but the innermost sides of the innermost cells remain open. This method continues, with the tissue advancing toward the center, even after archegonial initials have appeared at the top. When the central cavity is entirely closed, walls are formed on the centripetal ends of the cells. Consequently, along the line of

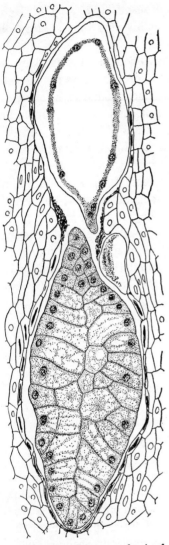

FIG. 321.—*Taxus canadensis:* female gametophyte cellular throughout, but before the appearance of archegonia. The upper gametophyte is in the free nuclear stage, and there is an abortive gametophyte between them, at the right; ×286.—After DUPLER.[176]

closure, two cell walls are in contact. This is doubtless the reason why many female gametophytes split so easily in the middle.

In *Taxus,*[176] the first walls, perpendicular to the megaspore membrane, extend to the middle of the megaspore cavity, so that the cells are like long tubes, which have been called "alveoli." In nearly all cases the walls on the centripetal ends of the alveoli form late. Subsequent divisions divide each of the alveoli into a large number of cells. In *Taxus,* the gametophyte is cellular throughout before any archegonial initials appear; this is true also of *Torreya* and others (fig. 321).

There are long alveoli in *Microcachrys tetragona,* but here, judging from LAWSON's figures,[350] the centripetal end of the alveolus has a wall from the start.

In general, the development of the female gametophyte is much as in the angiosperms, except that there are none which are cellular from the beginning, as in the long, narrow embryo sacs of *Ceratophyllum submersum* and *Monotropa hypopitys.*

It sometimes happens that more than one megaspore germinates. This is rather common in *Taxus canadensis,* where more than one megaspore mother-cell occurs frequently. All four megaspores of a tetrad may germinate, as well as one or two of a second tetrad. DUPLER[176] found several ovules in which three female gametophytes had reached the archegonium stage, with a couple more in the free nuclear stage. In *Taxus baccata* several investigators have failed to find more than one megaspore germinating. DUPLER's findings are conclusive for *T. canadensis*. More than one megaspore has been observed to develop in *Sequoia*,[344] *Cunninghamia*,[401] *Sciadopitys*,[349] *Taxodium*,[139] and *Cryptomeria*.[345] More than one is rare in *Pinus*.[196]

In the early stage of the megaspore, no megaspore membrane, distinct from the ordinary cellulose wall, can be distinguished; but as the free nuclear stage advances, and the cellular stage begins, a genuine spore coat appears, and may reach considerable thickness. The thickness of some megaspore membranes, as given by THOMSON,[633] are as follows: *Biota orientalis*, 1.7 microns; *Sequoia sempervirens*, 2.7 microns; *Pinus sylvestris*, 3 microns; *P. resinosa*, 4.2 microns; *Abies balsamea*, 4.6 microns; *Larix americana*, 4.7 microns. These measurements indicate the range of thickness in the order.

The chemical composition of the membrane is very complex. On the outside it is suberized, and, on the inside, chemical tests indicate a substance related to pectin. Between the two, there is cellulose which gradually changes into the suberin of the outside.

THOMSON[633] describes two layers, an exosporium and an endosporium, and there is no doubt that stained material, which is easily photographed, seems to support his view. However, three layers can be photographed in *Dioon edule*, where it is doubtful whether there is more than one. It is more than doubtful whether there are two layers originating like the exine and intine of microspores.

In spores which are to be shed, spore coats are highly developed, and the megaspore of gymnosperms still retains a highly developed spore coat. When the megaspore began to be retained in the megasporangium (ovule) there was no longer need for a protective coat, and it became more and more reduced, still appearing in the conifers, but not so thick in living forms as in the carboniferous gymnosperms. In the Gnetales[633] the coat is very thin—1.3 microns in *Welwitschia*—and in the angiosperms it has disappeared as a recognizable spore coat.

During its early development, the female gametophyte is surrounded by the spongy tissue, which is gradually absorbed. In later stages, while there is not such a definite surrounding tissue as the "endosperm jacket" of the cycads, the cells in contact with the megaspore membrane are more or less modified, and some have applied the term "tapetum" to these surrounding cells.

The archegonia.—It would seem that most, or even all, of the superficial cells at the top of the female gametophyte are, potentially, archegonium initials. The number which becomes recognizable as initials is small, and the number reaching maturity may be still smaller.

There are two general types of archegonial groups in conifers. In the Abietaceae and many others, the archegonia are separated by vegetative cells of the gametophyte. In the Cupressaceae and Taxodiaceae they are in contact with each other, forming an archegonium complex. In some, the complex is at the apex of the gametophyte, as in *Thuja, Libocedrus, Tetraclinis,* and *Juniperus;* while in others it is lateral, as in *Sequoia, Actinostrobus, Callitris,* and *Widdringtonia.*

The number of archegonia is much larger where there is an archegonium complex than where the archegonia are separated by vegetative tissue. In *Thuja* the number is usually 6; in *Juniperus communis,* 4–10, usually 7; in *Libocedrus decurrens,* 10–15; in *Biota orientalis,* 9–24; in *Callitris verrucosa,* 17–20; in *Actinostrobus pyramidalis,* 25–30; in *Widdringtonia cupressoides,* 30–100, variously placed, but never apical; and in *W. juniperoides* the number reaches 200.

In forms with archegonia separated by vegetative cells, the numbers are smaller and the position nearly, but not quite, apical; for the archegonia are usually in a circle, surrounding the center. In *Pinus strobus, P. rigida,* and *P. resinosa,* the usual number of archegonium initials is 3; in *P. laricio,* there are usually 5, occasionally 6, and sometimes only 2 or 3. In *Torreya taxifolia,*[152] there is almost invariably only 1 archegonium; but in other genera a single archegonium is very rare. Both types, the separated archegonia and the archegonium complex, occur in *Sequoia.*

The archegonium initial first becomes recognizable by elongating and enlarging somewhat, while the adjoining cells divide. Its nucleus moves to the peripheral end of the cell. Early in June, in the Chicago region, archegonium initials are recognizable in *Pinus laricio;* and in *P. banksiana* they may be seen a week or 10 days earlier. Within a week after the initial becomes recognizable, its nucleus divides, giving rise to the central cell and the primary neck cell (fig. 322).

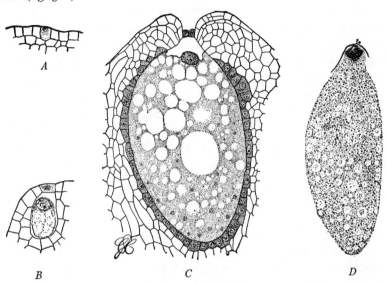

A

B   *C*   *D*

FIG. 322.—*Pinus laricio:* development of the archegonium; *A*, archegonium initial, May 28; *B*, neck and central cells, June 2; *C*, two-celled neck and enlarged central cell, June 18; *D*, mitosis cutting off ventral canal cell, June 21; ×104.—From COULTER and CHAMBERLAIN, *Morphology of Gymnosperms*[154] (University of Chicago Press).

After the primary neck cell is cut off, it soon divides, but it is nearly a month before there is a division of the central cell. During this period, the central cell enlarges immensely, and a very definite archegonium jacket is formed, which plays for the central cell such a rôle as the "endosperm jacket" plays for the female gametophyte. With its enlargement, the central cell becomes very vacuolate, and, besides the large vacuoles, a peculiar type of vacuole appears, the "proteid vacuoles," which look so much like nuclei that HOF-MEISTER[259] believed the eggs of gymnosperms differed from those of angiosperms in being multinucleate. HOFMEISTER resented STRAS-

BURGER'S correction of the mistake, perhaps because STRASBURGER was 20 years younger.

The primary neck cell early undergoes an anticlinal division, and a second anticline makes a plate of four cells. Later, there is usually a pericline, making two tiers of cells. In each tier there may be two divisions, so that the neck of the archegonium consists of eight cells. One or more of these mitoses may fail to take place, so that the number is usually less than eight. Occasionally, there are more than two tiers, and occasionally only one. In *Podocarpus coriacea*,[140] the number is variable, ranging from 2 to 25. In *Tsuga canadensis*,[404, 405] there is only one tier, and it may be only two-celled. *Austrotaxus*[498] is exceptional in having as many as 16 neck cells, all in one tier.

There is no neck canal cell in any gymnosperm. In the evolution of the archegonium the neck canal cell made its final appearance in the heterosporous pteridophytes, all of which have a single small neck canal cell.

The division of the central cell to form a ventral canal cell, or nucleus, and the egg, occurs shortly before fertilization, so that the development of the egg is almost entirely the development of the central cell. In the Abietaceae there is a distinct ventral canal cell (fig. 323). In the rest, there is a nuclear division, but no wall is formed between the two resulting nuclei. It is a curious fact that those in which no wall is formed between the two nuclei are the ones in which the sperms are distinct cells. In *Pinus*, with a distinct ventral canal cell, the sperm has become reduced to a naked nucleus.

In *Pinus*, the ventral canal figure is usually small, cutting off a small ventral canal cell which promptly degenerates (fig. 323 *A*,*B*). Occasionally, the figure is comparatively large, and cuts off a large ventral canal cell (fig. 323 *C*,*E*). When a large cell is cut off, it sometimes happens that the wall between the two nuclei breaks down. The ventral canal nucleus, then being surrounded by the general mass of the cytoplasm of the egg, grows and equals the egg nucleus in size and, apparently, in development. It might be fertilized, or it might fertilize the egg (fig. 323 *E*). HUTCHINSON[275] observed both these cases in *Abies balsamea*.

LAND[337] found cases in *Thuja occidentalis* which led him to believe that both the egg and the ventral canal nucleus had been fertilized, for there were two groups of nuclei, one at the base and the other at the top of the egg.

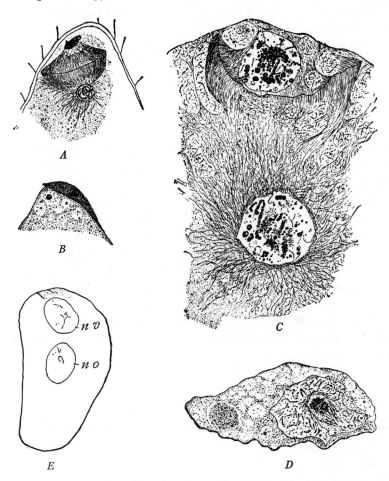

Fig. 323.—*Pinus laricio:* formation of ventral canal cell; *A*, typical mitotic figure; *B*, ventral canal cell disorganizing; *C*, unusually large mitotic figure cutting off a large ventral canal cell; *D*, a large ventral canal cell; *E*, the wall between the ventral canal cell and the egg has broken down leaving both nuclei free in the egg: *nv*, nucleus of ventral canal cell; *no*, nucleus of egg; *A–C*, ×500; *E*, ×100.—After CHAMBERLAIN.[104]

In *Torreya*,[152] it is probable that no ventral canal mitosis occurs. The material was so abundant and the observer so competent that the mitosis could hardly have escaped observation, had it been present.

There can be no doubt that in the evolution of the archegonium there has been a gradual reduction in the length of the neck and in the number of neck canal cells, which, phylogenetically, are probably eggs. In the lower Filicales there are two neck canal cells; in the higher homosporous forms, only one neck canal cell with two nuclei; and in the heterosporous genera, even the mitosis has failed to take place, so that there is only one neck canal cell with one nucleus. In the gymnosperms the mitosis which, in the pteridophytes, gives rise to the neck canal and ventral series, is suppressed, so that the ventral canal mitosis takes place in the cell which, in *Pteris*, gives rise to a primary neck canal cell and a central cell.

There can hardly be any doubt that the ventral canal cell is a reduced egg, just as in *Taxus*, and several other genera with unequal sperms, the smaller sperm is strictly the homologue of the larger one. In tracing the evolution of the archegonium, the bryophytes show a nearly equal division, so that the egg and ventral canal cell can be distinguished only by their relative positions; and, in a few cases, there are several equal eggs.

After the ventral canal mitosis, fertilization follows promptly, the interval between the mitosis and fertilization usually not exceeding 5 days.

CHAPTER XV

CONIFEROPHYTES—CONIFERALES—*Continued*

FERTILIZATION

The pollen tubes press and digest their way through the nucellus, destroying much of its tissue; but there is no such complete destruction as in the cycads, where the pollen tubes hang free for a greater part of their length. In conifers, the pollen tubes reach the megaspore membrane, with both gametophytes in various stages of development.

In *Torreya taxifolia*[152] the pollen tube completes its passage through the nucellus while the female gametophyte is still in an early free nuclear stage, with only 16 or 32 free nuclei (fig. 325). At this stage, the pollen tube has broadened at the base, and the body cell has enlarged, but will enlarge much more before division. Just as the pollen tube is about to discharge its two very unequal sperms, it is broader than the egg (fig. 326). It should be noted that the interval between the stages shown in these figures is about 7 weeks.

In *Callitris verrucosa*[491] the pollen tube arrives when the female gametophyte is in the 128 nucleate stage.

In *Taxus canadensis*[176] the female gametophyte is more advanced when

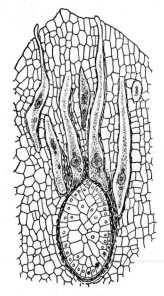

Fig. 324.—*Taxus canadensis:* nucellus showing seven pollen tubes, three of which show the body cell just ready to divide. The female gametophyte has not yet reached the archegonium initial stage; ×92.—After Dupler.[176]

the pollen tube reaches it, and is cellular throughout, but the archegonium initials are not yet recognizable (fig. 324). The body cell has rounded off and has enlarged, but its nucleus is still in the resting condition.

The arrival of the pollen tube while the female gametophyte is in a comparatively early stage of development is more frequently found where the male gametes are highly organized cells.

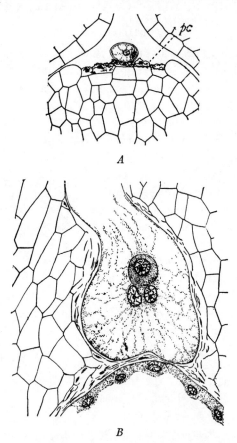

A

B

FIG. 325.—*Torreya taxifolia: A*, two-celled microspore on degenerating cells at tip of nucellus; *pc*, pollen chamber; *B*, enlarged end of pollen tube in contact with the female gametophyte which is still in the free nuclear stage (June 21, 1904); ×460.—After COULTER and LAND.[152]

In forms like *Pinus*, where the sperms are nearly or quite naked nuclei, the cellular condition is reached by the female gametophyte,

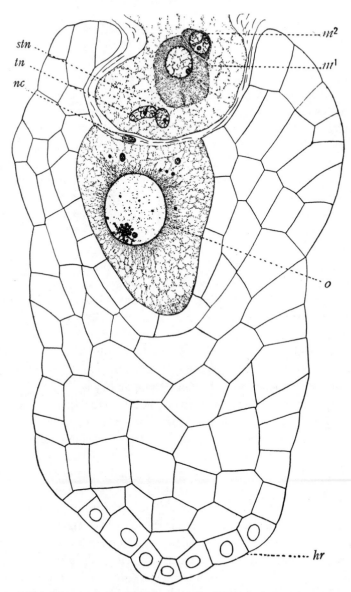

FIG. 326.—*Torreya taxifolia:* pollen tube in contact with the egg: m^1 and m^2 the two unequal sperms; *stn*, stalk nucleus; *tn*, tube nucleus; *nc*, neck cell; *o*, egg nucleus; *hr*, haustorial cells. Cells at the top of the female gametophyte are growing up around the tube; August 12, 1904; ×460.—After COULTER and LAND.[152]

and the archegonium is in a rather advanced stage of development before the pollen tube comes into contact with the megaspore membrane.

In any case, the division of the body cell to form the two sperms takes place shortly before fertilization, so that it is more or less simultaneous with the division of the central cell to form the egg and the ventral canal cell, or ventral canal nucleus.

The neck cells in many cases disorganize, and the megaspore membrane at the top of the female gametophyte is dissolved or becomes so weak that it is easily broken when the pollen tube arrives.

When the pollen tube reaches the egg, the behavior differs. In the Abietaceae the tip of the tube ruptures, forming a pore through which the contents are discharged into the egg. The pollen tube itself does not enter.

In the other families more or less of the tip of the pollen tube enters the top of the egg before the discharge takes place. Many of the observations upon which this statement is based should be confirmed or corrected, for there is, at the time of the discharge, a large vacuole at the top of the egg, and the vacuole often has such a strong plasma membrane that it might be mistaken for the end of a pollen tube. There have been occasional misinterpretations of pollen tubes ever since they were thought to be embryos.

The pollen tube, when it comes into contact with the egg, has been growing more and more turgid, so that, when the rupture comes, the contents of the tube are discharged with considerable violence. Some forms, like *Pinus*, have been studied so thoroughly by so many investigators that anything exceptional is easily distinguished from the normal behavior. A few other forms have been studied almost as thoroughly by several investigators. Unfortunately, many of the genera have been described by a single investigator in a single paper, and the investigations have too often been based upon exotic material or material growing naturally, but collected and sent to the investigator from a considerable distance. The variations which are known to occur in *Pinus* should be borne in mind while weighing accounts based upon comparatively limited material.

In *Pinus* both sperms, together with the stalk and tube nuclei and some of the protoplasm, are discharged into the egg. In *Taxus baccata* only the larger sperm enters the egg, the smaller sperm and both the stalk and tube nuclei remaining in the pollen tube. In *Taxus canadensis* all four nuclei enter the egg. In *Torreya taxifolia*[152] only the larger sperm enters. In the Podocarpaceae all four, with some of the prothallial nuclei, enter, but all except the functional sperm degenerate at the top of the egg. In the Araucariaceae both sperms and some small nuclei enter the egg. It should be remembered that the stalk, tube, and prothallial nuclei look alike at this time. The sperm nuclei have become so large that they are easily distinguishable from the rest, reaching a length of 150 microns in *Araucaria braziliensis*. GHOSE[209] claims that the pollen tube penetrates the egg.

In *Cephalotaxus drupacea* and *C. fortunei* both sperms get into the egg, but one remains at the top and disorganizes there.

In the Taxodiaceae generally only one sperm gets into the egg, but in *Sciadopitys* both get in. Here it should be noted that the archegonia are scattered in *Sciadopitys*, while in the rest there is an archegonium complex.

In *Juniperus* usually only one sperm gets into the egg. It is large in proportion to the diameter of the egg, and its wall is torn off and remains at the top of the egg, while the nucleus, surrounded by much of its cytoplasm, moves down to fuse with the egg nucleus. When the second sperm enters it remains at the top of the egg, apparently undisturbed, recalling the condition in cycads, where even the ciliated band is not disturbed when a second sperm enters the egg. The first sperm opens the way into the egg so that a second sperm enters easily.

With the sperm, more or less cytoplasm enters the egg, where it remains at the top and mingles with the general cytoplasm. When the sperm is a highly organized cell, the cell wall comes off soon after the sperm enters the egg, and the nucleus, with most of its surrounding cytoplasm, moves down and unites with the egg nucleus. The cytoplasm of the sperm forms a dense sheath, surrounding the fusing nuclei. The sheath is particularly conspicuous in *Juniperus*,[414, 418,] *Thuja*,[337] *Torreya*,[152] and *Tetraclinis*.[495]

Whether the sheath carries any hereditary characters is doubtful since, in most conifers, only the nucleus reaches the egg.

Nuclei left at the top of the egg nearly always degenerate promptly. Occasionally a nucleus divides, but no embryo is formed, and
there seems to be no influence upon the development of the functional embryo, which is at the opposite end of the egg.

What causes the sperm to move toward the egg nucleus has not
yet been determined. In most cases there is a mechanical impulse
when the sperm is discharged from the pollen tube, but this is not
sufficient to account for much of the movement. Chemotactic experiments,which succeed so well with pteridophytes, fail just as they
do in cycads. One thing is certain: something brings the nuclei together, and the nuclear membranes are dissolved at the line of contact, so that the two nuclei become surrounded by a common membrane contributed by both gametes.

It is a curious fact that the first two cases of fertilization described
for conifers were abnormal. STRASBURGER,[598] as early as 1878, in his
Befruchtung und Zelltheilung, figured two gamete nuclei of about
equal size in *Picea vulgaris*. Nearly 20 years later, COULTER[147]
described two fusing gametes of about equal size in *Pinus laricio*.
There can hardly be any doubt now that the "sperm," in both these
cases, was an enlarged ventral canal nucleus, since normal fertilization has been observed so often in both these species, and the sperm
nucleus has been proved to be very small in comparison with that of
the egg (fig. 327).

In the nineties it used to be taken for granted that gamete nuclei
fused in the resting condition, the assumption being based upon the
appearance of this stage in angiosperms. As technique improved, it
became evident that this would not hold for *Pinus*[104] (fig. 327 *B, F*).
Even COULTER'S[147] earlier account, showing two gamete nuclei of
nearly equal size, also showed them in the spireme stage, although
this fact was not mentioned in the paper (fig. 328). Later, the independence of the two groups of chromatin was observed in *Juniperus*,[414, 418] and probably any detailed observation, with modern technique, will show such a behavior to be general, if not universal. In
Lilium, upon which the most plausible claim for fusion in the resting
condition was based, it is now known that the two gametes form
two spiremes and that there is not any fusion of chromatin.

The most detailed investigation of the behavior of chromatin at fertilization is HUTCHINSON'S[275] account of *Abies balsamea*. He found the separate spiremes of the two gametes and their segmentation forming two groups of chromosomes, each with the *x* number.

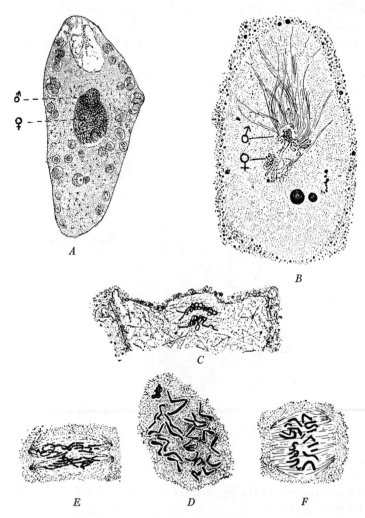

FIG. 327.—Fertilization in *Pinus*: *A, Pinus sylvestris*, sperm nucleus much smaller than the egg nucleus; June 19; ×135; after BLACKMAN;[56] *B, P. laricio*, nuclei of egg and sperm in spireme stage; ×500; after CHAMBERLAIN;[104] *C–F, P. strobus*, later stages than *B*, all showing that there has been no fusion of chromatin; ×315; after Dr. MARGARET FERGUSON.[196]

Two spindles are formed, which soon come together and appear as one.

The most unexpected feature in his account is that the chromosomes become paired (fig. 329). In this diagram, only two of the 16 chromosomes of each gamete are shown. The chromosomes of the egg nucleus are shown in black, and those of the sperm, in outline.

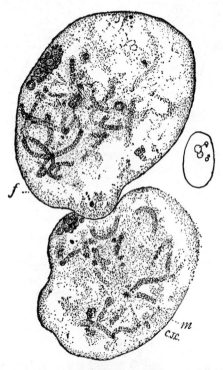

FIG. 328.—*Pinus laricio:* union of two nuclei originally described as male and female, but which are, doubtless, the egg nucleus and the ventral canal nucleus. *f,* female; *m,* male. The chromatin is in the spireme stage; ×500.—After COULTER.[147]

The chromosomes of the egg and sperm pair, and then twist about each other, as in the third and fourth figures of the diagram. They then split transversely, giving rise to groups of four, which resemble the tetrads of the reduction division (fifth and sixth figures of the diagram). The distribution of the chromosomes then takes place as shown in the final figure of the diagram.

In a form with short, thick chromosomes, at early metaphase of the first division in the fertilized egg, it would be easy to count only the x number of chromosomes; but each of such chromosomes would really be quadrivalent, and in the anaphase the $2x$ number would appear.

This is the only account of such a behavior of chromosomes at fertilization in any gymnosperm, although HUTCHINSON believes that my own figures and especially Dr. MARGARET FERGUSON'S[196]

FIG. 329.—*Abies balsamea:* diagrams showing the behavior of the chromosomes at fertilization and at the first mitosis of the fertilized egg. The chromosomes of the egg nucleus are shown in black; those of the sperm, in outline. Only two of the sixteen chromosomes of each gamete are shown.—After HUTCHINSON.[275]

more detailed drawings, are better interpreted according to his diagram.

In *Puccinia graminis* the two gamete nuclei appear at the beginning of the aecium and divide in pairs throughout the aecium stage and through the urediniospore and teliospore stages, coming together under one membrane only at the close of the teliospore stage. In the crustacean, *Cyclops*, the two gamete nuclei also divide in pairs throughout a lesser part of the life-history before they come together under one nuclear membrane. In *Abies* the chromosomes of the gamete nuclei are distinct after the two groups of chromosomes are included within a single nuclear membrane. Then there is a pairing of male and female chromosomes. That such a pairing takes place at the reduction division, every cytologist has observed. In *Abies* such a pairing also takes place at the reduction division. Whether such a pairing as HUTCHINSON described for *Abies* may not be general is at least worth a careful study. It should be noted that the chromosomes in *Abies balsamea* are large and much more favorable for study than those of *Pinus* or *Juniperus*.

In a recent paper, BEAL[35] describes the first mitosis in the fertilized egg of *Pinus banksiana* (fig. 330). He finds two groups of chromosomes, as others have found them, and finds that the two spindles quickly merge into one multipolar diarch spindle, on the equator of which the chromosomes lie in one group, with the chromosomes of the two gametes indistinguishable from each other. Each chromosome splits longitudinally, and the halves pass to the poles, 24 chromosomes to each pole. He finds no pairing or transverse segmentation.

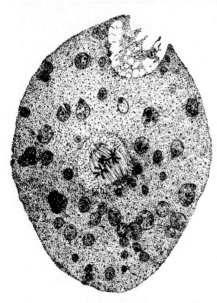

Of course, this does not prove that there is no pairing or transverse segmentation in *Abies;* and the situation described for *Abies* does not prove that there is a pairing and transverse segmentation in *Pinus*. Both accounts need either confirmation or correction. It seems unlikely that two conifers, in the same family, would differ so decidedly.

FIG. 330.—*Pinus banksiana:* first division of fertilized egg; ×150.—From an unpublished drawing by J. M. BEAL.[35]

Referring again to the first two cases of fertilization in gymnosperms, described by STRASBURGER,[598] in 1878, for *Picea vulgaris*, and by COULTER,[147] in 1897, for *Pinus laricio*, we must note that in both there was doubtless a fertilization of the egg by the nucleus of the ventral canal cell. My own work on *Pinus* made this interpretation practically a certainty.[104] IKENO[281] found fertilization of the egg by the ventral canal nucleus in *Ginkgo*, and SEDGWICK[537] found that in *Encephalartos*, in all probability, the same thing occurs. HUTCHINSON[275] finds that this occurs occasionally in *Abies*.

Double fertilization, as it occurs in angiosperms, may not occur in gymnosperms; but it is worth noting that LAND[337] found fertilization of both the egg and ventral canal cell nucleus in *Thuja;* and HUTCHINSON[275] found the same thing in *Abies.* In both, there were two similar groups of cells, one at the top and the other—the young embryo—at the bottom.

The term "fertilization" is not easy to define. Practically, when teachers order slides showing fertilization from biological supply companies, they accept anything showing the sperm within the egg.

CHAPTER XVI

CONIFEROPHYTES—CONIFERALES—*Continued*

THE EMBRYO

In dealing with fertilization we have already begun a description of the embryogeny, for we have described the fertilized egg and some features of its first mitosis. The fertilized egg is the first cell of the $2x$ generation. Although some of the early cells of the $2x$ generation take no part in the formation of root, shoot, cotyledons or leaves, the entire $2x$ generation, up to the ripe seed, should be included in any account of the embryo.

The proembryo.—In all the living pteridophytes, the first division of the fertilized egg is followed by the formation of a cell wall. There is no free nuclear stage for, throughout the entire group, the egg is small and easily segmented. As the egg increased in size, probably in some extinct heterosporous ancestors of the gymnosperms, a free nuclear stage appeared, and became more prolonged as the egg continued to increase in size. The climax was reached in living cycads, where *Dioon* shows more than a thousand free nuclei before wall formation begins. In the higher cycads, like *Zamia*, the number of free nuclei becomes as low as 256. In the living Coniferophytes, *Ginkgo*, with 256 free nuclei, has the highest number. In the conifers the eggs are comparatively small, and the number of free nuclei correspondingly low. In only one species in the entire conifer line has a wall been reported at the first division of the fertilized egg. In the immense *Sequoia sempervirens*, which has an egg only 100 microns in diameter (almost as small as some of those in living pteridophytes), there is no free nuclear stage. A strong cell plate appears at the telophase of the first division of the fertilized egg, and a distinct wall is formed before the second division occurs (fig. 331).

In the rest of the conifers, as far as they have been studied, the embryogeny begins with a free nuclear period.

Pinus will serve as a thoroughly investigated example. In the free nuclear divisions the figures are entirely intranuclear, and there is a great display of achromatic structures, especially at the first mitosis (fig. 332). The next two mitoses follow in such rapid succession that the entire free nuclear series may be secured at one collection (fig. 333). These four nuclei, which constitute all of the free nuclear period, are formed at about the level of the egg nucleus. After the second mitosis, they pass to the bottom of the egg, where the third mitosis, closing with wall formation, takes place.

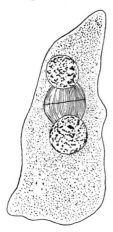

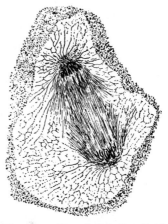

FIG. 331.—*Sequoia sempervirens:* first division of the fertilized egg. A strong cell plate is formed on the spindle, and the wall will be completed before the second division begins; ×500.—After LAWSON.[344]

FIG. 332.—*Pinus laricio:* first division of nucleus of fertilized egg. The figure is entirely intranuclear; ×500.—After CHAMBERLAIN.[104]

The positions of nuclei are worth noting. Throughout the development of the archegonium, from the first appearance of the archegonium initial up to the formation of the ventral canal cell, the nucleus is at the top. After the ventral canal division, the nucleus moves down to the middle of the egg; and after two mitoses, the four nuclei move down to the bottom of the egg. Perhaps pollen tubes and the disorganization of the nucellus may have something to do with the earlier position, and nutrition, which, in later stages, comes more from beneath, may cause the later movement.

When walls come in at the close of the third mitosis they form two tiers of cells with four cells in each tier. The cells of the upper tier

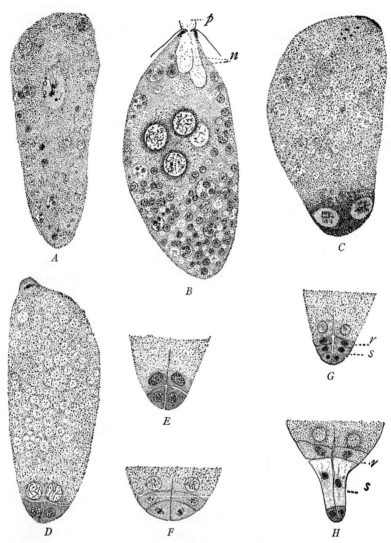

FIG. 333.—*Pinus laricio: A*, the two spirems of the gamete nuclei within the egg nucleus; a detail is shown in fig. 327 *B; B*, four-nucleate stage; proteid vacuoles are particularly distinct and, at the top, are two large vacuoles which might be mistaken for pollen tubes; *C*, third mitosis, showing two of the four dividing nuclei; *D* and *E*, eight-celled stage; *F*, three tiers of four cells each, with nuclei of the lowest tier dividing; *G*, four tiers of four cells each; *H*, cells of the suspensor tier elongating; *p*, pollen tube; *n*, vacuoles; *r*, rosette tier; *s*, suspensor tier; *A-C*, June 25; *D-G*, July 2; ×104.—From COULTER and CHAMBERLAIN, *Morphology of Gymnosperms*[154] (University of Chicago Press).

then divide, so that there are three tiers; and a division in the lowest
tier completes the intra-oval stage of the embryogeny. Some details
of these mitoses are shown in Dr. NILSINE KIHLDAHL'S[322] study of
Pinus (fig. 334). The walls dividing the lower part of the egg into

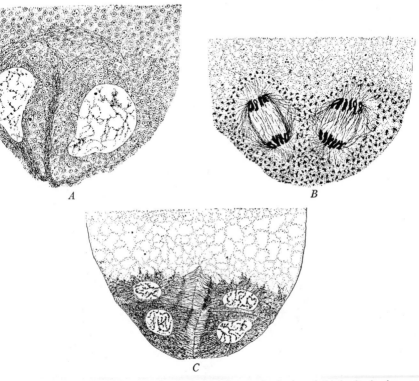

FIG. 334.—*Pinus laricio: A*, achromatic structures as beginning of third mitosis of
fertilized egg; *B*, late anaphase of third mitosis which will give rise to two tiers of four
cells each; *C*, late telophase of same mitosis with walls nearly complete. The cells of the
uppermost tier never have any wall on the side next the general cytoplasm of the egg;
×350.—After Dr. NILSINE KIHLDAHL.[322]

four tiers are formed on the central spindle in the usual way, while
the walls dividing each tier into four cells are formed on the strong
threads radiating from the poles of the figure.

Root, shoot, cotyledons, leaves, and secondary suspensor cells
(embryonal tubes) all come from the lowest tier, the other three tiers
contributing nothing to these structures.

Four free nuclei seem to be quite general in the Abietaceae, Taxodiaceae, and Cupressaceae, although mistakes could be made in stating the number. One might think that there would be eight free nuclei in *Thuja;* but LAND's[337] complete series showed that, while

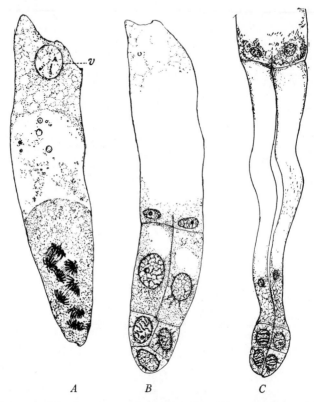

FIG. 335.—*Thuja occidentalis: A*, third mitosis in fertilized egg. Walls will come in at the close of this mitosis, forming eight cells; *B*, organization of tiers; *C*, elongation of suspensor; *v*, ventral nucleus; ×425.—After LAND.[337]

there are four mitotic figures lying in a common mass of protoplasm, definite walls are formed at the close of this mitosis (fig. 335).

The largest number of free nuclei in the conifers is found in the Araucariaceae. BURLINGAME[85] found 32 in *Araucaria braziliensis;* and EAMES[181] found usually 32 with occasionally 64 in *Agathis australis.*

Except for the Araucariaceae, the number of free nuclei in the Taxares is regularly higher than in the Pinares. *Phyllocladus*,[323] *Austrotaxus*,[498] and *Cephalotaxus*[143] have 8; *Podocarpus coriaceus*,[140] *P. macrophyllus*, and *P. totora*,[83] 16; and *Taxus baccata*,[285] 16, with an occasional 32, before walls are formed. *Torreya*[152] is exceptional, however, in having only four free nuclei when walls come in.

The significance of the longer and shorter free nuclear periods will be discussed in the chapter on "Phylogeny."

In *Pinus* the four tiers of cells, with four cells in each tier, are almost geometrical in their symmetry and arrangement; and their function is just as definite. The upper tier, with the distal ends of its cells open to the general mass of the cytoplasm of the egg, is active in the nutrition of the parts below, as long as any food material remains in the egg. The next tier below is called the "rosette," from its appearance in vertical view. Its cells are actively meristematic and often develop into embryos. The cells of the next tier elongate immensely, to hundreds of times the length of the original tier, and constitute the suspensor, which may be called the primary suspensor to distinguish it from the structures which appear later and might be mistaken for it.

Only a part of the cell progeny of the lowest tier develop into embryos, and none of the other tiers have any part in the formation of the root, shoot, cotyledons, or leaves.

A differentiation of the proembryo into tiers is characteristic of conifers, and even in the massive proembryo of the cycads and *Ginkgo* there is a differentiation into regions, although not so sharply marked.

In the Abietaceae there are, prevailingly, four tiers; in the Taxodiaceae and Cupressaceae, three tiers; in the Araucariaceae there are three tiers (fig. 336), the upper forming the suspensor, the middle one giving rise to the embryo, and the lower merely forming a temporary protective cap, which soon disorganizes.

In *Cephalotaxus* three tiers are described: the upper, a rosette; the next below, the suspensor; and the lowest, the group of embryo cells. In the lowest group the lowest cell, or sometimes two cells, acts as a protective cap, as in the Araucariaceae (fig. 337).[600]

Although the development of the embryo is a continuous process,

it is convenient, for the sake of reference, to have some name for the
stages before the growing sporophyte breaks through the base of the
egg. The term "proembryo" has long been used for this part of the
embryogeny.

Later embryogeny.—While stages in the development of the embryo have been studied, often rather thoroughly, ever since the time

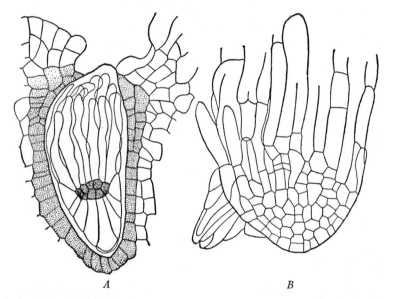

A   *B*

FIG. 336.—*Araucaria braziliensis: A*, the proembryo fills the entire egg: the shaded
cells are the embryo proper; the cells above form the suspensor; and the cells below, the
protective cap; *B*, later stage; the protective cap at the left is being pushed off; many
of the cells above are "embryonal tubes." ×153.—After STRASBURGER.[600]

of HOFMEISTER,[259] investigations of later stages had been comparatively desultory, until BUCHHOLZ[67–82] made a critical examination
of nearly all the genera of the order. With a new and ingenious technique, he was able to remove the embryos entire and uninjured.
With such preparations, many of them examined in the living condition, and all of them after critical staining, it was easier to observe
and safer to interpret, especially in the numerous cases of polyembryony. More than one embryo is so common in the gymnosperms
that it might be called their most distinguishing characteristic (fig.

338). While more than one, and often many, begin to develop, the ripe seed usually has only one which has developed sufficiently to produce a seedling.

More than one embryo may originate in different ways. More than one egg in a gametophyte may be fertilized and one embryo may develop to a considerable extent from each fertilized egg. This is *simple polyembryony*. When more than one

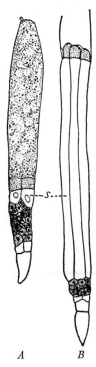

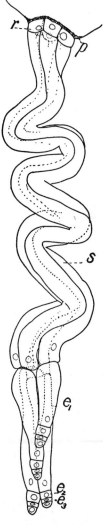

FIG. 337.—*Cephalotaxus fortunei: A*, proembryo, still within the egg, showing the rosette, suspensor (*s*), embryo, and protective cap: *B*, later stage, after breaking through the base of the egg; ×63.— After STRASBURGER.[600]

FIG. 338.—*Pinus banksiana:* cleavage polyembryony: *s*, primary suspensor; e_1, e_2, e_3, first, second, and third secondary suspensor cells (embryonal tubes); *r*, rosette; *p*, basal plate above rosette formed from disorganized remains of egg; ×100.— After BUCHHOLZ.[68]

embryo comes from a single egg by the splitting of the product of a single fertilization, the term *cleavage polyembryony* is used. Both types are widely distributed in the conifers.

In the Abietaceae, cleavage polyembryony is a constant feature of *Pinus*, *Cedrus*, *Pseudolarix*, and *Tsuga;* while simple polyembryony is the rule in *Larix*, *Picea*, and *Pseudotsuga*. In *Abies*, cleavage occurs in rare cases: simple polyembryony is the rule.

In the Taxodiaceae, cleavage polyembryony is excessive in *Sciadopitys*, is not so frequent in *Taxodium*, and does not occur in *Sequoia*.

In the Cupressaceae, cleavage polyembryony occurs, at least occasionally, in *Juniperus*, *Thuja*, *Biota*, *Actinostrobus*, *Widdringtonia*, and *Callitris*, but not in *Tetraclinis*.

In the Araucariaceae, neither *Araucaria* nor *Agathis* has any cleavage polyembryony.

In the Podocarpaceae cleavage polyembryony is not so prevalent. A form of polyembryony described as determinate cleavage polyembryony has been described for *Dacrydium*,[80] and in *Podocarpus coriaceus* some of Coker's figures suggest cleavage polyembryony, but most species of *Podocarpus* (for example, *P. spicatus*[74]), and also *Phyllocladus*, *Saxegothea*,[497] and *Microcachrys*[350] seem to have simple polyembryony.

In the Taxaceae JÄGER[285] found that in *Taxus baccata* some of the upper suspensor cells occasionally break away and form small embryos; but even this last trace of polyembryony is usually lacking, and it does not occur in the other genera.

Simple polyembryony occurs throughout the order except, of course, in forms like *Torreya*, with only one archegonium.

BUCHHOLZ[67-82] believes that cleavage polyembryony is a primitive character, and that simple polyembryony has been derived from it. In some forms, like the Araucariaceae, *Cephalotaxus*, and some species of *Podocarpus*, the cap, very probably not a primitive feature, may prevent cleavage; and in others occasional cleavage is interpreted as a reversion. With this interpretation the *Pinus* type is very primitive, and the *Araucaria* type, very advanced.

The rosette cells, where they are present, are embryonic, and often produce embryos (fig. 339 *F*). They are highly developed in *Pinus*, where all four of them often produce embryos; so that, with the other four embryos, a single fertilized egg may produce 8 embryos. When three eggs are fertilized, as often happens, 24 embryos may start in a single seed. Since it is possible that six or seven eggs may be fertilized, there could be 48, or even 56, embryos in a young seed. Rosette embryos are also the rule in *Cedrus*, but rare in *Abies* and *Tsuga*. In the rest of the Abietaceae, except in *Pseudotsuga*, there are rosette cells, but they do not develop into embryos.

Rosette embryos are found in *Sciadopitys*, but not in *Taxodium;* they are found in *Arthrotaxis*, but not in *Sequoia*. The initials for rosette cells may occur in *Podocarpus spicatus*, and they are found in *Cephalotaxus*, where they may develop into embryos; but they are not found in *Taxus* or *Torreya*.

Rosette cells sometimes elongate like suspensor cells and function like them.

COKER noted that, in *Podocarpus coriaceus*,[140] a single apical cell, and, later a group of cells, are binucleate. BUCHHOLZ found the same condition in *Dacrydium cupressinum*, and, in a forthcoming paper, has greatly extended the range of forms which show this character to 12 species, so that all members of the Podocarpaceae, except *Saxagothea* and *Microcachrys*, probably have binucleate embryonic cells.

A suspensor, at least in the form of embryonal tubes, characterizes the entire order, and perhaps the entire gymnosperm phylum. The primary suspensor cells, which are well illustrated by the four elongating cells of the suspensor tier in *Pinus*, do not divide. When there are two or more cells in the suspensor, looking as if they had come from transverse divisions in the primary suspensor cells, the additional cells have come from transverse divisions in the lowest tier of cells of the proembryo (fig. 339 *A* and *E*). Later, such a secondary suspensor cell may divide periclinally. These secondary suspensor cells have been called "embryonal tubes" and in later embryogeny they may become very numerous.

In some of his more recent publications BUCHHOLZ has made use of the term *prosuspensor*. This part of the suspensor system seems to be more than the group of greatly elongating cells which emerges from the proembryo. It is a special part of the suspensor system which elongates very greatly, and in such forms as *Sciadopitys*, may precede the formation of the primary suspensors. Each embryo of *Sciadopitys*, which appears later, is borne on its own primary suspensor. Thus, *Pinus* may be considered as having no prosuspensor, but a group of four primary suspensors placed parallel to each other, followed by the embryonal tubes, which together constitute the secondary suspensor. *Dacrydium* has a prosuspensor, but omits the formation of the primary suspensor, and forms, instead, a massive secondary suspensor on one or more of the several embryos. The very long suspensors which appear on the early embryos of podocarps would therefore be described as prosuspensors. Prosuspensors seem to be recognizable in conifers above the level of the Abietaceae.

There can be no doubt that the highly developed suspensor pushes the growing embryo down into the gametophyte, which is richly stored with starch and other foodstuffs. As the foodstuffs become liquid, the tissues surrounding the embryos break down, so that a large cavity is formed. The elongating suspensor, as it kinks and coils, fills most of this cavity, thrusting the embryo deeper and deeper into the gametophyte. After the embryo has reached its maximum length, the suspensor, together with the remains of the egg and nucellus, forms a dry cap which may protect the root end of the embryo as it breaks through the testa.

In the early embryogeny there is frequently a definite apical cell, segmenting like the apical cell of many pteridophytes (fig. 339). In *B* and *C* of this figure, the apical cell and its segments are indicated by stronger lines, while the subdivisions of the segments are indicated by lighter lines. At the stage shown in *D* there is no longer any segmentation of the higher fern type, but a growth by a group of initials.

There are apical cells in other conifers, *Sciadopitys*, *Thuja*, *Juniperus*, and others, but the apical cells do not cut off so many segments. Embryos with caps, and many embryos without cleavage polyembryony, like *Picea*, *Larix*, and *Abies*, have no apical cells. In *Thuja occidentalis* and *Taxus*, there seems to be an apical cell.

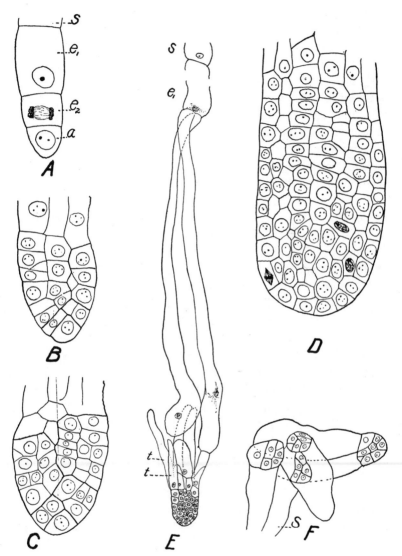

FIG. 339.—*Pinus banksiana*: *A*, young embryo with suspensor (*s*), apical cell (*a*), first embryonal tube (*e₁*), and second embryonal tube (*e₂*); *B* and *C* apical stages, showing apical cell and some segments; *D*, later stage with growth by group of cells; *E*, embryo showing part of suspensor (*s*), with first embryonal tube (*e₁*), below it, two long embryonal tubes, and still lower more embryonal tubes (*t*); *F*, four young embryos from rosette cells; *A-D*, ×300; *E*, *F*, ×80.—After BUCHHOLZ.[68]

An apical cell with definite segmentation is characteristic of the higher Filicales, not only during embryogeny, but throughout the whole life-history. In the lower Filicales apical cells are not so definite. In some of the lycopods an apical cell is very definite in the early development, but later is replaced by a group of initials. This behavior is also true of many fern gametophytes. So, it seems safe to assume that the apical cell, as it appears in the embryogeny of some conifers, is a primitive character, inherited from some filicinean progenitor, and appearing for a short time in the embryo. Those who lay great stress upon recapitulation will include this apical cell in their defense of the theory.

At the stage of development shown in fig. 339 D, at least the lower half of the embryo is meristematic. Later, the meristematic region becomes localized, first near the base, where the root is being organized, and then higher up, where a meristematic region gives rise to stem, cotyledons, and leaves.

The meristematic group of cells of the young root is small. It gives rise to the periblem and plerome of the root. The root cap comes from the periblem. There is no dermatogen in the early embryogeny (fig. 276).

Investigators interested in vascular anatomy have begun their study with the mature embryo, or later, and morphologists have done their most intensive work on the proembryo. Some, like BUCHHOLZ, have been adding to our knowledge of intermediate stages; but these studies have not extended much beyond the apical cell and early meristematic stages.

From the appearance of the cotyledons to the mature seed, a considerable amount of topographic work has been done. Polycotyledony is prevalent in conifers, and there has long been a controversy over its origin, some claiming that it is a primitive condition, while others believe that it has been derived from dicotyledony by a splitting of the two cotyledons.

HILL and DE FRAINE,[249-251] relying principally upon vascular anatomy, claim that polycotyledony has been derived from dicotyledony by a splitting of the two cotyledons. SISTER HELEN ANGELA made a series of diagrams, based on vascular anatomy, showing intergrading forms from polycotyledony to dicotyledony, in both conifers and cycads. She believed that polycotyledony is the primitive condition.

BUCHHOLZ,[67-82] studying a great number of species in critical stages, concluded that polycotyledony is primitive, and that the lower numbers are due to fusions. He lays little stress upon vascular anatomy as a factor in this problem, because the primordia of the cotyledons are well developed before any vascular structures appear. He found that the average number of primordia in the younger embryos, with fusing cotyledons bearing double primordia, was in excess of the average number found in the older stages, after any fusions or splitting of cotyledons had been completed.

Forms with a large number of cotyledons, like the Abietaceae, are primitive in other features; and forms with 2 or 3 cotyledons, like some of the Cupressaceae, are advanced in other respects; but, of course, this is not a very convincing argument. There is no doubt that the number of cotyledons is sometimes reduced by the abortion of one or more. It is not so easy to prove whether a primordium, notched at the top, is splitting, or is the result of fusion. BUCHHOLZ'[68] work seems to show a fusion (fig. 340). The fact that the primordia are easily distinguishable before any vascular strands appear would indicate that the vascular structures do not cause any splitting. It is certain that vascular strands, growing faster than the surrounding parenchyma, cause lobing, serration, and other margins of leaves; but here, the strand is present at an early stage. In conifers the primordia of cotyledons, appearing in advance of the strands, could not be formed in such manner.

After the proembryo breaks through the base of the egg the elongating suspensor cell thrusts the embryo tier deeper and deeper into the gametophyte. The base of the egg is partly dissolved and partly fractured as the embryo goes through. In forms with cleavage polyembryony, the cells of the elongating suspensor, and also those in the embryo tier at the tip, split apart. The abundant starch grains surrounding the embryo disappear, especially for a long distance immediately in front, and their place is taken by soluble foodstuffs, which are taken in by the rapidly growing embryos.

The gametophyte tissue in contact with the embryo not only loses its starch and subsequent foodstuffs, but its cell walls break down, so that a cavity is formed behind the embryo. The tissues of the nucellus also break down. While this breaking-down of tissues is going

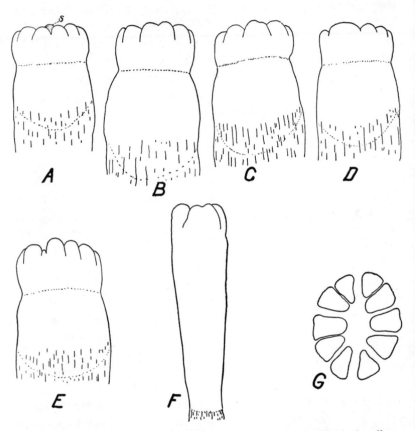

FIG. 340.—Reduction in the number of cotyledons: *A-E*, *Cedrus libani: A*, ordinary embryo, with no fusion of cotyledons; *B* and *C*, earlier and later stages in fusion; *D*, the large cotyledon has probably arisen by fusion; *E*, reduction in number of cotyledons by abortion of a cotyledon, the small cotyledon (third from the left) is disorganizing; *F, G, Pinus banksiana: F*, two cotyledons fusing; *G*, transverse section of the group of cotyledons, indicating two groups; *s*, stem tip; ×32.—After BUCHHOLZ.[68]

on around the embryo, the cells at the periphery of the gametophyte divide and grow actively, until the embryo completes its intraseminal development.

Even before fertilization, the stony layer of the testa has begun to develop (fig. 341). At this time three layers are recognizable, the outer and inner fleshy layers, with the stony layer between them. The cells of the stony layer interlock somewhat, but they do not intertwine as in the cycads. Their walls become thicker as their cell contents disappear. The inner fleshy layer may be considered as

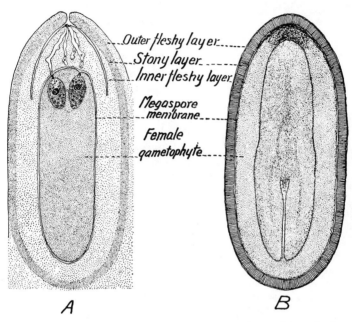

Outer fleshy layer
Stony layer
Inner fleshy layer
Megaspore membrane
Female gametophyte

A   B

FIG. 341.—*Pinus laricio: A*, young seed at time of fertilization; *B*, nearly ripe seed. The inner and outer layers have nearly disappeared.

made up of all the tissues between the stony layer and the female gametophyte.

In the cycads, the outer fleshy layer usually becomes variously colored, with red, orange, or cream colors predominating; this outer coat persists for a long time, finally drying and becoming very tough and leathery. In conifers, it is seldom colored while it is young and fleshy. Later, it becomes brownish and very thin, and may disappear entirely, so that the stony layer is the outer layer of the seed.

The inner fleshy layer, at the time of fertilization, is the thickest of the three layers. It becomes partly absorbed and partly crushed by the growing gametophyte, until, in the ripe seed, it is only a thin, papery membrane, somewhat thicker at the top, where it consists of the disorganizing nucellus.

FIG. 342.—*Pinus edulis: A*, seedling with tips of cotyledons still inside the seed: *B*, later stage with cotyledons expanded and young leaves appearing. No spurs at this stage. The portion below the cotyledons and down to the break is hypocotyl. About two-thirds of the hypocotyl is shown, one-half natural size.

Many conifer seeds will germinate immediately, without any resting period; but some of them remain dormant for a long time. As already noted, the cone scales of *Pinus mucronata*, an endemic California species, may open only when there is a fire, or an unusually warm summer.

At germination the testa is carried up at the tips of the cotyledons, which, at first, are curved because their tips are held together inside the seed coat (fig. 342).

All forms which have spur shoots, like *Pinus*, or appressed leaves, like *Thuja*, or phylloclads, like *Phyllocladus*, have simple needle leaves in the young seedlings. These simple needle leaves also appear in adult plants when a bud develops on account of a wound.

We believe in the recapitulation theory, but we also believe that it has been called upon to explain things not at all related to it. In support of the theory we should lay the greatest stress upon the life-histories of pteridophytes in their relation to the evolution of the seed. Some features of vegetative anatomy seem best explained in accordance with the theory. We are inclined to believe that the juvenile leaves of conifers are really a recapitulation of an early ancestral condition, and that spurs, appressed leaves, and phylloclads came later.

FIG. 343.—*Pinus palustris:* seedling near New Orleans, Louisiana. Most of the pines in the background are *Pinus taeda.*

Just how far the seedling must develop before it should be called a tree is a matter of individual taste. Farmers use the term "sapling" for stages between the seedling and the tree. The term is convenient, but it makes two points to determine instead of only one. Most botanists would call the plant shown in fig. 343 a seedling. It is *Pinus palustris*, is several years old, and all the leaves are on spurs. The plant is about 3 feet in height.

The anatomy of the seedling has already been considered in chapter xi.

CHAPTER XVII

CONIFEROPHYTES—GNETALES—EPHEDRA

Professor CHARLES R. BARNES used to say that a character which would make a species in the thallose jungermanias would make a genus in the mosses. It seems to be a matter of taste whether the Gnetales should be put into one family, with three genera, or into three families, with one genus in each. All agree that there are only three genera, *Ephedra*, *Welwitschia*, and *Gnetum*. MARKGRAF,[381] in the second edition of ENGLER and PRANTL'S, *Die natürlichen Pflanzenfamilien*, makes three families, Ephedraceae, Welwitschiaceae, and Gnetaceae. Since the number of families seems to be a matter of taste, we prefer to treat the assemblage, as most taxonomists treat it, under one family, the Gnetaceae.

The characters which keep the three genera together in one order and in one family are: vessels in the secondary wood; compound strobilus in both male and female; the long micropylar tube formed by the inner integument; opposite leaves; dicotyl embryos; no resin canals. All of the Gnetales have all of these characters, although some of them are not confined to this group. Many other gymnosperms have dicotyl embryos, most of them have a compound ovulate strobilus, many have opposite leaves, some have a more or less elongated micropylar tube; but no other gymnosperms have this combination of characters. The compound male strobilus and vessels in the secondary wood are not found in other gymnosperms. The combination of characters is sufficient to keep the three genera together, while the compound male strobilus and vessels in the secondary wood are sufficient to separate them from the rest of the gymnosperms.

Some of the characters belong to angiosperms as well as to Gnetales, and have tempted botanists to look upon the Gnetales as the ancestors of the angiosperms. A strong objection to such a theory of relationships is that no Gnetales have been found below the Tertiary, while angiosperms were abundant in the Cretaceous, and certainly existed in the Jurassic.

The archegonium and embryogeny keep *Ephedra* definitely in the gymnosperms; while other features keep the other two genera with *Ephedra*. Otherwise, only the naked ovule would keep *Welwitschia* and, especially *Gnetum*, out of the angiosperms.

The three genera are so different in appearance and in the details of life-histories that no one could have given rise to either of the others. Their connection with any of the rest of the living gymnosperms is just as doubtful as any relationship with the angiosperms. They are gymnosperms because they are seed plants with naked ovules, and *Ephedra*, carrying the other two genera with it, has a gymnosperm life-history. Otherwise the whole assemblage would be an isolated group, without even a problematical relationship.

It seems best to treat the three genera separately, and, on the basis of the evolution of the female gametophyte, the order of treatment should be *Ephedra*, *Welwitschia*, and *Gnetum*.

EPHEDRA

Ephedra is a low, profusely branching shrub (fig. 344). In the region shown in the illustration, near Palm Springs Canyon, California, it is very abundant and often serves as a sand binder. Some North African species trail over other plants and climb somewhat.

Geographic distribution.—It is a xerophytic genus, at its best in mountainous or rocky places, or in sandy, desert regions, like that shown in the illustration.

MARKGRAF,[381] in *Die natürlichen Pflanzenfamilien*, estimates the number of species at 35. PEARSON[446] lists 32, not including the well-marked *Ephedra compacta*, found near Tehuacan, Mexico.

The species are somewhat equally divided between the Western and Eastern hemispheres. PEARSON assigns 17 species to the Old World and 14 to the New, with 6 to North America (there should be 7 with *E. compacta*), and 8 to South America.

In North America they are most abundant in New Mexico, Arizona, and California, although they are found in the states bordering these on the north. Only one species, *Ephedra antisyphilitica*, gets as far east as Texas. There are some in northern Mexico, but none have been reported between northern Mexico and the small *Ephedra compacta*, near Tehuacan. In South America they are most abundant in the Andes regions of Bolivia and Paraguay, but in Paraguay they also extend across the desert plains even to the Atlantic Ocean. A few are found farther south in Chili and Patagonia.

In the Eastern Hemisphere, the western limit is the Canaries and Madeira. There are species in the western Alps, in western France, and in some places along the shores of the Mediterranean and Black

Fig. 344.—*Ephedra:* near Palm Springs, California. *Ephedra*, in this region, often acts as a sand binder.

Sea. The genus crosses Arabia and Persia, through northern India, and then northeast through China, across the upper basins of the Yang-tse-Kiang and Hoang-Ho rivers. *Ephedra distachya* gets into Siberia, very far north for a genus which belongs typically to a warm climate.

No species are common to the Western and Eastern hemispheres, and no species seems to cross the Equator.

The geographic distribution, with such scattered patches, would indicate great age; but, as already noted, there is scarcely any geological history, no material having been found below the Tertiary.

THE SPOROPHYTE—VEGETATIVE

The general appearance of the genus is sufficiently characteristic to make it easily recognizable. Nearly all are straggling shrubs,

FIG. 345.—*Ephedra trifurca:* female plant near Tucson, Arizona. The larger branches at the surface of the ground, and even below it, are 5 cm. in diameter.

usually less than two meters in height, and some less than half that height. *Ephedra compacta*, a very compact, profusely branching form,

near Tehuacan, Mexico, is usually about 30 cm. in height, and seldom reaches 50 cm. On the other hand, the stem of the South
American *E. triandra* sometimes reaches a diameter of 30 cm. and a
height of several meters. What the age of these large plants might
be has not been determined. LAND[338] reported 40 rings in an old
plant of *E. trifurca*. Since this is the largest number of rings reported
for any species, *Ephedra* is a short-lived plant.

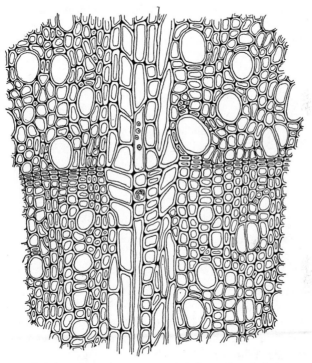

FIG. 346.—*Ephedra trifurca:* transverse section of part of stem about 1 cm. in diameter, showing numerous vessels of various sizes. The largest vessels are formed earlier
in the season, as may be seen from the vessels above the growth-ring. A large medullary ray is shown in the middle of the figure; ×170.

Branching begins very early, buds appearing even in the axils of
the cotyledon. In older plants the first branches are often covered
by soil (fig. 345). When the soil is loose, and conditions are favorable,
buds at the nodes may grow out into long rhizomes, and buds on
the rhizomes may develop into new plants. LAND[340] found numerous

plants of *Ephedra trifurca* developing in this way. Several conifers are reproduced by underground buds.

The seedling has a strong tap root, which persists for a long time, but is gradually overtaken by adventitious roots. Root hairs are abundant, but there is no mycorrhiza.

The leaves are small and rudimentary, and, even when young, are of scarcely any importance in the vegetative economy of the plant. They are opposite or in whorls of three, very rarely of four. The leaves of American species are usually in whorls of three. In all cases the whorls alternate.

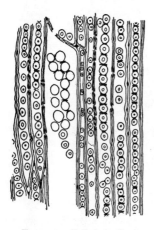

FIG. 347.—*Ephedra trifurca:* longitudinal radial section of stem about 1 cm. in diameter, showing one large vessel and several tracheids; ×170.

There is hardly anything which could be called a blade. A thick and often fleshy midrib has a thin border, thicker and sheathing at the base, and with scarcely any stomata. The border, at first whitish, soon becomes brown, and withers. An abscission layer develops early, and the leaf falls off, leaving a broad scar. The leaf trace is double, and extending into the leaf is its only vascular feature. The double trace does not extend beyond the node above its insertion. In both leaf and stem the trace is endarch.

Histology.—At the apex of the stem and root there are no separate initials for plerome, periblem, or dermatogen, and in the root there is probably no dermatogen at all. A general meristem differentiates later into the body regions.

The most striking histological feature of *Ephedra*, and of the other two genera, is the presence of vessels in the secondary wood (fig. 346). The vessels are modified tracheids of all sizes, from that of the ordinary tracheid up to several times that diameter, the largest being formed early in the spring, smaller ones later, and still later in the season none at all. The pits, at first bordered, enlarge and lose both torus and border, so that they become mere perforations. Such perforations often fuse, and when they fuse on the oblique end walls the structure becomes more and more like the continuous tube of the angiosperms. There is no other general breaking down of the oblique walls to form continuous vessels.

Most of the wood consists of tracheids with bordered pits, usually uniseriate, and more abundant on the radial face, but there is also abundant tangential pitting (fig. 348).

Medullary rays are very long and very wide (fig. 348). Only about one-third of the two long rays is shown in the figure, with the top of another at the lower left. The cells of the rays are of various shapes and sizes: isodiametric, elongated, and curved. The walls are thick, lignified, and pitted, but the pits are small and simple.

Rays in young plants are uniseriate, but, later, they become multiseriate by longitudinal divisions in the uniseriate ray, by the incorporation of adjoining cells, or by the fusion of uniseriate rays. When there is a fusion of uniseriate rays, separated by a few tracheids, the tracheids are incorporated in the large resulting ray. Such rays have no relation to leaf traces.

With practically all of the cells thick walled and lignified, it is natural that the wood should be very hard. In young stems the rigidity is also increased by lignification of the pith just above the

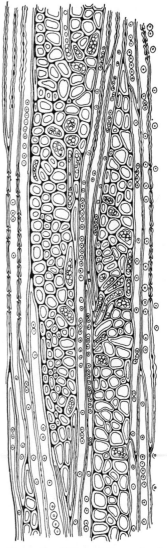

FIG. 348.—*Ephedra trifurca:* longitudinal tangential section, showing the ends of two large medullary rays, and a tip of a ray at the lower left. Many cells of the ray are pitted, and in the long tracheids there is both radial and tangential pitting; ×170.

nodes, giving the general impression of partitions in bamboos and other grasses.

The small, more or less upright, green stems, which give *Ephedra* such a characteristic appearance, do the photosynthetic work. The long-fluted internodes and reduced leaves make these small shoots look like *Equisetum*, and their internal structure also resembles that of the ancient pteridophyte (fig. 349). They grow from a small meristem at the base, and many of them fall off at the end of the growing season, thereby effecting a very advantageous reduction in the transpiration surface. In some there is a vigorous development of secondary wood, and these, later, produce whorls of small branches. Branches of all sizes are shown in fig. 345.

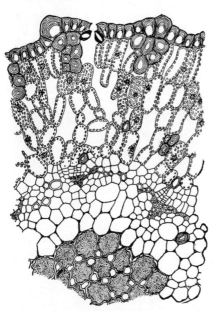

FIG. 349.—*Ephedra trifurca:* transverse section of a small upright green twig, about 1 mm. in diameter, showing two ridges, the depression between them, and a stoma at the base of the depression. There are thick-walled cells under the ridges, and a zone of chlorophyll cells extending down to the vascular region; ×270.

The epidermal cells are thick walled, with a group of very thick-walled cells under the ridges; stomata are distributed at the bottom or along the sides of the depression between ridges. Between these thick-walled cells and the vascular region is a zone of very thin-walled cells with abundant chloroplasts and numerous intercellular spaces. The vascular cylinder is an endarch siphonostele. In the center of the pith is a group of rather thick-walled cells with very dense contents, perhaps tannin: there is no resin in the order.

THE SPOROPHYTE—REPRODUCTIVE

Ephedra, and also the other two genera, are dioecious, but in all of them there are traces of an ancestral bisporangiate condition. By hunting through a large patch, a monoecious individual can generally be found, and in *E. foliata* they are rather common. Staminate and ovulate strobili are found on the same plant, and LAND found bisporangiate flowers in *E. trifurca*. WETTSTEIN[670] found similar flowers in *E. campylopoda*, and others have reported them for other species (fig. 350). When both sexes are in the same strobilus, the staminate flowers are below and the ovulate at the top, as in the bisporangiate strobili already described for *Picea* and other conifers.

The staminate strobilus.—The staminate strobili are in whorls of 2, 3, or 4 at the nodes of the small green branches. The whorled condition of the leaves of the vegetative shoot is also present in the floral axis. There is no doubt that the staminate structure is a compound strobilus, a feature which, with vessels in the secondary wood, separates the Gnetales from the rest of the gymnosperms.

FIG. 350.—*Ephedra campylopoda:* bisporangia strobilus; ×7.—After WETTSTEIN.[670]

The male strobilus consists of a short axillary shoot, bearing 2–8 opposite pairs of bracts, of which the lower one or two pairs are sterile, while the rest bear solitary flowers (fig. 351). In the axil of a fertile bract is a shoot, bearing two thin, opposite scales, which have been interpreted as a perianth. Between these scales the axis is prolonged, and bears the microsporangia at its top. Whether the scales should be called a perianth, is doubtful; but it is certain that they are reduced opposite leaves, more or less united at the base, covering the axis before the elongation which pushes the stamens out into a favorable position for shedding their pollen.

The structure bearing the two scales at the base, and the sporangia at the top, has been called a "sporangiophore," a good name because it is efficient for reference, like placenta and receptacle, and is just as noncommittal. In some species one or more—usually more—sporangia are sessile at the top of the sporangiophore. In *Ephedra trifurca* there are 5 or 6 sporangia, and each one is borne on a filament, which may be called a sporophyll, just as reasonable an interpretation as to call the structure a branching sporangiophore.

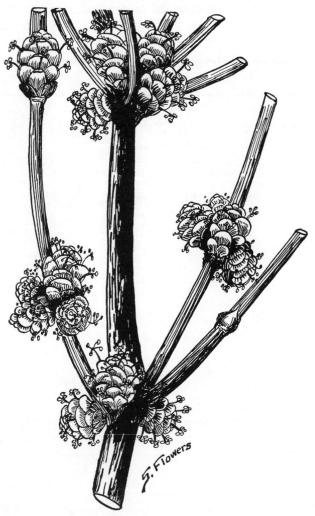

FIG. 351.—*Ephedra viridis:* part of staminate flower; ×2.—From an unpublished drawing by Dr. S. FLOWERS.

The sporangia usually have more than one loculus and have been called synangia; but while the multilocular condition is evident, any actual fusion still remains to be proved.

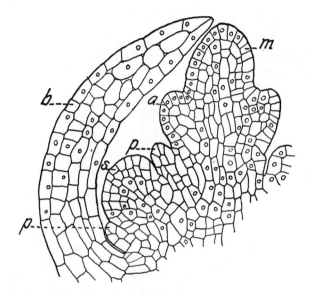

Fig. 352.—*Ephedra campylopoda:* longitudinal section of tip of staminate strobilus: *m*, apical meristem of strobilus; *b*, bract; *p*, "perianth"; *s*, sporangiophore; *a*, *Anlage* which is to develop into *b*, *s*, and *p*; ×160.—After Strasburger.[596]

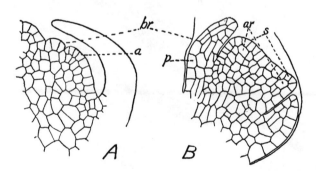

Fig. 353.—*Ephedra trifurca: A*, longitudinal section at tip of male strobilus, December 20, 1902; *B*, longitudinal section of male flower, a month later: *br*, bract; *a*, sporangiophore; *p*, perianth; *s*, microsporangia; *ar*, archesporial cell; ×150.—After Land.[338]

As long ago as 1872, STRASBURGER[596] worked out the early development of the bract, the two scales, and the sporangiophore of *Ephedra campylopoda* (fig. 352). From his figure it is obvious that the sporangiophore, bearing the two scales, is in the axil of a bract.

FIG. 354.—*Ephedra viridis:* part of ovulate plant; ×2.—From an unpublished drawing by Dr. S. FLOWERS.

The most complete account of the life-history is by LAND,[338, 339] who studied abundant material, both living and fixed, of *E. trifurca*, through spermatogenesis, oogenesis, fertilization, and some stages in the embryogeny (fig. 353). The bract appears close to the stem tip, and the sporangiophore (a in fig. 353) soon appears in its axil. The two scales (p, in the figure) appear at the base of the sporangiophore, and the hypodermal archesporial cells become recognizable, not at the center of the top, but in a circle around it.

From this point up to the microspore, the development is about as in any eusporangiate microsporangium. The wall of the mature microsporangium in *Ephedra trifurca*[338, 339] is very thin, with usually one layer of crushed wall cells between the epidermis and tapetum. The tapetal cells are very large, several times the diameter of the epidermis and wall cells together. In the vicinity of Mesilla Park, New Mexico, the locality of most of LAND'S material, the reduction division, by which the microspore mother-cell gives rise to four microspores, takes place about March 12. At the first division in the spore mother-cell, a wall begins to form, as if the bilateral type, characteristic of monocots, would result; but the incipient membrane disappears and spores of the tetrahedral type are formed.

The ovulate strobilus.—The ovulate strobilus can be distinguished from the staminate, even in the early stages, because it is elongated and pointed, while the staminate is globular (fig. 354). The ovulate strobili, like the staminate, are in whorls of 2, 3, or 4, at the nodes of the small green branches.

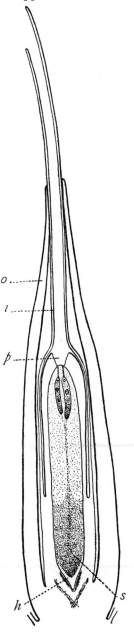

FIG. 355.—*Ephedra trifurca:* longitudinal section of ovule, showing nucellus with deep pollen chamber (p), inner (i) and outer (o) integuments, and female gametophyte with reproductive storage (s) and haustorial (h) regions; ×48.—After LAND.[338]

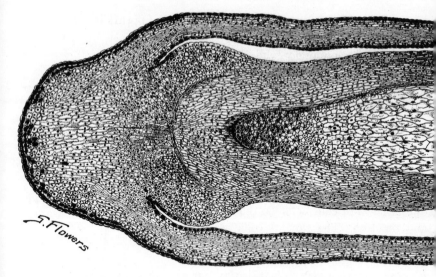

Fig. 356.—*Ephedra viridis:* longitudinal section of ovulate flower, showing

There are more bracts than in the staminate strobilus, usually four or more pairs of sterile ones, and a terminal ovule. The ovule has two integuments, the outer consisting of four bracts, coalescent at the base, and the inner, of two bracts, also coalescent at the base, and, at maturity, splitting at the top. The inner integument, at the time of pollination, elongates immensely, and, at its tip, is a sparkling pollination drop. The topography of the ovule at this stage is well shown in the much copied figure by LAND[338] (fig. 355), and in a recent figure by FLOWER (fig. 356).

STRASBURGER found a row of three megaspores in *Ephedra campylopoda*, and JACCARD found the same number in *E. helvetica*. LAND,[338] in *E. trifurca*, found about equal numbers of threes and fours (fig. 357). Of course, in rows of three, only the lower two are megaspores: the upper one is still a $2x$ cell of the sporophyte.

THE GAMETOPHYTES

Gametophytes of Eastern Hemisphere species have been studied by STRASBURGER,[596] JACCARD,[283] PEARSON,[440] BERRIDGE and SANDAY,[48] and Dr. STEPHANIE HERZFELD.[243] LAND'S[338, 339] work on the American *Ephedra trifurca* is the most complete account.

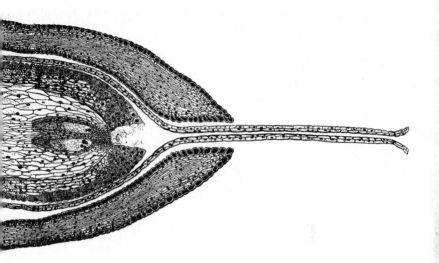

s diagrammed in fig. 355.—From an unpublished drawing by Dr. S. FLOWERS

The male gametophyte.—*Ephedra trifurca* will serve as a type. As in all seed plants, the microspore is the first cell of the male gametophyte. At its first division, a prothallial cell is cut off by a wall. At the second division a prothallial nucleus is formed, but there is no wall separating it from the rest of the spore, which is the antheridium initial (fig. 357). The initial then divides, forming a tube cell and a generative cell, which divides to form the nuclei of stalk and body cells. These two nuclei lie in a common mass of cytoplasm, and are never separated by a cell wall. At this stage the pollen is shed.

When it reaches the ovule, the generative cell divides, giving rise to two nuclei which are alike in size and appearance. The exine cracks longitudinally, and the intine slips out, becoming prolonged into a short pollen tube (fig. 358).

The female gametophyte.—The megaspore is the first cell of the female gametophyte (fig. 359). Its germination begins, as in all gymnosperms, with a period of simultaneous free nuclear divisions (fig. 359 *B*). The free nuclear period lasts about 20 days and walls begin to appear at the 256 nucleate stage (about April 1, in 1903, which was a very dry season).

Wall formation begins at the outside and rapidly proceeds toward the center until the gametophyte is cellular throughout. Even before the gametophyte is completely cellular, there is a differentiation into an upper reproductive region, consisting of large elongated cells, and a lower nutritive region, with small cells (figs. 355 and 356). Later, the lower part is further differentiated into an upper storage region, below which the cells act as a haustorium (fig. 355 *h, s*).

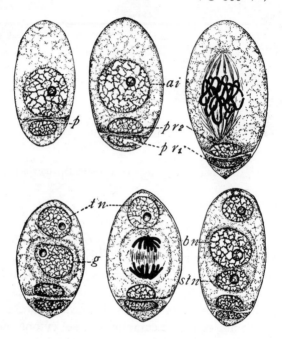

FIG. 357.—*Ephedra trifurca:* development of male gametophyte: *p* and *pr 1*, first prothallial cell; *pr 2*, second prothallial cell; *ai*, antheridial initial; *tn*, tube nucleus; *g*, generative cell; *bn*, nucleus of body cell; *stn*, nucleus of stalk cell; ✕1,500.—After LAND.[338]

Usually there are two archegonia, occasionally only one, and rarely three. The archegonial initial soon cuts off a neck cell, which divides several times, forming four or five tiers, before any anticlines appear (fig. 360). As many as eight tiers were observed, and since each divides anticlinally into four or more cells, there are seldom less than 32 neck cells, and often more. Some of the divisions are so irregular that the neck is not sharply marked off from the surrounding cells (fig. 360 *C*).

When the nucleus of the central cell divides, no wall is formed between the ventral canal nucleus and that of the egg. The ventral canal nucleus may then move down with the egg nucleus, or may remain at the top of the egg.

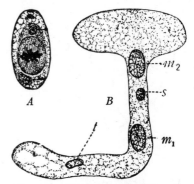

FERTILIZATION

A dense mass of cytoplasm, which is evident below the nucleus of the central cell, becomes denser, surrounds the egg nucleus, and extends for a long distance below it as fertilization takes place (fig. 361). Similar

FIG. 358.—*Ephedra trifurca: A*, pollen grain just before formation of pollen tube; the nucleus of the body cell is dividing to form two sperms; *B*, pollen tube: m_1 and m_2, the two sperms; *s*, nucleus of stalk cell; *t*, tube nucleus; ×500.—After LAND.[338]

masses have already been noted in connection with both egg and sperm nuclei of conifers.

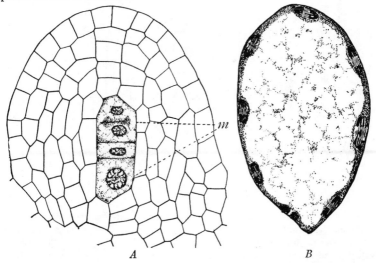

FIG. 359.—*Ephedra trifurca: A*, row of four megaspores, in which the lower megaspore is enlarging, the one above it is breaking down, and the mitosis for the formation of the other two megaspores is in late telophase; *B*, simultaneous free nuclear division to form the 64-nucleate stage of the female gametophyte; *m*, megaspores; ×500.—After LAND.[338]

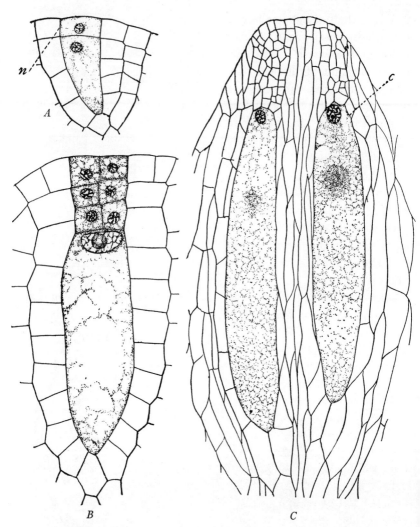

FIG. 360.—*Ephedra trifurca:* *A*, neck cell and central cell of archegonium; *n*, neck cell; *B*, neck consisting of three tiers, central cell not yet divided; *C*, later stage, with neck cells not easily distinguishable from surrounding cells; and central cell (*c*) still not divided: *A* and *B*, ×500; *C*, ×112.—After LAND.[338]

At the time of pollination, the pollen grains fall on the pollination drop and are drawn down the long micropyle. By this time such a deep pollen chamber has been formed by the breaking down of cells in the upper part of the nucellus that the pollen grains fall directly upon the female gametophyte. There would be no place for a pollen tube, were it not for the very long neck of the archegonium. The short pollen tube forces its way through the neck of the archegonium and discharges all four of its nuclei into the egg.

Whether there is any "double fertilization," like that in the angiosperms, is questionable; but several observers have noted divisions at the top of the fertilized egg, as well as at the bottom. Land[339] found jacket cells disintegrating at the time of fertilization, so that their protoplasm and nuclei mingled with those of the egg. The second male nucleus and ventral canal nucleus were also in this region. As the fertilized egg nucleus divided, there were also numerous divisions at the top of the egg. These small cells are soon absorbed by the growing embryos, functioning like the endosperm of angiosperms, and Land[339] believes

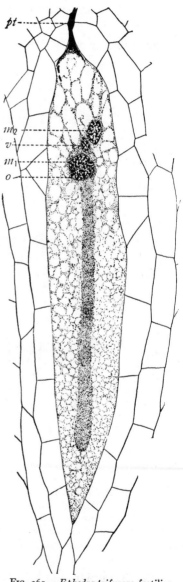

Fig. 361.—*Ephedra trifurca:* fertilization: *pt*, pollen tube; *o*, egg nucleus; *m₁* and *m₂* sperms; *m₁* is fusing with the egg nucleus; *v*, ventral canal nucleus; ×215.—After Land.[339]

that there is a suggestion of the origin of endosperm in the angiosperm sense (fig. 362). LAND[339] did not show a definite fusion of the second male nucleus with the ventral canal nucleus.

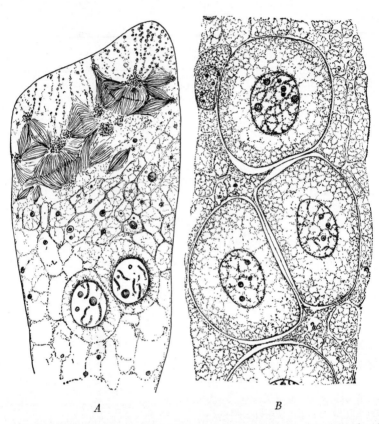

A　　　　　　　　　　　　　　　*B*

FIG. 362.—*Ephedra trifurca:* proembryos: *A*, group of spindles from second male cell and, below them, small cells which have come from jacket cells, or from the division of the non-functioning proembryonal cells, or both; farther down, two functional proembryonal cells; *B*, three of five proembryonal cells, also jacket nuclei in egg cytoplasm, and free masses of cytoplasm; ×500.—After LAND.[339]

Miss BERRIDGE and Miss SANDAY[48] found a similar situation in *Ephedra distachya*, but thought the nuclei at the top of the egg fused in pairs and formed functional embryonal cells. Nuclei in pairs are not rare; but LAND[339] found many binucleate cells in the normal jacket.

Dr. STEPHANIE HERZFELD[243] figured and described a fusion of the second sperm nucleus with the ventral canal nucleus, and did not hesitate to call it double fertilization in the angiosperm sense (fig. 363).

In conifers there have been reports of divisions in the top of the egg, variously attributed to divisions of the second sperm, or the ventral canal nucleus; and HUTCHINSON[275] described and figured the fusion of the second sperm with the ventral nucleus in *Abies balsamea*.

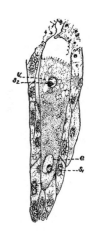

That nuclei in the rich protoplasm at the top of the egg should divide, seems very natural, whether the division might be preceded by any fusions or not; and it also seems probable that any such product would serve to nourish the growing embryo; but that there is any genetic continuity between this phenomenon and the double fertilization in angiosperms—in other words, that the angiosperms inherited double fertilization from the gymnosperms—seems more than doubtful.

FIG. 363.—*Ephedra campylopoda:* "double fertilization": *e*, egg nucleus; *s₁*, first sperm; *v*, ventral nucleus; *s₂*, second sperm.—After HERZFELD.[243]

EMBRYOGENY

STRASBURGER,[597] in 1876, outlined the embryogeny of *Ephedra altissima*, and LAND, in 1907,[339] made a thorough investigation of *E. trifurca*.

There is a free nuclear period with, usually, 8 free nuclei, which do not sink to the bottom of the egg, but are somewhat evenly distributed throughout the protoplasm (fig. 362). Around each of these nuclei there is organized a cell, which is a young embryo. So there is polyembryony without any cleavage. Usually from three to five of the young embryos begin to develop (fig. 362). The nucleus of the embryo cell divides, but the formation of a wall between the two nuclei is delayed until a suspensor tube has been formed. The em-

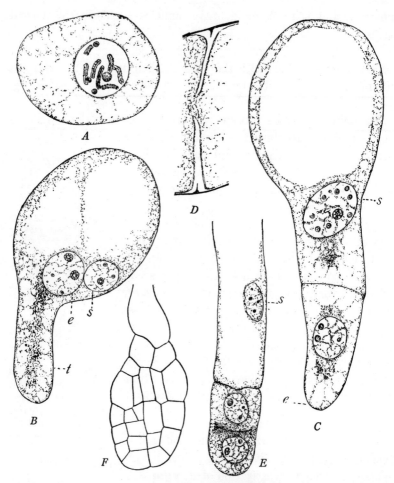

Fig. 364.—*Ephedra trifurca:* early development of embryo: *A*, unicellular embryo; *B*, the nucleus has divided; *C*, embryo and suspensor; *D*, mode of formation of wall separating embryo and suspensor; *E*, division of embryo initial cell; *F*, embryo and secondary suspensor; *A*, *B*, *C*, and *E*, ×500; *D*, ×1,900; *F*, ×250; *e*, embryo nucleus and embryo cell; *s*, suspensor nucleus and suspensor cell; *t*, suspensor tube.—After LAND.[339]

bryo nucleus passes into the tube, followed by the suspensor nucleus, and a wall is formed between them, beginning at the outside and progressing to the center (fig. 364 D).

The embryo cell then divides and the embryo develops. While three or four may reach the stage shown in fig. 364 C, the ripe seed scarcely ever contains more than one embryo. If conditions are favorable, there is no resting period: the seed germinates at once and the seedling becomes established the same season.

CHAPTER XVIII

CONIFEROPHYTES—GNETALES—WELWITSCHIA

The most bizarre of all gymnosperms, if not of all seed plants, is *Welwitschia* (fig. 365). It has been found only in the coastal region of Southwest Africa, north and south of Walvis Bay, with northern

FIG. 365.—*Welwitschia mirabilis:* large ovulate plant, about 20 miles east of Walvis Bay, on the Namib plateau.—From a photograph by PEARSON.

limit 14° S. latitude and the southern, near Hope Mine, 22° 85′ S. latitude, the only extra-tropical station yet reported. So the range, north and south, is about 700 miles. In some places plants have been observed within a few meters of the sea, and they are seldom found more than 20 miles inland. Dr. WELWITSCH discovered the plant in latitude 15° 50′ S. in August, 1860, and sent material to Sir JOSEPH HOOKER,[272] with the suggestion that it be called *Tumboa mirabilis;* but Dr. HOOKER, in his classical account, named it *Welwitschia*, in honor of the discoverer; and practically all of the important literature has treated it under that name, in spite of international congresses. At Dr. HOOKER'S request, the Brussels congress, in 1910, placed *Welwitschia* on the list of *nomina conservanda*, thus making the official name the same as that in the most important literature.

A couple of years ago a newspaper report, in typical newspaper reporter style, claimed that a new field of *Welwitschia*, some 2,500 acres in extent, had been discovered in the Kaokoveld, a vast tract of jungle along the northern frontier of Southwest Africa. PEARSON[446] mentions the Kaokoveld, not as a jungle, but as a desert littoral, extending some 300 miles south of Choricas, with *Welwitschia* in particularly large numbers. He says that the region is little known, and is exceptionally difficult for travelers, and that it is likely to contain still unreported *Welwitschia* localities.

On the coast of Damaraland, a few miles northeast of Cape Cross, another patch is reported, and is said to be reproducing abundantly from seed. Still another locality is reported, about 100 miles east of Cape Cross, exceptionally far inland.

While the genus extends over a considerable range, north and south, it occurs in scattered patches hard to reach. It is an extreme xerophyte, growing on rocky plains or on beds of streams, which are nearly always dry. In most of its habitats the rainfall does not exceed 1 inch a year; and near Walvis Bay, the best-known locality, the average rainfall for ten years was only about one-third of an inch. However, there are heavy dews.

Any botanist, contemplating a trip to *Welwitschia* localities, had better find out in advance how long it will take and how much it will cost.

THE SPOROPHYTE—VEGETATIVE

The plant has the shape of a turnip, or of an inverted cone, rarely more than 45 cm. above ground, and frequently almost covered. PEARSON[446] found plants with only a piece of the rim, with one leaf, above ground. The stem is elliptical, in top view, and the largest diameter may reach more than 4 feet, 1.2 meters. Below the surface of the ground the stem tapers abruptly, and an extremely long tap root extends downward to the water table; for, in such a dry country, little or no water is taken in, except by the root.

The plants sometimes grow in clusters of two or three, or even four or five, probably coming from seedlings of an older plant; and such plants, coming into contact, become fused together, so that points of union are indistinguishable. It might be called a natural graft.

The stem.—The tip of the young axis is convex, but growth at the apex soon stops, while it continues near the periphery, making the apex depressed (fig. 366).

HOOKER[272] called the part of the stem above the leaves the *crown*, and the part between the crown and root, the *stock*. The whole plant is covered by a periderm, which is thicker on the crown, and everywhere harder and darker than the parts beneath. On the crown of an old plant it may reach a thickness of 2 centimeters. On the root it is sometimes loose enough to peel off like the bark. It is thickest at the top of the periphery of the crown, and diminishes to less than half the maximum thickness at the bottom of the depression, and at that level on the outer surface. Its thickness diminishes rapidly near the leaf, and there is none at all in the leaf groove.

The periderm grows from a phellogen, or, more probably, from a series of phellogens.

Between the leaf and the stem apex the most striking feature of the crown is a series of ridges, which would be somewhat semicircular in longitudinal section, extending the whole breadth of the leaf, almost half of the entire circumference (fig. 366). The ridges are marked by pits and scars, showing the position of the inflorescences which have fallen off. The ridge is certainly not a leaf. It develops from the adaxial surface of the leaf groove, but only a too rigid morphology could make it a branch on that account. Whether there is any bract at the base of the inflorescence still remains to be determined.

Ridges develop on the stock, below the leaf groove, and are probably just as numerous as those above, but not so conspicuous. PEARSON found that they occasionally bore inflorescences. However, they are small and comparatively inconspicuous.

In old plants the crown sometimes becomes cracked radially, from the circumference almost to the center. Longitudinal cracks also

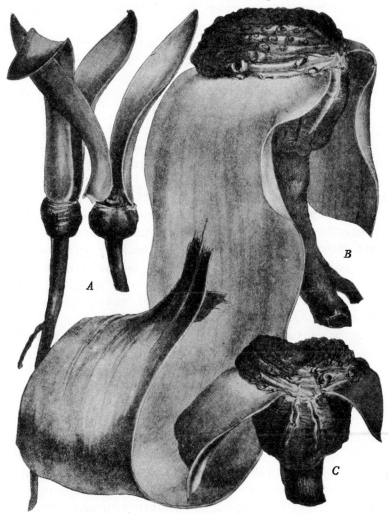

Fig. 366.—*Welwitschia mirabilis:* *A*, young plants with entire leaves; *B*, older plant with leaf splitting at tip; *C*, top view, showing depression between leaves; one-half natural size.—After Hooker.[272]

appear in the stock, reaching from the leaf groove almost to the root, but they are not so deep as those in the crown.

The leaf.—There are only two leaves, the original pair of leaves of the seedling persisting throughout the life of the plant, which is esti-mated at more than 100 years. The leaves are entire, until they reach a length of 15–20 cm., when they begin to split at the tip (figs. 365, 366, and 369). Still older leaves, lying on the ground and flap-ping in the wind, are split into ribbons. The leaves are thick and leathery and the venation is parallel; consequently, the splits are long and straight. The cells exposed by the splitting become suber-ized so quickly that the plant suffers no damage.

The leaves grow from the base of a groove, which extends nearly half-way around the top of the crown, and functions as a moist chamber. The base of the leaf remains permanently meristematic, while the tip keeps wearing and dying off. In old plants the leaves are about 2 meters long.

WELWITSCH did not believe that the plant had any leaves at all, but only two cotyledons, which persisted throughout the life of the plant. HOOKER's material was too old either to correct or confirm that view; but he adopted it tentatively, remarking that it would be easy to determine the facts as soon as anyone got a seedling. These have now been seen by many observers. There are two cotyledons and, at right angles to them, the two leaves (fig. 380).

The root.—As already indicated, the root is very long, and must go down to the water table. People have tried to dig it up, but, after digging for several feet, have concluded, probably correctly, that it kept on going down until it reached the water. *Dioon spinulosum,* growing on a rock, with scarcely any soil, had roots hanging down the vertical face of the rock for 12 m., when—still about 5 cm. in di-ameter—they disappeared in a crack in the rock. The roots of cy-cads, in regions as dry as the *Welwitschia* country, go down to the water table and keep the plants green, while the grass is yellow, or even scorched. The roots of *Welwitschia* must go down as deep.

Histology.—The most spectacular feature of the histology is the great display of spicular cells. They are usually branching, very thick walled, lignified outside and cellulose inside, and incrusted with crystals of calcium oxalate (fig. 367). These cells, branching and interlocking, are formed in the stem, root, and leaf, and they make free-hand sectioning impossible. One might as well try to cut sections of a thick Scotch plaid blanket as to try to cut a stem of *Welwitschia* without imbedding. The dry wood is light and not hard, but a treatment of 2 or 3 weeks in 20 per cent hydrofluoric acid should precede any attempt at imbedding. With such treatment Dr. LA DEMA M. LANGDON cut very satisfactory thin paraffin sections, 3 cm. square, including the leaf groove, of a plant 15 cm. in diameter.

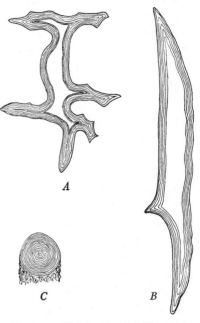

Except in the leaf, the arrangement of the bundles is irregular. Occasionally, in younger stems, and especially in roots, there is a zonation, doubtless representing growth-rings; but it is doubtful whether such rings are annual. It is more likely that they were formed some season when there was a heavy rain. We have already noted that the normal rainfall in the *Welwitschia* country is about 1 inch; but there have been floods.

FIG. 367.—*Welwitschia mirabilis:* spicular cells from the perianth of the staminate flower: *A*, branching cell, the branching represented in only one plane; *B*, a nearly straight cell; *C*, transverse section showing lumen nearly closed and surface incrusted by small crystals of calcium oxalate; ×225.— From COULTER and CHAMBERLAIN, *Morphology of Gymnosperms*[154] (University of Chicago Press).

A median longitudinal section of a stem, with a crown 15 cm. in diameter, shows a cup-shaped plate of vascular tissue about as thick as the leaf groove, and extending from one leaf groove to the other. This is the principal vascular system from which bundles extend upward to the crown and inflorescences, and downward to the stock and root.

Although the bundles are collateral, endarch, with a cambium, the xylem of any individual bundle has no recognizable growth-rings.

In such rings as have been mentioned, each ring has its xylem and phloem, as in polyxylic cycads. In transverse section, the bundles are long and narrow, with the xylem cells in rather straight rows for about twenty cells back from the tip, where they become very irregular in size and arrangement. It is in this irregular region that one might possibly find some record of seasonal changes. It is not easy to recognize growth-rings in woody monocots; in fact, it has been assumed that they do not exist; but they are easily seen in *Aloe bainesii*, not quite so easily in *A. ferox* and *Yucca filamentosa*. However, the rings are there, and they are seasonal.

In the branching inflorescences the bundles are more regular, the transverse section showing rows of xylem usually one cell wide, with thin-walled parenchyma between (fig. 368). The walls of the xylem elements are extremely thick, and, in a bundle like that shown in the figure, more than half of the cells have spiral or annular markings. The protoxylem tracheids of the lower part of the hypocotyl and root are reticulate, and in the leaf, spiral or annular; but all three kinds may be found together. In the secondary wood, the tracheids have bordered pits, often with reticulations between the pits.

The cells of the phloem are long and narrow, with prominent nuclei and sieve areas on the ends, and, also, to some extent, on the side walls.

Long, very thick-walled fibers occur singly or in twos or threes in the pith; they are abundant just outside the phloem, and throughout the cortex they form long, straight bundles, showing ten to twenty or more fibers in transverse section, with a single section showing more than 200 such strands.

Stomata are rare on the branches of the inflorescences. The outer walls of the epidermal cells are thick, with three easily recognizable layers; the outer, rather thin and, apparently, not cutinized; a middle layer, somewhat cutinized and containing very small crystals of calcium oxalate; and an inner layer of cellulose.

Dr. WELWITSCH, in a letter to Dr. HOOKER, said the plant exuded resin like a conifer. There is some exudation, not resin, but more or less mucilaginous, coming from the disorganization of spicular cells, or from lysigenous cavities.

The tough, leathery leaves reach a thickness of 2 mm. Stomata are more numerous on the upper side, but there are many on the lower side; PEARSON[446] counted 108–125 to the square millimeter on the upper side, and 87–96 on the lower.

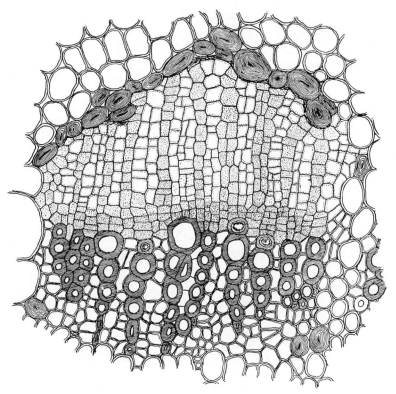

FIG. 368.—*Welwitschia mirabilis:* transverse section of flower stalk, next to the last branch below the cones. Only one or two cells of each xylem row are pitted: the rest have annular, spiral or reticulate marking; ×370.

In transverse section, the leaves show a single row of collateral endarch bundles, each surrounded by transfusion tissue, and with strands of thick-walled fibers between the transfusion tissue and the xylem. There is a strong palisade both above and below, with bundles of thick-walled fibers alternating with the palisade. Surrounding the bundles is a thin-walled parenchyma, and, everywhere, except in the bundles themselves, great numbers of spicular cells. A leaf could hardly be better adapted to desert conditions.

THE SPOROPHYTE—REPRODUCTIVE

Both staminate and ovulate strobili are compound, and are borne in great numbers on branching shoots arising from the rim, just above the leaf groove, although an occasional inflorescence is found below the groove.

FIG. 369.—*Welwitschia mirabilis:* part of the crown of an old plant, showing one of the much split leaves and about a dozen branched flower stalks with staminate strobili at the tips.—From a negative taken by PEARSON, January, 1907, on the Nahib Plateau near Walvis Bay, South Africa. The scalpel in the middle of the picture indicates the size.

THE STAMINATE STROBILUS

The stalk, bearing the strobili, branches more or less dichotomously, two, three, or even four times (fig. 369). In January, 1907, when PEARSON made the exposure from which this figure was made, pollen was beginning to shed from the lower stamens of the most advanced cones.

The cones are beautifully geometrical in the arrangement of their parts. CHURCH'S[132] drawing of this cone does not exaggerate the regularity (fig. 370). In the lower part of the middle cone the flowers are pushing out beyond their subtending bracts and, especially in the middle row, the six stamens can be seen on the rim of the staminate tube, with the funnel-shaped end of the integument in the center of each group of stamens.

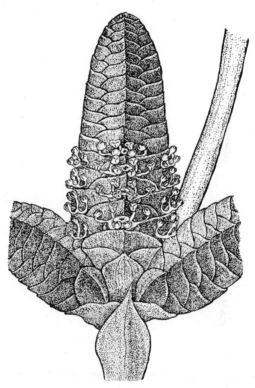

FIG. 370.—*Welwitschia mirabilis:* one complete strobilus and parts of two others: ×5.2.—After CHURCH.[132]

The arrangement of the flowers is strictly cyclic. Two opposite bracts alternate with two opposite bracts at right angles to them, throughout the entire cone, and in the axil of each bract, except a few at the base, is a single flower. More than any other feature, this flower has been called upon to link the Gnetales with the angiosperms. Its floral diagram might well pass for that of an angiosperm flower (fig. 371). The decussate arrangement of bracts in the cone is continued in the four parts of the perianth of the flower. There are six trilocular stamens, one opposite each of the smaller bracts of the perianth, and two opposite each of the larger ones. The stamens are borne on a tube, and below each stamen is a protuberance, which can be a nectary when one wishes to emphasize the resemblance to an angiosperm flower.

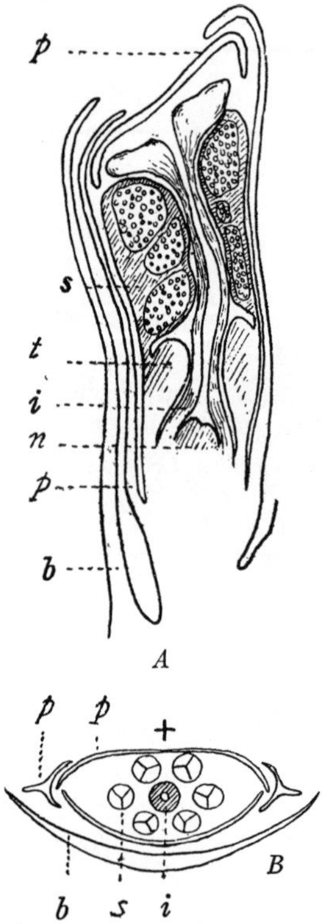

FIG. 371.—*Welwitschia mirabilis;* staminate flower: *A*, longitudinal section of flower with nearly ripe pollen: *p*, bract of perianth; *s*, trilocular anther; *t*, protuberance on inner face of stamen tube; *i*, inner integument; *n*, nucellus of sterile ovule; *b*, bract. *B*, floral diagram: lettering as in *A; t*, axis of cone.—From COULTER and CHAMBERLAIN, *Morphology of Gymnosperms*[154] (University of Chicago Press).

The most remarkable thing about this flower is that it is bisporangiate. In the center is an ovule, with a well-developed nucellus, but never with any sporogenous tissue. There is an inner integument, which elongates considerably, although it never reaches the extreme length of the inner integument of the ovulate flower. However, the integument of this sterile ovule has an expanded funnel-shaped tip, which has caused some to write about stigmas. Outside the inner integument is the perianth, consisting of four bracts: two at the ends, small and sharply angled at the midrib, and two at the sides, parallel with the large bract in the axil of which the flower stands. Thus, each flower is a strobilus in the axil of a bract, and the whole cone is a compound strobilus. The parts of the flower are in two's or four's. In those Cruciferae which have tetradynamous stamens, the positions of the two missing stamens are clearly marked by nectaries. In *Welwitschia* the two stamens at the ends, in the floral diagram, are generally larger than the other four, so that, if two stamens are really missing, they would have alternated with the two stamens opposite each of the larger bracts of the perianth. No traces of rudiments have been found, and since insect pollination has never been proved for any gymnosperm, nectaries would hardly be anticipated.

The anthers are trilocular, resembling somewhat the sporangia of *Psilotum*.

Floral development.—A longitudinal section of a strobilus, about 1 cm. in length, shows a very complete series of stages in floral development, from the beginning of the bract to nearly mature pollen.

The first protuberance to appear below the apex of the strobilus is a bract. The conical structure which soon appears in its axil is the beginning of the flower, and its apex finally develops into the sterile ovule. The first floral organs to appear are the bracts of the perianth, soon followed by the staminal rings. PEARSON says the two lateral stamens appear first, followed immediately by the other four, which grow faster, so that they all look alike; CHURCH says they appear simultaneously. If the two outer ones appear before the other four, the appearance in succession would favor the view that there are two cycles of stamens and that two of the outer set have been lost. There are six vascular strands in the staminal tube, one going to each filament. The fact that the two strands going to the two lateral stamens are inserted lower down than the other four favors PEARSON'S view.

As soon as the rudiments of the stamens can be recognized, the integument appears as a ring about the base of the nucellus. Therefore, the development is acropetal throughout. Later, there is a great development of both staminal tube and the integument. Some of the stages of floral development are shown in fig. 372.

In studying the floral development, one cone was sectioned in which the sterile ovule terminated the cone axis. The flower was large and the pollen mother-cells had rounded off, while the next flowers below were in an early sporogenous stage.

During the elongation of the staminal tube, the reduction division takes place in the pollen mother-cells, the second division following the first so closely that the young microspores have a typical tetrahedral arrangement.

THE OVULATE STROBILUS

The ovulate strobili, like the staminate, are borne in considerable numbers on branching flower stalks (fig. 373). The young strobili are green, but, at maturity, the color changes to a brilliant red—as brilliant as that of the Christmas *Poinsettia*.

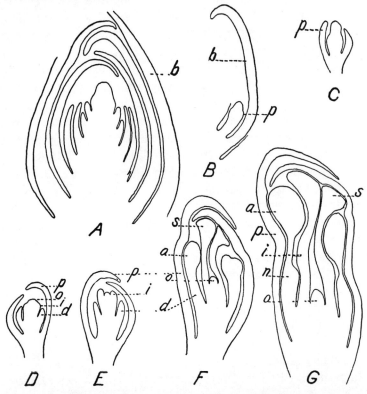

Fig. 372.—*Welwitschia mirabilis:* floral development: *A*, longitudinal section of tip of staminate cone; *B*, bract with young flower in its axil; *C-G*, older stages; *b*, bract; *p*, perianth; *o*, ovule; *i*, inner integument; *d*, staminal disk; *a*, anther; *s*, "stigma"; *n*, nectary-like swelling of staminal disk; all ×50.

While the strobilus is compound, its component strobili are much simpler than those of the male, for there is no trace of a bisporangiate condition.

A few of the lower bracts have no flowers in their axils, and the flowers in the axils of a few of the upper ones do not mature. Each strobilus produces from fifty to seventy flowers, many of which develop more or less; but the number of seeds which will germinate is

A

B

FIG. 373.—*Welwitschia mirabilis: A,* flower stalk with ovulate strobili of various ages, one-half natural size; *B,* tip of flower stalk with staminate strobili, natural size. This is not a satisfactory representation of the staminate strobili: fig. 370 is more accurate.—After HOOKER.[272]

comparatively small. We have planted about thirty seeds which seemed to have reached the maximum size and which appeared to be viable. These had not been taken from the plant more than 2

years earlier. Only three germinated, and only one lived more than
a year. The one shown in fig. 381, was nearly 4 years old when the
photograph was taken. PEARSON, in 1910, germinated seeds collected in 1907, and estimated to be at least one year old at that time.

In comparing the floral diagram with that of the staminate flower
it is evident that it not only lacks any stamens, but there are only

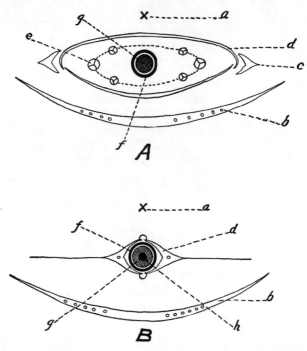

FIG. 374.—*Welwitschia mirabilis:* *A,* floral diagram of staminate flower: *x, a,* axis of
strobilus; *g,* nucellus of sterile ovule; *f,* integument; *e,* cycle of stamens; *d,* inner bract
of perianth; *c,* outer bract of perianth; *b,* bract in the axil of which the flower stands.
B, floral diagram of ovulate flower: *h,* embryo sac; other lettering as in *A.*—After PEAR-
SON.[446]

two bracts in the perianth. The two broad bracts, which are so conspicuous in the male, are lacking; but the two bracts at the ends,
which are comparatively inconspicuous in the male, are developed
into broad, thin wings (fig. 374).

The floral development throughout is acropetal. The perianth
first appears as a ring at the base of the nucellus, but soon grows

more rapidly at the sides, producing the broad, thin wings. While the wings are extremely thin, an abundance of wavy fibers makes them rather tough. They doubtless function in seed dispersal.

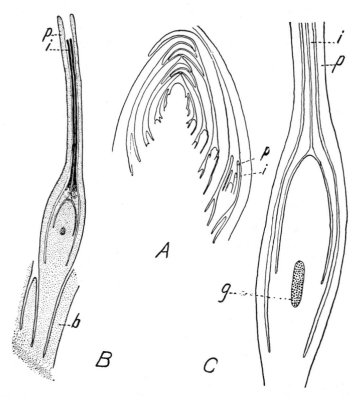

Fig. 375.—*Welwitschia mirabilis:* development of ovulate flower: *A*, longitudinal section of tip of ovulate cone: the lowest flower at the right shows the nucellus, with inner integument (*i*) and (*p*) outer integument (perianth); the flower next above shows the same structures in earlier condition; *B*, older ovulate flower, with the female gametophyte in an earlier free nuclear stage; *b*, bract; *C*, still later stage, with female gametophyte (*g*) in late free nuclear stage; *A*, ×20; *B* and *C*, ×50.

At first the perianth, which PEARSON prefers to regard as an outer integument, much exceeds the inner integument, but, as the time of pollination approaches, the inner integument grows rapidly until it protrudes beyond both the subtending bract and perianth (figs. 375 and 373).

There is a single archesporial cell which divides, forming a primary wall cell and megaspore mother-cell. There is no spongy tissue, either at this stage or later. The reduction divisions were not observed, but PEARSON concluded, from early stages in the female gametophyte, that the lower cell of the row develops in the usual way.

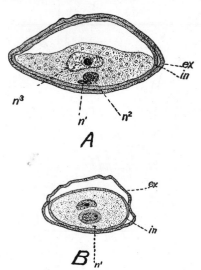

THE MALE GAMETOPHYTE

The microspore is the first cell of the male gametophyte. PEARSON[446] followed the development from the first appearance of the archesporial cells up to the shedding of the pollen. The two spore coats, exine and intine, are of about equal thickness and usually become more or less split apart (fig. 376).

The divisions which take place in the microspore before the stage shown in fig. 376, have not been described; but from PEARSON'S figures and description it is evident that the first division forms

FIG. 376.—*Welwitschia mirabilis: A*, three-nucleate stage of pollen grain, ×940; *B*, shedding stage, ×600: *ex*, exine; *in*, intine; *n^1*, *n^2*, and *n^3* interpreted respectively as prothallial, generative, and tube nuclei. —After PEARSON.[446]

a prothallial nucleus (PEARSON says there is certainly no prothallial cell) and an antheridium initial, and the antheridium initial, at its first division, produces a tube cell and a generative cell.

In this three-nucleate stage the pollen grain reaches the ovule. The pollination drop, characteristic of gymnosperms, appears at the tip of the projecting micropylar tube, which is the greatly prolonged inner integument.

HOOKER[272] suspected that *Welwitschia* was insect pollinated; and BAINES found a parasitic insect, *Odontopus expunctulatus*, on plants at Haikamchab. PEARSON not only found the insect on both male and female plants, but found pollen on its legs and abdomen. He concluded that it would be impossible for it to crawl over ovulate cones without effecting pollination. But whether the insect is the principal agent in pollination may still be doubtful. It is very probable that in most wind-pollinated plants, even in gymnosperms, pollen may occasionally reach the pollination drop on the stigma through the agency of insects.

Reaching the pollination drop in the three-nucleate stage, the pollen is drawn down through the long micropyle to the nucellus of the ovule. The pollen tube may begin to develop, even in the micropyle. There is no pore, but the exine splits longitudinally throughout the entire length.

In the young pollen tube the generative cell and the tube nucleus enlarge, and the prothallial nucleus can no longer be distinguished. There is no stalk cell. The nucleus of the generative cell soon divides, forming the two sperm nuclei, which lie in a common mass of protoplasm, with no wall between them.

Except for the prothallial nucleus, this is a typical angiosperm history, and even the prothallial cell occurs sporadically in angiosperms.

THE FEMALE GAMETOPHYTE

The megaspore is the first cell of the female gametophyte. The divisions of the megaspore mother-cell have not been worked out, and no chromosome counts have been made anywhere; but PEARSON's figures show that the archesporium was doubtless hypodermal and that the lowest megaspore of a row germinates. He figures the mature megaspore, the four-nucleate stage of the female gametophyte, and later free nucleate stages. The nuclear divisions are doubtless simultaneous, for simultaneous divisions were observed at two stages. A striking feature of the development of this gametophyte is that no large central vacuole is formed, the nuclei being equally distributed throughout, up to what would be the 1,024 nuclear stage, if all divisions were simultaneous and all nuclei divided (fig. 377). Actual calculation placed the number between 1,015 and 1,360.

At the close of the free nuclear period, walls come in irregularly, often inclosing a dozen nuclei in one cell. In this condition, there are occasional nuclear divisions, but nuclear fusions are the rule and they continue, sometimes giving the impression of amitotic divisions, until nearly all of the cells become uninucleate (fig. 377).

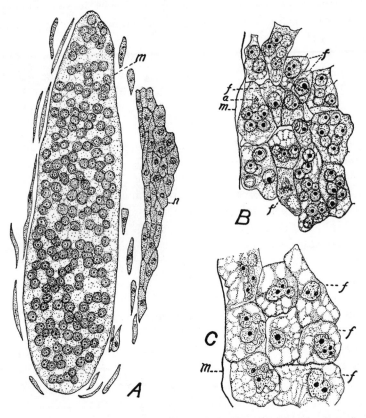

FIG. 377.—*Welwitschia mirabilis: A*, late free-nuclear stage of female gametophyte: *n*, cell of nucellus; *m*, megaspore membrane; *B*, early cellular stage, with most of the cells still multinuclear; at *f*, nuclear fusions have taken place until the cells are uninuclear; *f*, at bottom, shows that cells may divide after the fusions; *a*, in the middle cell at the left, shows that nuclei may divide before fusion; *C*, four of the cells, *f*, have become uninuclear and nuclear fusions are advancing in the rest, *m; A*, ×305[439]; *B* and *C*, ×350.[446]—After PEARSON.

The cells of the lower part of the gametophyte contain more nuclei than those in the micropylar end, the former often containing a dozen, while the latter contain two or three, or sometimes half a dozen. Fusions are completed earlier in the micropylar region, but finally nearly all of the cells become uninucleate. In their further development, the two regions continue to be different.

A remarkable feature in the development of this gametophyte is that there are no archegonia. Cells which might be regarded as archegonial initials, elongate, break through the megaspore membrane, and grow up into the nucellus, looking like pollen tubes, and growing up into the nucellus just as pollen tubes grow down. They are called "prothallial tubes." They grow about half-way through the nucellus, where they meet the pollen tubes coming down. Nuclear details have not been worked out, but if the nucleus in a prothallial tube has been formed by the fusion of several nuclei, fertilization and chromosome numbers would present an interesting problem.

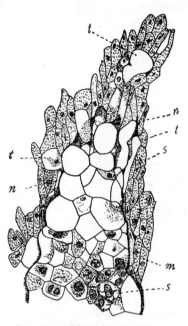

FIG. 378.—*Welwitschia mirabilis:* upper part of nucellus with prothallial tubes going up to meet the pollen tubes which will be coming down: *t*, prothallial tubes; *s*, sterile cells of upper region of female gametophyte; *n*, nucellus; *m*, megaspore membrane; ×140.—After PEARSON.[439]

After the cells in the lower part of the gametophyte have become uninucleate through the extensive nuclear fusions, mitosis, with the formation of cell walls, is resumed. The chromosome numbers, at first very large, become smaller as divisions continue, and the cells also become smaller. This behavior stops before fertilization, but is resumed as soon as fertilization has taken place, a feature quite characteristic of angiosperms.

While the gametophyte is characterized by the x number of chromosomes, and the sporophyte is characterized by $2x$ chromosomes, we should still regard the prothallium of *Welwitschia* as gametophyte in which the normal x number of chromosomes has been modified by extensive nuclear fusions. We see no reason for adopting the term "trophophyte," which has been proposed.

Fertilization.—The pollen tubes growing down into the nucellus and the prothallial tubes growing up into it meet, and fertilization takes place (fig. 378). A pollen tube and a prothallial tube come into contact, the tube walls at the point of contact become dissolved, and

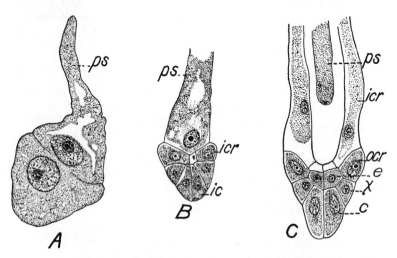

Fig. 379.—*Welwitschia mirabilis:* early embryogeny: *A*, first division of zygote; *ps*, primary suspensor cell and, below it, the cell from which the embryo is to develop; *B*, later stage, with inner cortical ring (*icr*) and terminal initial cells (*ic*); *C*, still later stage; *ps*, primary suspensor; *icr*, cells of inner cortical ring; *ocr*, cells of outer cortical ring; the embryonic plate (*e*), ring (*x*), and cap (*c*), are each represented in section by two cells; *A*, ×700; *B* and *C*, ×305.—After PEARSON.[446]

the nucleus of the prothallial tube passes into the pollen tube, where it fuses with one of the sperm nuclei. PEARSON found no independence of the chromatin of the gametes, as it had already been described for *Pinus* and *Juniperus*, but found a complete fusion, with a resting nucleus, before any division of the zygote. Nearly all of the cytoplasm is contributed by the pollen tube. The zygote nucleus passes from the pollen tube into the prothallial tube on its way down to the endosperm.

Embryo.—The zygote elongates and its nucleus divides. As in *Ephedra*, the wall begins to form at the periphery and closes in to-

ard the center. The wall is complete before another mitosis takes
lace, so there is no free nuclear stage (fig. 379).

FIG. 380.—*Welwitschia mirabilis:* seedling in greenhouse at the University of Chi-
go.

The upper cell elongates and becomes the primary suspensor:
e embryo is derived from the lower cell. The primary suspensor
ll elongates but does not divide. The inner cortical ring cells
ongate immensely (compare *icr* in *B* and *C* of fig. 379), sur-
unding the primary suspensor cell. The outer cortical ring cells

then behave like the inner cortical ring cells, elongating and surrounding the inner cortical ring cells, so that a transverse section shows the primary suspensor in the middle, surrounded by two cortical rings, the inner consisting of eight cells and the outer of sixteen. Later, a third ring of cortical cells (x in fig. 379 C) is cut off and is added to the suspensor. And finally, even a fourth ring is cut off and is added to the suspensor.

Fig. 381.—*Welwitschia mirabilis:* same seedling as that in fig. 380, two years later

The cells (C) undergo division, forming a cap, which is cast off later, as in *Cephalotaxus*.

The stem, leaves, cotyledons and root are formed from the four cells of the plate (e, in C of fig. 379).

As the embryo grows down into the endosperm, the suspensor becomes coiled and twisted in typical gymnosperm fashion and, after the cap has been cast off, the outer cells become dermatogen, and the meristems of the root and shoot are organized.

The seedling.—The seedling has two cotyledons and two leaves (fig. 380). The cotyledons persist for two or three years and then fall off: the two leaves, at right angles to the cotyledons, persist throughout the life of the plant. The cotyledons and leaves are, at first, erect; but, before the end of the first year, the cotyledons begin to droop and the leaves become horizontal (fig. 381).

In the axil of each cotyledon a bud appears and becomes flatter and broader until the two buds meet, forming a continuous plate, under which the stem apex, now arrested, is buried. Meanwhile, the tissues above and below the base of the leaves grow so that the leaf bases become buried in a deepening groove.

At the lower part of the hypocotyl, a lateral outgrowth, called the feeder, acts as a haustorium until the food supply of the seed is exhausted.

The times for various stages are given by PEARSON as follows: most of the stages in the development of both male and female gametophytes can be secured in January. In 1904, at Haikamchab, there was little fertilization before the end of the second week in January. At Welwitsch, in 1907, the last week in January, fertilization and proembryos were abundant; and in March, 1909, embryos were more advanced. At Haikamchab on May 10, 1861, BAINES collected ripe seeds. So the intraseminal growth of the embryo is less than 4 months.

CHAPTER XIX

CONIFEROPHYTES—GNETALES—GNETUM

The final genus in the gymnosperm phylum is *Gnetum*—in general appearance almost as much out of place in this assemblage as *Welwitschia*, for most of its more than thirty species are lianas. Only a few are trees or shrubs.

In striking contrast with *Ephedra* and *Welwitschia*, both extreme xerophytes confined to desert habitats, *Gnetum* belongs to the luxuriant tropics, and most of its species, when not in fruit, might be mistaken for dicotyls.

Tropical Asia and the islands between Asia and Australia have nineteen of the thirty-four species given by PEARSON.[446] The two African species are north of the *Welwitschia* country, in Cameroons and Angola. Of the twelve American species, three are in the Guineas, along the northern coast of South America, seven belong to the Amazon country of Brazil, one to Ecuador, and one to the West Indies. There are none in North America, Australia, or Europe.

No species have yet been found common to both Western and Eastern hemispheres, but some in India and the islands between India and Australia are found on both sides of the Equator.

THE SPOROPHYTE—VEGETATIVE

The lianas, which are characteristic of the genus, twine, climb, or trail over other vegetation, reaching the tops of the tallest trees, with rarely any leaves for the first 40 or 50 feet. *Gnetum gnemon*, in the Moluccas, and widely cultivated, is a tree, and since it is the best-known species, one is likely to picture the tree habit when one thinks of *Gnetum*. A species in New Guinea, *G. costatum*, also has the tree habit; and there are also a few shrubs.

The leaf.—The large, oval, entire leaves, with netted veins, make the plants look like dicotyls. There are branches of limited and unlimited growth, but the difference between the two kinds is not so extreme as in *Pinus* or *Ginkgo*, and in *Gnetum gnemon* the two kinds look much alike. In climbing species, leaves are borne only on shoots of limited growth. On the long shoots the leaves are usually reduced to scales. All leaves are opposite and decussate. There is a short petiole, with no stipules, and the leaves vary so much in size and shape that such characters are of little value in taxonomy; but they are so typically dicotyledonous in appearance that a botanist, not familiar with *Gnetum*, would guess the plant to be a dicotyl (fig. 382). The plant shown in the figure was raised from a seed at the University of Chicago. When it was about 20 years old and 4 inches in diameter, it was moved from the old greenhouse to the new, where it survived only a few months. A cutting is still alive and is about 2 inches in diameter. Many cuttings were made, but only two were successful. However, as in many conifers, there is occasional vegetative propagation. One season, several leaves from the plant already mentioned produced buds at the margins,

FIG. 382.—*Gnetum gnemon:* young plant raised from seed at the University of Chicago. The plant is about two years old.— From COULTER and CHAMBERLAIN, *Morphology of Gymnosperms*[154] (University of Chicago Press).

as in *Bryophyllum*. Some of the buds had a couple of leaves, but none developed beyond this stage. A similar case was noted at the botanical garden at Utrecht.

The histological structures are so advanced that they are responsible for an undue amount of theorizing.

The stem.—A transverse section of a young stem of *Gnetum gnemon* shows an endarch siphonostele, with strong bundles, large rays, and a cortex, partly of thin-walled parenchyma and partly of suberized fibers, and with a zone of spicular cells just outside the phloem (fig. 383).

The protoxylem is very scanty, and the markings are spiral. Vessels in the secondary wood are of all sizes, from that of ordinary tracheids up to those with four or five times that diameter. The pitting is multiseriate and extends all the way around and on the end walls, which soon break down, so that there are continuous tubes, as in angiosperms.

The end walls of the cells, which are to form vessels, may be quite oblique or perfectly transverse. There is a single perforation, formed by the enlargement or fusion of bordered pits and the disappearance of the middle lamella—a more advanced type than that of *Ephedra*, where the end walls have several perforations, and more like that of angiosperms, which have a single perforation. It should be noted that the mode of formation of the more or less freely open tube of *Gnetum* is not like that in the angiosperms, where the single large perforation of the lower dicotyls has been developed from a scalariform type. THOMPSON[631] regards this difference in the development of the vessels as so fundamental that vessels in the secondary wood should not be regarded as any evidence in favor of the theory that angiosperms have come from Gnetales, or that the two have had a common ancestor.

In many angiosperms the end walls break down while still very thin, and without any connection with pitting, and even in some (in which secondary thickening has begun), the breaking-down does not seem to depend upon pits.

The phloem consists of very uniform cells. There are no companion cells in *Gnetum gnemon*, although such cells occur in *G. latifolium* and *G. scandens*. However, these companion cells are not cut off from a mother-cell, as in angiosperms, but arise independently from the cambium. Here, again, the angiosperm feature, the companion cell, should not be urged as evidence in favor of relationship, be-

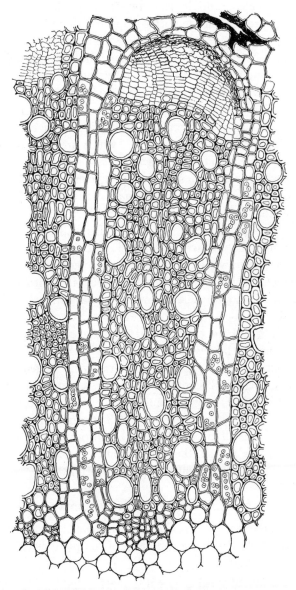

FIG. 383.—*Gnetum gnemon:* transverse section of bundle of young stem; ✕175

cause the mode of origin is different. Physiologically, the companion cells are the same in both groups, but there is no phylogenetic connection.

The root.—The root of *Gnetum gnemon* is diarch, with an extremely scanty amount of primary xylem, only a single row of cells with occasionally a couple of cells in the protoxylem lying side by side (fig. 384). The vessels are of various sizes and are much larger than those of the stem, with several times as great a diameter, as may be seen by comparing figs. 383 and 385, which are both from *Gnetum gnemon*, and drawn to the same scale. Vessels of lianas are likely to be larger. The phloem, as in the stem, consists of very uniform cells and, just beyond it, are numerous fibers (fig. 385). The rays are broad and thin walled, and are packed with starch, in striking contrast with those of the stem, which are thick walled and pitted. The difference in structure accounts for the fact that the wood of the stem is very hard, while that of the root is very soft.

The tracheids have uniseriate bordered pits, with conspicuous bars of SANIO (fig. 386). The pits of the vessels are smaller and multiseriate, with few bars of SANIO, or even none at all.

The breaking of the end walls of the large cells to form the continuous lumen of the vessels is easily seen in the root (fig. 387). At first, the border of the large perforation may be ragged, but it soon becomes smooth, and sometimes the passage may be even more complete than that shown in the figure.

On the whole, *Gnetum*, in its outward appearance and in its internal structure, has almost reached the angiosperm level; and, since it has no record as a fossil, the temptation to connect it in some way with the angiosperms has often been irresistible.

THE SPOROPHYTE—REPRODUCTIVE

Like the other two genera, *Gnetum* is dioecious; but also, like them, it shows very clearly that a condition of complete dioecism has not yet been attained.

The staminate strobilus.—The staminate strobilus is a long slender axis, bearing numerous decussate pairs of bracts, which are concrescent throughout practically their whole length, making them

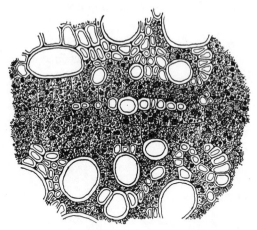

Fig. 384.—*Gnetum gnemon:* transverse section of central part of a root 6 mm. in diameter, showing a single row of primary xylem cells, with protoxylem two cells wide at the extreme tips; ×175.

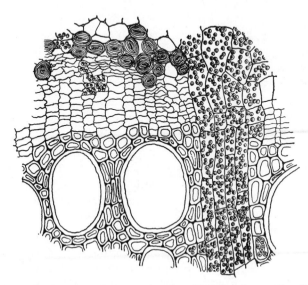

Fig. 385.—*Gnetum gnemon:* transverse section of peripheral part of bundle of root; ×175.

look like cups. In their axils, all the way around the axis, the staminate flowers are borne.

As in *Welwitschia*, ovulate flowers are associated with the staminate, and the ovules develop much farther, producing megaspores, which sometimes germinate. Such gametophytes disorganize in early free nuclear stages; occasionally they develop farther and even produce good seeds. In *Welwitschia*, the sterile ovules, although reaching the size at which the archesporium appears in functional ovules, show no trace of the beginning of sporogenous tissue. The

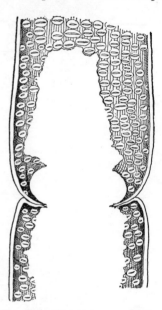

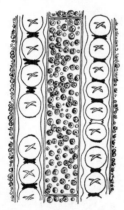

FIG. 386.—*Gnetum gnemon:* longitudinal section of tracheids and parenchyma of root, showing bars of SANIO; ×375.

FIG. 387.—*Gnetum gnemon:* longitudinal section of two cells of root, showing perforation which makes the lumen continuous; ×375.

staminate flower has a sterile ovule, and thus is bisporangiate. In *Gnetum*, the association is not so close, for there are no bisporangiate flowers—only ovules and stamens in the axil of the same bract (figs. 388). If the sterile ovule is only slightly developed, it does not appear to inhibit the development of the microsporangia near it; but when the ovule reaches such an advanced stage as that shown in fig. 388 C, the microsporangia near it abort, and only those lower down produce good pollen. In very rare cases, stamens have been found in ovulate strobili.

In the two African species, *Gnetum africanum* and *G. buchhol-zianum*, the staminate strobilus has no trace of ovulate flowers.

The staminate flower consists of a stalk with two anthers at the top and a sheathing perianth at the base. The anthers are uni-

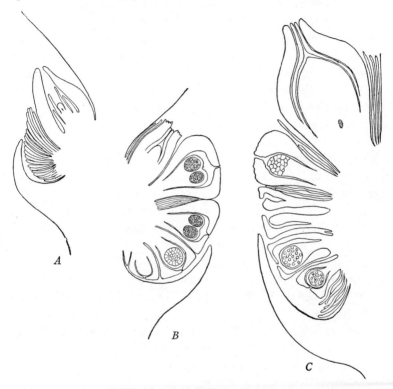

FIG. 388.—*Gnetum gnemon:* longitudinal sections with flowers in axils of bracts: *A*, ovule in ovulate strobilus, showing two integuments and perianth; *B*, staminate stro-bilus, showing sterile ovule with inner integument and perianth; oldest sporangia at the top; *C*, staminate strobilus with functional sporangia at the bottom; sporangia near the large ovule, in which the gametophyte has reached the free nuclear stage, are abortive; ✕23.—From COULTER and CHAMBERLAIN, *Morphology of Gymnosperms*[154] (University of Chicago Press).

locular. In the development of the microsporangium, the tapetum is formed from the sporogenous tissue and not from the wall cells. There is no endothecium. As the microsporangium matures, all cells between the spores and the epidermis break down, and the epidermis, becoming hard, is the outer protecting layer. This condition is universal in Pteridophytes and in the Carboniferous gymnosperms.

The ovulate strobilus.—The ovulate strobilus has received more attention than the staminate, doubtless because it can be collected during several months and is quite conspicuous for some time before the seeds ripen and fall off (fig. 389). The figure shows some ovulate strobili of the plant of *Gnetum gnemon* (fig. 382) grown at the University of Chicago. At this time the plant was about 20 years old and this was the first and only time it ever produced strobili. The characteristic leaves, bearing such a close resemblance to dicotyls, are also well shown in this figure.

The axis of the ovulate strobilus in *Gnetum gnemon* has a pair of opposite sheathing bracts at the base, followed by five or six whorls of ovules, with five to seven ovules in a whorl (fig. 390). Sometimes there is a terminal ovule. Although there are so many ovules, most of which reach the pollination stage, and even the fertilization stage, only a few, perhaps from two to five, complete the entire development and become capable of germination.

In the development of the strobilus the pairs of concrescent bracts, usually about seven, forming a series of cups, are first to appear, followed by the nucelli of the ovules in a ring in the axils of the bracts (fig. 391).

Ovules in ovulate strobili have two integuments and a perianth, while those in the staminate strobili lack the outer integument. In the latter case, a rudiment of the outer integument appears, but soon aborts. In normal ovules the order of appearance is perianth, outer integument, inner integument. As in the other two genera, the inner integument becomes prolonged into the characteristic micropylar tube. In the mature seed it becomes reduced to a thin, papery layer. The outer integument finally becomes differentiated into an outer fleshy layer and an inner stony layer, so that the seed has three seed coats, as in the cycads, a stony layer in the middle, with a fleshy layer outside, and a thin, dry, membranous layer inside. These three layers are very common in gymnosperms, and have led some into curious interpretations. The three layers appear in typical form in the cycads, where it is said that the integument is differenti-

FIG. 389.—*Gnetum gnemon:* ovulate strobili on the plant shown in fig. 382. The plant, at this time, was about 15 feet high and had been topped twice to keep its height within the capacity of the old greenhouse.—From a negative by Dr. CHING YUEH CHANG.

ated into a stony layer in the middle, with a fleshy layer on each side. Such a statement involves the assumption that the nucellus and integument are united, except at the "free" part of the nucellus, an assumption originating from the fact that some very ancient seeds have the integument and nucellus free from each other throughout. In *Gnetum*, the outer integument becomes differentiated into an

Fig. 390.—*Gnetum gnemon:* Typical ovulate strobili collected in the Philippines. Three young strobili, like the one from which fig. 388 was made, are shown at the left. The others show ovules in various stages of development; about natural size.—From a negative by Dr. W. J. G. Land.

inner stony layer and an outer fleshy layer. In an attempt to unify, some have regarded the outer integument as having been differentiated from the inner during phylogeny. They were probably never more united during phylogeny than they are now in ontogeny. In *Lyginopteris*, the outer layer of the integument becomes stony, while the cupule serves as an outer fleshy layer. Physiologically, the three layers are efficient during the development of the seed and, at maturity, they are protective. Their function is as uniform as that of tendrils, and their homology may be as various.

The archesporium is hypodermal, dividing into a primary sporog-

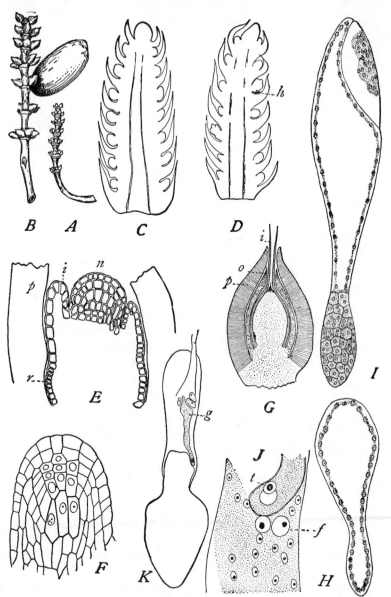

FIG. 391.—*Gnetum gnemon:* *A*, young ovulate strobilus; *B*, older strobilus with one mature seed; *C* and *D*, sections of young strobili; *h*, hairs; *E*, young ovule; *n*, nucellus; *i*, inner integument; *r*, rudimentary outer integument; *p*, perianth; *F*, nucellus with three megaspore mother-cells; *G*, advanced ovulate flower; *i*, inner integument; *o*, outer integument; *p*, perianth; *H*, free nuclear stage of female gametophyte; *I*, female gametophyte with free nuclei above and cellular tissue below; a second gametophyte is shown at the upper right; *J*, fertilization; *t*, pollen tube; *f*, two eggs; and there are several free nuclei of the gametophyte; *K*, late embryo sac; *g*, zygote; *C*, ×24; *D*, ×45; *G*, ×33; *I*, ×50; *J*, ×340; *K*, ×50.—After LOTSY,[371] except *F*, which is after STRASBURGER.[603]

enous cell, which is also the megaspore mother-cell, and a primary wall cell, which builds up an extensive tissue above the mother-cell. Often, there may be more than a single sporogenous cell.[371]

The megaspore mother-cell produces four megaspores, of which more than one may germinate.[371] COULTER found that twelve and twenty-four are the x and $2x$ numbers of chromosomes in *Gnetum gnemon*.[148]

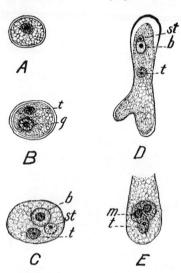

FIG. 392.—*Gnetum:* male gametophyte: *A*, young microspore: *B*, a little older; *t*, tube nucleus; *g*, generative cell: *C*, *t*, tube nucleus; *b*, body cell; *st*, stalk nucleus; *D*, end of pollen tube; *st*, stalk nucleus; *b*, body cell; *t*, tube nucleus: *E*, end of pollen tube, later stage; *t*, tube nucleus; *m*, sperms. *A-C*, *Gnetum gnemon*, ×1,200; *D*, *E*, *G*, sp.; *D*, ×550; *E*, ×800.—After THOMPSON.[630]

THE MALE GAMETOPHYTE

The microspore is the first cell of the male gametophyte. The microspore of *Gnetum gnemon*, up to the shedding stage, is shown in *A*, *B*, and *C* of fig. 392. In this series, by THOMPSON,[630] there does not seem to be any prothallial cell, the first division giving rise to a tube nucleus and a generative nucleus, the latter soon dividing to form a stalk nucleus and a body nucleus. No cell walls are either figured or described; but in *Gnetum* sp., in *D* and *E* of the same figure, a body cell is organized.

In the complete elimination of even a single prothallial cell, *Gnetum* has reached the angiosperm condition, where there are no prothallial cells, except in extremely rare cases, where they are regarded as reversions.

At the first division of the microspore of *G. africanum*, PEARSON found a very delicate wall, which soon disappeared, and no wall was formed at the second division.

It is easy to follow the growth of the pollen tube, because the pollen grains frequently germinate while still in the micropylar tube. The exine is cast off, and the intine grows into a tube, beginning near the tube nucleus. By this time, a definite body cell has been organized about the body nucleus, and, with the tube nucleus, it passes into the pollen tube, while the stalk nucleus remains behind. PEARSON does not regard this nucleus as a stalk nucleus, but as prothallial. Some of the pollen grains reach the nucellus directly and germinate there. Germination at a distance from the nucellus adds another angiosperm feature to the growing list.

The nucleus of the body cell divides as the pollen tube grows down into the nucellus, but no wall is formed between the two nuclei. They may differ somewhat in size, and THOMPSON[630] thinks it probable that only the larger one functions, and that the other disorganizes.

THE FEMALE GAMETOPHYTE

The megaspore is the first cell of the female gametophyte. As in all other gymnosperms, its germination begins with a series of free nuclear divisions, but, unlike all other gymnosperms, the gametophyte—at least the micropylar end of it—remains in the free nuclear stage, up to the time of fertilization (fig. 393). There has been some difference of opinion regarding the lower part of the gametophyte. LOTSY[371] described a tissue which he interpreted as homologous with the antipodal cells of angiosperms, only more extensive. COULTER[148] thought that LOTSY[371] had mistaken the extensive nutritive tissue at the base of the gametophyte, undoubtedly a sporophytic tissue, for a part of the gametophyte itself. A study of the figures and descriptions of both authors, and also the later work of THOMPSON,[630] together with the re-examination of COULTER'S material, make it certain that there is a considerable amount of cellular tissue at the base of the gametophyte and definitely within the megaspore membrane. THOMPSON shows very clearly the origin of this tissue, which develops from the free nuclear condition, just as in *Welwitschia* (fig. 394). The first walls are formed irregularly, without any connection with the mitotic figures, and inclose several nuclei in each cell. The nuclei, which are rather small, then begin to fuse, and the cells become uninucleate, with one large nucleus in each cell. Consequently, the tissue corresponds to the antipodal cells of angiosperms, which, in many cases, are quite numerous before fertilization. This tissue is shown in Lotsy's figure (391) and in Thompson's figure (395 C). Coulter's figure (393) shows too young a stage to have the antipodal tissue organized. A later stage which, unfortunately, his material did not contain, would have shown antipodal tissue and the pavement tissue.

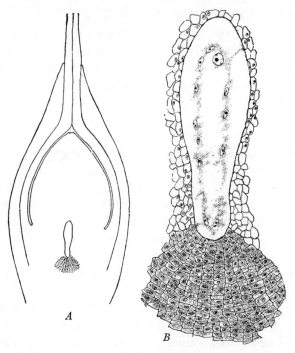

Fig. 393.—*Gnetum gnemon:* *A*, ovule showing position of female gametophyte and pavement tissue; *B*, detail of female gametophyte in free nuclear stage, with the nutritive pavement tissue beneath; *A*, ×54; *B*, ×300.—After Coulter.[148]

Qualitatively, this gametophyte has nearly reached the angiosperm level. Although the free nuclear stage is much more extensive than in any angiosperm, it is still in this stage at the time of fertilization. There is no archegonium, or even the archegonium initial, which is still retained in *Welwitschia*. Gnetum has reached the final stage in the reduction of the archegonium. Phylogenetically, neck cells and ventral canal cells are gametes and, in the bryophytes, may possibly function as such. In the heterosporous pteridophytes the reduction has proceeded until there is only one neck canal cell. There is no neck canal cell in known gymnosperms, and many gymnosperms have lost the wall between the ventral canal nucleus and that of the egg. In *Torreya* it is very doubtful whether there is even a mitosis: the central cell becomes the egg. *Welwitschia*, going a step farther, has lost the mitosis which gives rise to the neck cell and central cell, so that the archegonium initially functions as an egg. In *Gnetum* there is not even an archegonium initial: a free nucleus, organizing some cytoplasm about itself, functions directly as an egg.

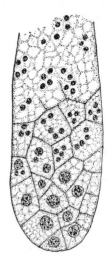

Without such a series in mind, some have tried to homologize the angiosperm synergids with various lost structures of the archegonium. There is no relation. The synergids are new advanced structures, having no connection with gymnosperm archegonia.

After fertilization the rest of the gametophyte becomes cellular. As yet, there is no evidence that any of the tissue has come from a fusion with a male nucleus, or that a fertilized egg has developed "endosperm" instead of an embryo. It used to be said that the endosperm of gymnosperms is formed before fertilization, while that of angiosperms was formed after fertilization. In *Gnetum* most of this tissue is formed

Fig. 394.—*Gnetum gnemon:* development of tissue at the base of the female gametophyte; ×300.—After Thompson.[630]

after fertilization, and, in this respect, follows the angiosperm method, although no "double fertilization," like that described by Herzfeld for *Ephedra*, has been reported.

FERTILIZATION AND EMBRYOGENY

The most interesting feature about fertilization in *Gnetum* is that it occurs while the female gametophyte is still in the free nuclear stage. One or more eggs are organized from the free nuclei, looking like the eggs of angiosperms. The pollen tubes, some of which begin their development in the micropylar tube, at some distance from the nucellus, grow through the nucellus and reach the egg. The two sperm nuclei are formed from the body cell, while the tube is still only about half-way through the nucellus. According to THOMP-SON,[630] the two sperm nuclei differ somewhat in size, and the smaller one may disorganize before the sperms are discharged. LOTSY[371]

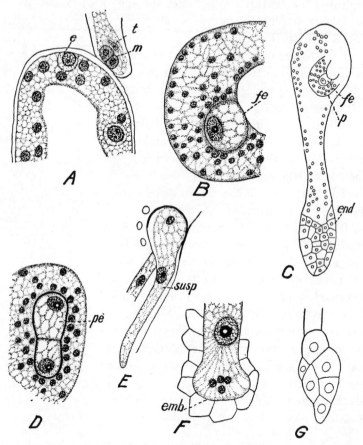

FIG. 395.—*Gnetum: A-E, G. gnemon; F, G, G. moluccense: A,* upper part of female gametophyte in free nuclear condition, with two eggs (*e*), and pollen tube with tube nucleus (*t*) and two sperm nuclei (*m*); *B,* fertilized egg (*fe*) surrounded by free nuclei; *C,* topographic sketch showing position of *B; fe,* fertilized egg; *p,* mass of protoplasm surrounding the egg; *end,* cellular part of the female gametophyte; *D,* two cells (proembryo, *pe*) resulting from first division of fertilized egg; *E,* suspensor developing from proembryo cell; *F,* end of suspensor with four nuclei which will give rise to the embryo, *emb; G,* young embryo. *A, B,* ×400; *C,* ×100; *D, E,* ×300; *F,* ×200; *G,* ×50.— After THOMPSON.[630]

described sperm nuclei of equal size, and believed that both were functional, since fertilized eggs were usually found in pairs. LOTSY believed that the number of pollen tubes which had entered an egg could be determined by counting the number of pairs of zygotes.

THOMPSON'S figure (395 D) is described as a two-celled proembryo. It looks much like a pair of zygotes, as described by LOTSY. If it is a two-celled embryo, as seems likely, there is no free nuclear stage in the embryogeny, and *Gnetum*, like *Sequoia*, has reached the angiosperm level in another feature of its development.

Whether the figure represents a two-celled proembryo or a pair of zygotes, the next stage is the development of a tube, the suspensor, from each of the two cells (fig. 395 E). The nucleus divides, and, of the resulting nuclei, the one in advance undergoes free nuclear division, producing four nuclei, from which the embryo is organized (fig. 395 F, G). The other nucleus does not divide.

It is very desirable that fertilization and embryogeny be worked out in cytological detail, not only in *Gnetum*, but in the other two genera. Investigators familiar with other gymnosperms may have wondered why LOTSY, PEARSON, and THOMPSON, with material at hand, left some features undecided; but the reason is evident when one attempts to make preparations, especially of the male gametophytes of *Welwitschia* and *Gnetum*. However, the problems can be solved if fresh material is fixed in very small pieces, for these two genera are no more difficult than *Ephedra*, in which LAND gave a very complete account of spermatogenesis.

The intermediate and later stages in the embryogeny are still to be described.

CAYTONIALES

At this time no account of the gymnosperms would be quite complete without some mention of the Caytoniales inasmuch as they possess some gymnosperm features and are so regarded by some botanists. THOMAS'[623] account, which refers to the order as *angiosperms*, was based upon megasporophylls, fruits, and seeds of *Gristhorpia nathorsti* and *Caytonia sewardi;* microsporophylls or stamens, *Antholithus arberi;* and fragments of associated leaves, *Sagenopteris phillipsi*. These investigations revealed a closed carpel with stigma and anthers with four rows, both characters certainly angiospermic. Later, HARRIS,[232] describing material collected from Greenland, came to the conclusion that the carpels were open at the time of pollination and that the pollen grains were drawn in through the micropyle to the nucellus; these are just as certainly gymnospermic characters. For the present, we are not inclined to ascribe the order to either group, but await the finding of additional material, with both reproductive and vegetative structures preserved, which will make it possible to establish the position of the Caytoniales.

CHAPTER XX

PHYLOGENY

Throughout the preceding chapters, remarks have been made and opinions have been expressed in regard to the relationships of various groups; but it seems best to assemble some of the scattered views, add some arguments, and to consider the evidence upon which botanists founded their theories of phylogeny.*

Similarity of structures has been relied upon in all attempts to arrange plants in a natural, or genetic, sequence. Morphologists of the older school believe that most of this evidence, especially that afforded by embryology, is reliable; modern morphologists believe that some of this evidence, but not so much of it, is due to genetic relationship. There are ecologists and physiologists who would go still farther and claim that external form and internal structure are due, almost entirely, to environment and function.

Heredity and environment determine the form, structure, and life-history of a plant. Morphologists have overemphasized the influence of heredity, while ecologists and physiologists have overemphasized the influence of environment.

It is becoming more and more evident that some of the things which have been attributed to heredity may be due to environment; but, as an acute observer remarked some 2,000 years ago, you do not gather figs from thistles; and very probably, if there had been constant experimentation from that time up to the present, not a single member of the fig family could have been transferred to the sunflower family. However, it must be recognized that there is such a thing as ecological anatomy, and also that phylogenetic anatomy is equally important. When pumpkin seeds and corn are planted in the same hill, the phylogenetic factor determines that one shall produce pumpkins, and the other, corn. Physiological and ecological

* Some of the views, expressed in this chapter, even with their phraseology, were presented in a symposium before the International Congress of Plant Sciences, at Ithaca, New York, August 19, 1926.[124]

factors may have a great influence upon the size and quality of the products, but they are still pumpkins and corn.

The apple, pear, and quince resemble each other rather closely, and we believe that their structural similarities are due to genetic relationship; in the same way, the cherry, peach, and plum have a genetic relationship which is indicated by similar structures. In each group the three members have come from a common ancestor in the remote past; and, farther back, these two common ancestors may have come from some still more remote ancestor.

The morphologist stresses mutation, smaller variations, hybridizing, and natural selection in accounting for changes, and he is too likely to overlook the influence of soil, climate, and other conditions.

The aquatic form of *Polygonum amphibium* differs so much from the land form that they were described as two species. How far is the capacity for such immediate responses inheritable? Would *Proserpinaca palustris*, grown in a mesophytic habitat for a thousand generations, lose the capacity for producing dissected leaves when grown in water?

Most botanists believe that the land flora came from an aquatic ancestry. When algae transmigrated to the land it became necessary to develop protective, conducting, and supporting structures. The theories of CHURCH,[133] as expressed in his *Thallassiophyta*, the views of SCOTT, as set forth in his *Extinct Plants*[534] and in the third edition of his *Studies in Fossil Botany*,[533] and also the views of SEWARD, as presented in his *Fossil Plants*[547] and in his *Plant Life through the Ages*,[548] are suggestive.

Let us suppose that some algae became stranded. Those which did not die developed conducting cells, at first merely elongated, then with thickenings and with groupings into bundles. Later, more algae transmigrated, and, having the same conditions to cope with, developed elongated cells with thickenings and groupings like the previous transmigrants. The modern botanist, finding the two descendents resembling each other, assumes that they are related.

Paleobotanists are often entirely dependent upon such evidence, because the wood may be the only part preserved; but morphologists, especially anatomists, lay no less stress upon the evidence of anatomy.

No botanist will deny that heterospory has arisen independently in various groups of plants, and that it has arisen in the same way in the most diverse cases—by the disorganization of young megaspores which have been absorbed by growing megaspores.

We have already remarked that the Cycadofilicales were mistaken for ferns until their seeds were discovered, and it is possible that the discovery of seeds may transfer more of the oldest recognized members of the Filicales to the Cycadofilicales.

In the angiosperm flower there seem to be some rather definite lines of evolution—from spiral to cyclic arrangement of parts, and, in the cyclic forms, from pentacyclic to tetracyclic, from hypogyny to epigyny, etc. On the basis of these tendencies, the Archichlamydeae have been arranged in a line from the Amentiferae to the Umbelliferae; the Sympetalae, in a line from Ericaceae to Compositae; and the monocotyls, in a line from the Pandanales to the Orchids. This does not mean that each order must be derived from the one below it; but it is probable that some tetracyclic flowers have come, by direct descent, from pentacyclic flowers. However, the possibility that similar structures may be due to parallel development must always be recognized. It may be that most of the forms in the three great lines of angiosperms have come, by parallel development, from a few great centers like the *Ranunculus—Rose—Legume plexus* in the Archichlamydeae.

Similarly, there are lines of evolution in the gymnosperms, which does not mean that each family is derived from the one ranked before it, or even that the genera within a family are mentioned in genetic sequence.

The sequence of families in an order, and the sequence of genera in a family, is generally based upon the evolution of some one important structure. For example, in the Fucaceae, *Fucus*, with eight eggs in the oogonium, is placed first, while forms with four, two, and only one egg, come later. There can be no doubt that reduction in the number of eggs in this family is an evolutionary tendency, and, in this respect, *Fucus* is the most primitive. But, in the most primitive form of plant body, conceptacles cover the entire plant. On this basis, *Hormoseira* should stand at or near the beginning, although only four of its eight nuclei become nuclei of functional eggs. *Fucus*, on this basis, would stand not at the beginning but near the end of the line.

In the gymnosperms, also, the arrangement will depend upon the structure chosen as a basis.

In the cycad, *Macrozamia*, there is a group of species closely resembling *M. spiralis*. It would be dubious to arrange these species in linear order, each species derived from the one before it. Probably some of the species have come, independently, from the highly variable *M. spiralis*. However, if two of the species differed somewhat from *M. spiralis*, but resembled each other in the structure of the gland and venation of the leaf, it would seem more probable that one of them had come from the other than that both had developed, independently, identical minor features.

Even the open carpel, from which the gymnosperms are named, is not more universally present than the free nuclear period at the germination of the megaspore. This free nuclear period is more characteristic of living gymnosperms than the single cotyledon is of monocots, or the two cotyledons are of dicots; but it would be hard to defend a claim that it is due to inheritance. It is a natural consequence of heterospory. Homosporous forms do not have any free nuclear period, and, as heterospory was beginning to emerge from homospory, there may have been no free nuclear period. Some living heterosporous pteridophytes have no free nuclear period, but with heterospory in such an advanced stage as in *Selaginella* and *Isoetes*, the early nuclear figures are too small to segment the comparatively large mass of protoplasm, and a free nuclear stage results. After a free nuclear stage has been established, it might persist, even in small megaspores, as in *Taxus*.

A free nuclear stage in the embryo of gymnosperms, immediately following fertilization, occurs in all gymnosperms except *Sequoia* and, perhaps, *Gnetum*. It resembles that which occurs at the germination of the megaspore, and occurs for the same reason—the early nuclear figures are too small to segment the comparatively large mass of cytoplasm. The free nuclear periods in the young gametophyte and embryo do not indicate relationships. They are merely similar responses to similar conditions.

The seed is the final stage in the evolution of heterospory. There were, doubtless, cases in which it would have been difficult, or impossible, to draw a line between a heterosporous pteridophyte and a seed plant. If the retention of the megaspore makes the sporangium, with its contained megaspore, a seed, while a sporangium which sheds its megaspore, even at an advanced stage of development, has not yet reached the seed condition, a single individual might be partly fern and partly seed plant. Such a condition sometimes occurs in *Selaginella*, and may have occurred rather frequently as the early gymnosperms were evolving from the heterosporous pteridophytes.

During this period of transition, it would not be surprising to find the leaf remaining at the fern level. In very recent times, numerous varieties of apples, of various aspect, have arisen, while the leaves remained about the same. In the same way, the fern leaf was retained by the early gymnosperms.

In vascular anatomy the Cycadofilicales are more advanced than the ferns with which they were associated. Circular pits are characteristic of the xylem of higher seed plants, while a scalariform marking is equally characteristic of ferns. The known Cycadofilicales have quite generally progressed beyond the scalariform stage, but we should expect to find it in their seedlings, for even the living cycads pass through a scalariform stage, and *Stangeria* does not get beyond it, except in a few tissues. The genus also retains a very fernlike leaf. This is instructive, for it shows that the fern leaf and vascular anatomy may be retained after the seed habit has become established. *Stangeria* was described as a fern, and even assigned to the genus *Lomaria*, until its seeds were discovered. And so the lower gymnosperms and plants, which had almost, but not quite, reached the seed condition, would naturally resemble each other so closely that they could not be distinguished by vegetative characters: and the resemblance would be due to genetic relationship.

Where complete life-histories are known, we believe that recapitulation is a definite help in solving relationships, especially in nearly related forms. Here, we should lay the greatest stress upon the origin and development of heterospory and the seed. Next, we should rank the evidence from vascular anatomy, like the occurrence of spiral, scalariform, and pitted structures, and exarch, mesarch and endarch bundles. The behavior of leaves, like the evidence from juvenile leaves, we should place last. On the whole, we believe in the recapitulation theory, but we feel certain that it has been called upon to explain things for which it is not responsible.

From time to time we have stated or assumed that, in some way or other, the gymnosperms have come from the pteridophytes, and most botanists will agree to this theory. WETTSTEIN,[670] a profound student of phylogeny, says that the gymnosperms represent a plant type which is traceable to the pteridophytes, by way of the Cycadofilicales. He thinks that the unity of the entire group is not such as to indicate the remnant of a former race, but rather, a terminal series going back to a common ancestry.

WETTSTEIN'S view is accepted by most botanists. Both cycadophytes and coniferophytes show an unmistakable pteridophyte ancestry. Have they arisen independently, or has one of them given rise to the other? If both have come from a common ancestor, the coniferophytes have progressed much farther and retain fewer of the ancestral characters. As far as any evidence from fossils is concerned the groups were never any more related than they are now.

In some way or other the Cordaitales, the lowest of the coniferophyte stock, came from the pteridophytes. Then the Cordaitales gave rise to the Coniferales and probably also to the Ginkgoales.

Long after the Cordaitales became differentiated from the pteridophyte stock, the Bennettitales and Cycadales arose, independently, from the Cycadofilicales. The cycadophyte line is much more homogenous than the coniferophyte, and, in our opinion, there is no doubt that it arose from the Filicales.

The coniferophyte line is not so homogeneous. Those who lay great stress upon the leaf gap and use the terms "lycopsida" and "pteropsida," insist that the coniferophyte line must have come from the Cycadofilicales, or at least from the Filicales, because all belong to the pteropsida. Others would minimize the value of the leaf gap in determining relationships, and say that lycopods do not have leaf gaps because the bundles are exarch and the leaf traces, being connected with the protoxylem, are already at the periphery of the stele, and naturally would not produce gaps. The lycopods, as a group, have comparatively small leaves, with entire margins, and, in this respect, bear a much closer resemblance to the coniferophytes, in which the small leaf, with entire margin, is dominant. Of course, some gymnosperms, notably the Cordaitales, have large leaves; and in some, like *Ginkgo*, the margin is not entire. But there are no big compound leaves, like those of the Cycadofilicales. Cones were already highly developed in the lycopods, long before they appeared in the cycadophyte line, and they appeared in the Cordaitales long before they appeared in any of the cycadophyte phylum.

As far back as they can be traced, the lycopod and fern phyla seem to be just as distinct as they are now. Throughout our long association in teaching and in conducting research, the late Dr. JOHN M. COULTER and myself, relying chiefly upon the importance of the leaf gap, assumed that the coniferophyte line has come from the Cycadofilicales. As the survivor of the pair, if I were still in active teaching, I should still teach that theory, but the teaching would lack the dogmatic confidence which characterized the earlier days. So let us assume, but with minds still open, that the Cordaitales have come, directly or indirectly, from ferns.

The major problems which remain concern the origin of the Coniferales, Ginkgoales, and Gnetales.

The Gnetales, like Minerva, seem to have sprung, full armed, from the head of Jove; but it is possible that the discovery of some new group, like the Caytoniales, may prepare the way for a less fanciful theory of origin. On the other hand, it is possible that thorough investigations of complete life-histories in the lower dicots, especially trees, will help to place the Gnetales where they really belong.

For a long time the Ginkgoales were classed with the Taxaceae. When motile sperms were discovered, *Ginkgo* was removed from the taxads, and made the sole living representative of an order. The leaves and long stalks of the female flowers are also characteristic of the new order. The mere fact that the sperms are ciliated does not seem sufficient to warrant a new order. In its early development, the sperm is almost identical with that of *Juniperus*, and *Juniperus* usually has a dense mass of kinoplasm, which may represent a blepharoplast. There seems little doubt that the sperms of *Juniperus* are descended rather recently, phylogenetically, from motile sperms;

and the sperms of *Taxus* do not seem to be very far removed from a swimming ancestry. *Ginkgo*, like the cycads, has retained the swimming sperms, after other structures have advanced. Nevertheless, the swimming sperm is a universal pteridophyte character, which *Ginkgo* has inherited directly or indirectly from the pteridophytes.

On the whole, it seems best to derive Ginkgoales from the Cordaitales. Some of the seeds assigned to Cordaitales bear a close resemblance to those of the living *Ginkgo*, especially in the archegonia and "tent pole" structure of the top of the female gametophyte. Material recently secured, and now under investigation, may throw some light on resemblances between *Cordaites* and *Ginkgo*. The seeds of the Cordaitales are already so advanced that they are far removed from the primitive seeds which must have existed while the lower coniferophytes were emerging from their heterosporous pteridophyte ancestry.

The Coniferales have so many cordaitean characters that they must have come from the Cordaitales, or the two groups must have developed independently from a common ancestor. In this case, it hardly seems necessary to call upon parallel development, as is generally done when there is difficulty in making a direct connection.

The Coniferales fall, rather naturally, into two great groups, the Pinares and Taxares, the former containing four families, Abietaceae, Taxodiaceae, Cupressaceae, and Araucariaceae; and the latter two families, the Podocarpaceae and Taxaceae.

Most of the literature dealing with the phylogeny of gymnosperms is concerned with the origin and relationship of these six families, and it is here that the most intensive investigations have been made. Life-histories in these six families are so well known that theories are based upon interpretation of a wide range of established facts.

More investigations and more theorizing have been devoted to the Abietaceae and Araucariaceae than to all the other four together. Which of these two families is more ancient? Did both arise independently from the Cordaitales or some other ancestor, or did one of them give rise to the other? These are questions which are not yet settled.

Most of the fossil material consists of stems, roots, and leaves, with a comparatively scanty amount of strobili, and still less of gametophytic structures. Consequently, theories have been based almost entirely upon comparative anatomy of the sporophyte.

According to JEFFREY, the most profound student of anatomy America has produced, and who, with his students, has developed the subject of comparative anatomy from both the phylogenetic and ecological standpoints, making abundant use of Mesozoic and Paleozoic material, the Abietaceae are the ancestral stock from

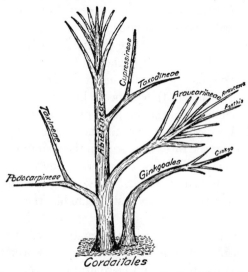

FIG. 396.—Genealogical tree of the Coniferales, showing their proximity to the Ginkgoales.—After JEFFREY.[301]

which the other five families have been derived. His views in regard to relationships in the coniferophyte phylum are summarized in a diagram taken from his book, *The Anatomy of Woody Plants* (fig. 396).

Some of the evidence for and against a derivation of the Abietaceae from the Cordaitales is as follows:

In spite of the antiquity of spur shoots in Ginkgoales and early members of the Abietaceae, the spur shoot must be regarded as a later development. The long shoot was the original form of the plant body. There are no spur shoots in the Araucariaceae, or in seedlings of the Abietaceae. As far as the theory of recapitulation is concerned, the long shoot is more primitive than the spur.

The crowded pitting and the absence of bars of SANIO are claimed to indicate a close relationship between the Araucariaceae and Cordaitales, but, in araucarian seedlings, the pitting is not crowded, and in xylem, near the pith of the ovulate cone, the pits are neither crowded nor alternating. On the contrary, there is a strong tendency to opposite arrangement, and there are definite bars of SANIO, which are lacking in adult wood of living araucarians.

The Abietaceae and Ginkgoales have opposite pitting and bars of SANIO, both of which features are absent from the Cordaitales. These features were developed later in *Pinus*, because they are absent from conservative regions, like the inner wood of the cone axis and the inner wood of the root, although they appear farther back from the primary xylem. In these conservative regions ray tracheids are also lacking, although they appear elsewhere. *Pinus* also lacks a torus in the membrane of the bordered pits near the primary wood, agreeing, in this respect, with Cordaitales. In the Araucariaceae the opposite is true, for the torus is present in the membrane of pits near the primary xylem, and absent elsewhere. If only the structure of the cone axis is considered, *Pinus*, representing the Abietaceae, has come from an ancestor with wood structure like that of the Cordaitales.

In general, JEFFREY believes that the structure of the wood indicates relationship between the Abietaceae and Cordaitales, rather than between Araucariaceae and Cordaitales.

The ovulate scale and bract are separate in the Abietaceae. This seems to be a primitive character. Whether they are fused or not in the rest of the Pinares may be questionable. There may be no more fusion than in a gamopetalous corolla. The "fused" condition may be due to zonal growth, which gives rise to perigyny and epigyny. However, in these cases, the condition is regarded as more advanced than in hypogyny. Similarly, the "fused" bract and ovuliferous scale may represent a more advanced condition than the separate bract and scale. Then, in this respect, the Araucariaceae would be more advanced than the Abietaceae.

Evidence from the gametophytes has received little attention; but, in our opinion, it is much more definite than the evidence from the anatomy of woody structures. The development of prothallial cells in the microspore is more extensive in the Araucariaceae, especially in *Araucaria*, than in any other known seed plant. There are often twenty or thirty prothallial cells, and as many as forty have been counted. Even the highest numbers recorded for any of the Abietaceae are insignificant in comparison. There is no doubt that the original gametophytes were green and independent. The retention of the gametophytes and their progressive reduction is well known. *Pinus* has only two evanescent prothallial cells, and the Cupressaceae, none at all. In this feature the Araucariaceae are the most primitive of living conifers. Not much is known about the male gametophyte of Cordaitales, but the best-preserved material indicates that there were many prothallial cells.

As far as the evidence from the female gametophyte is known, it is similar, except that in the Abietaceae there is a distinct ventral canal cell, while in the Araucariaceae no wall is formed between the ventral canal nucleus and that of the egg.

In the conifers a reduction in the number of free nuclei in the early embryogeny seems to be an evolutionary tendency. The Araucariaceae have thirty-two or sixty-four free nuclei, while in the Abietaceae the prevalent number is only four. In this feature the Araucariaceae are more primitive than the Abietaceae.

On the whole, it is certain that in gametophytic structures and in early embryogeny the Araucariaceae are more primitive than the Abietaceae, while, on the other hand, the anatomy of the sporophyte would indicate that the Abietaceae are more primitive.

If the geological record were complete, the comparative antiquity of *Pinus* and *Araucaria* and the rest would be settled definitely, although there would still remain the problem of determining whether their similarity was due to parallel development from a common ancestor, or to genetic continuity.

ZEILLER and FLICHE[719, 197] found pine cones of both the Strobus and Pinaster types already differentiated in the Jurassic of France; and NATHORST[411] concluded, on the evidence of winged pollen grains, that pines existed in the Triassic of Sweden. This would bring the Abietaceae into connection with the Cordaitales.

The Araucariaceae are also very ancient, and were believed to have been abundant in the Carboniferous, on account of the *Arau-*

carioxylon type of wood; but this wood probably belonged to the Cordaitales. The "parallel" veined leaves of Cordaitales once placed the monocotyls in the Carboniferous, and settled "by the sure testimony of history" that the monocots must be older than the dicots. However, the mere fact that the wood structure is so similar in the two cases should have some weight. SCOTT believed that the Araucariaceae have the longest fossil history of any of the Coniferales, overlapping that of the Cordaitales. Consequently, they might have come from the Cordaitales.

Material is being found farther and farther back, and claims are being made that both Abietaceae and Araucariaceae existed in the Permian.

The Taxodiaceae and Cupressaceae have not occasioned so much discussion, probably because it is rather generally agreed that they are a branch from the general abietineous stock. Their fossil record does not go as far back. They were abundant in the Cretaceous, and such names as *Cupressites*, *Widdringtonites*, and *Thujites* indicate their resemblance to living genera. *Cupressinoxylon* is Jurassic, and the family doubtless was more widely represented in that time, but material has not been identified with as much confidence. When FLORIN completes his work on cuticular structures, some of the material which has been identified tentatively may be assigned definitely to its proper place.

Both families have the ligneous resin canals and the marginal ray tracheids which characterize the Mesozoic Abietaceae. In tracing the origin of the two families, evidence from the Mesozoic *Sequoias* should be left out, for they are more like the Araucariaceae, and may belong with them.

In gametophytic characters the two families illustrate how one feature may advance while another retains its primitive character. In *Juniperus*, and in the Cupressaceae generally, there is no prothallial cell in the male gametophyte. In the pollen tube there are two male cells, which have progressed but little beyond the swimming sperm level. But in the female gametophyte, there is no wall between the ventral canal nucleus and that of the egg. Such features should be considered along with the evidence from comparative anatomy.

In general, the evidence indicates that the Taxodiaceae and Cupressaceae came from the Abietaceae, perhaps originating as a common line which later differentiated into the two families. JEFFREY, who strongly supports the theory that the Abietaceae are the ancestral stock, believes that the two families were differentiated from that stock earlier than the Araucariaceae. The other two families, Podocarpaceae and Taxaceae, constituting the Taxares, certainly belong together.

In the Podocarpaceae the scales of the ovulate cone, and the sporophylls and spores of the staminate cone, indicate relationship with the Abietaceae. The wood is similar to that of the Cupressaceae and Taxodiaceae. It seems possible that a thorough study of very young ovulate cones might limit somewhat the application of the old phrase "conifers without cones."

In the Taxaceae, *Cephalotaxus* seems to be the most primitive genus. The ovulate strobilus looks like a cone, and has several ovuliferous scales with young ovules, but usually only one ovule, the terminal one, develops. In *Taxus* usually one ovule develops. Occasionally two ovules develop and three have been known to start. A study of the development of the young ovulate strobilus in material which is fruiting superabundantly might be suggestive. Such material was noted on the estate of REGINALD CORY Esq., at Duffryn, near Cardiff, Wales. This *Taxus baccata* was pruned to form an out-of-door room—without a roof—and the pruning may have caused the extreme production of seed, which gave a reddish tinge to the walls. Possibly such material might show ovules in the axils of the numerous bracts, and indicate the ancestral condition of *Taxus*.

The Taxaceae are not known with certainty below the Cretaceous, although their morphological structure would indicate a greater age.

It seems safe to say that from the Carboniferous onward the two great lines, Cycadophytes and Coniferophytes, have been distinct. They have some common characters, but the general outline of the life-history is the same in all seed plants, and the pteridophyte structures from which the seed evolved are similar, even in lycopods and ferns. If the two great lines of gymnosperms had a common origin, it is still to be demonstrated.

CHAPTER XXI

ALTERNATION OF GENERATIONS

Throughout the book we have been repeating that the microspore is the first cell of the male gametophyte, the megaspore is the first cell of the female gametophyte, and that the fertilized egg is the first cell of the sporophyte. This may seem trite, but it is fundamental and the evolution of these structures in the gymnosperms is so suggestive that it seems worth while to consider them in relation to those which are lower and higher in the scale.

That the gametophyte and sporophyte generations alternate in seed plants is accepted by every botanist. Similar alternation is just as readily recognized in the pteridophytes and bryophytes; but, in the thallophytes, there is not the same unanimity of opinion, partly because the average botanist is not so familiar with life-histories in thallophytes and partly from failure to recognize the origin of alternation.

Below the level of sexuality there is no alternation of generations: merely cell division. A cell may grow larger than its neighbors, become surrounded by a thicker wall, and tide the plant over unfavorable conditions; but there is no alternation. If such a plant has differentiated chromosomes, we should regard their number as the x number.

When a plant reaches the level of sexuality, two cells (or their nuclei) fuse. When they fuse, each contributes the x number of chromosomes and the number is doubled, so that the resulting cell, the zygote, has $2x$ chromosomes.

At first, the fusion was probably only a stimulus to development, and a reduction of chromosomes occurred at the first two mitoses in the zygote. No plant body, except the zygote, was built up. *Spirogyra* and many of the Chlorophyceae show this condition, and many botanists do not recognize any alternation; but alternation has originated, and, from this beginning, the evolution of the $2x$ generation and the reduction of the x generation afford a splendid study in the comparative morphology of plants. If zoölogists knew this whole line of evolution and reductions they might find a reasonable interpretation for the three polar bodies.

In many algae reduction does not take place at the germination of the zygote, but there is a more or less extended period of cell division preceding it. In such cases the $2x$ body becomes large enough to be seen with the naked eye. It may or may not look like the x body. In *Zanardinia* the x and $2x$ bodies look alike; but in *Cutleria*, in the same family, they look different. In the Laminariaceae the $2x$ body has become immensely larger than the x body. In *Coleochaete scutata* the germinating zygote builds up a body which does not look like the structure that produced the gametes; but this new body, usually consisting of eight cells, has the x number of chromosomes, the reduction taking place during the first two mitoses in the zygote, as in *Spirogyra*. It would be interesting to know where reduction takes place in those species of *Coleochaete*, which have more than eight cells in the body produced by the zygote. As many as sixteen and thirty-two have been counted. All these zygotes produce spores. Consequently, the eight-celled body, in *Coleochaete*, although an x structure, is etymologically a sporophyte. Many x bodies produce spores, and, in this sense, are sporophytes; but the same plant body may produce both spores and gametes, as in *Ulothrix*. *Fucus*, a $2x$ body, produces gametes. When one's theories of alternation are based only upon plants from the bryophytes up, the fundamentals of the phenomenon may be overlooked. For this reason, we have reiterated: the spore is the first cell of the gametophyte, and the zygote is the first cell of the sporophyte. We might have said x and $2x$ generations; but from the bryophytes up, and in many thallophytes, x and $2x$ generations are synonymous with gametophyte and sporophyte generations. When plants which he regards as gametophytes produce spores, and those which he regards as sporophytes produce gametes, some botanists become confused. The trouble is that, in these cases, gametophyte and x generation and sporophyte and $2x$ generation are not synonymous. The terms "gametophyte" and "sporophyte" are not as broad as x and $2x$ generations.

The zygote is the first cell of the $2x$ generation, whether it divides many times, building up a more or less extensive $2x$ body, or does not divide at all. The zygote, even in *Spirogyra*, might be called a sporophyte; for it produces four nuclei, three of which degenerate, while the other remains as the only nucleus of the cell which grows into a new filament. In *Mesocarpus* the four nuclei organize protoplasm about themselves and become recognizable spores, so that the older taxonomists called the whole structure a sporocarp.

In *Riccia*, and in most of the liverworts, the sporophyte is parasitic upon the gametophyte. In the moss, while still parasitic, it is green and partly independent. In the ferns, and in all plants above that level, the sporophyte, although at first parasitic, finally becomes entirely independent of the gametophyte.

In the gymnosperms, and in all plants which have reached the seed level, the sporophyte is parasitic until the seed germinates.

In some of the extinct seed plants it is possible that the male gametophyte may have protruded somewhat from the spore, and may have developed some chlorophyll, but in all known gymnosperms, both living and extinct, the male gametophyte is contained within the spore until a pollen tube is formed by those gymnosperms which have pollen tubes. The vegetative part of the male gametophyte of gymnosperms is most extensive in the Araucariaceae, where it may consist of as many as forty cells. In most of the Podocarpaceae there is a vigorous development of prothallial cells, but the number is far less than the Araucariaceae. In the Abietaceae there are constantly prothallial cells, but not so many, and in *Pinus*, the most primitive genus, there are only two small evanescent cells. In the other three families, Taxodiaceae, Cupressaceae, and Taxaceae, prothallial cells are practically entirely lacking, so that the microspore, as in the angiosperms, is reduced to an antheridial initial.

In *Ginkgo* there is one evanescent prothallial cell and one more or less permanent prothallial cell. In the Cycads there is one rather permanent prothallial cell. Nothing is known definitely about the prothallial cell situation in any extinct forms; but it is very probable that there were numerous prothallial cells in the Cordaitales, and probably some in the Cycadofilicales and Bennettitales.

The gymnosperms show the end of the series in the reduction of the vegetative part of the male gametophyte.

The number of sperms is, dominantly, only two. *Microcycas* and *Cupressus* are notable exceptions in having a dozen or more sperms. Probably in extinct forms, near their pteridophyte ancestors, sperms were more numerous.

The female gametophyte is, necessarily, parasitic in all seed plants. In all known gymnosperms its development begins with a period of free nuclear divisions, which is followed by a period of wall formation. This sequence was already established in the heterosporous pteridophytes.

Aside from a general reduction in the size of the gametophyte, the main features are the reduction of the archegonium and a delay in wall formation.

In the most primitive archegonia, like those of *Pinus* and *Ginkgo*, there is a neck, consisting of two or more cells, and a ventral canal cell separated from the egg by a definite wall. In most, if not all of the Abietaceae, there is a definite ventral canal cell. In the rest of the Coniferales the wall between the ventral canal nucleus and the egg nucleus is lacking, and is also lacking in the Cycadales. Nothing is known about the ventral canal situation in any extinct gymnosperm; but we should expect to find a well developed ventral canal cell.

In *Torreya* there is not even a ventral canal nucleus, and in *Welwitschia*, not even a neck cell, the archegonium initial functioning as an egg. In *Gnetum* there is not even an archegonium initial. One or more of the free nuclei organize an egg, as in the angiosperms, and fertilization takes place with the upper part of the female gametophyte in the free nuclear condition, as in angiosperms. The lower part of this gametophyte, as often in the antipodal region in angiosperms, is already cellular at the time of fertilization, and, as in angiosperms, the rest of the gametophyte becomes cellular after fertilization.

Consequently, the reduction of the female gametophyte has almost reached the angiosperm level, the principal difference being that *Gnetum* has more antipodal cells and more free nuclei.

Not much is known of the female gametophyte of extinct gymnosperms; but the female gametophyte of *Cardiocarpus*, assigned to *Cordaites*, looks like that of *Ginkgo*. On the basis of similar structures, *Ginkgo* and *Cordaitales* are closely related. The megaspore membrane is highly developed in Cycadofilicales, and the gametophytes are cellular throughout.

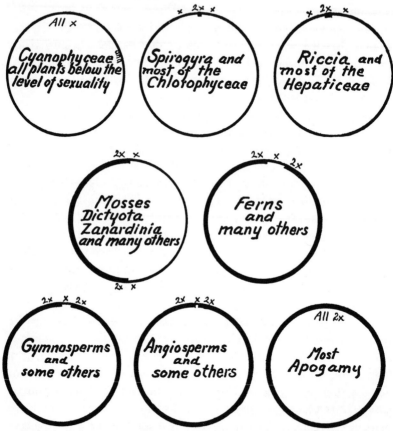

Fig. 397.—Diagrams indicating the comparative extent of the *x* and *2x* generations in various plants. In the second diagram, the extent of the *2x* generation is exaggerated; in the seventh and eighth, the *x* generation is exaggerated.

The female gametophyte of gymnosperms thus stands between those of the pteridophytes and the angiosperms.

In the alternation of generations the sporophyte of the gymnosperms has become as dominant as in the angiosperms. The male gametophyte has reached the angiosperm condition in the final elimination of all prothallial cells. The female gametophyte, while not so much reduced as the male, has nearly reached the angiosperm level.

The comparative display of the x and $2x$ generations may be illustrated by a series of diagrams (fig. 397). The broader line represents the x generation, and the thinner line the $2x$ generation.

In studying the alternation of generations it is interesting to note that the gametophytes, in the early stages of phylogeny, were green and independent, and that they later became parasitic and finally lost their chlorophyll, while the sporophytes, originally green and independent, became parasitic and lost their chlorophyll; then later, in the bryophytes, pteridophytes and seed plants—after passing through a parasitic stage in their ontogeny—again became green and independent.

Alternation of generations, viewed as an alternation of x and $2x$ phases in the life-history, is strictly antithetic. Since we believe that alternation of generations arose from the fusion of gametes, the resulting zygote being the first cell from which the evolution of the sporophyte began, we see no place for the old theory of homologous alternation, especially since it is based largely upon the phenomena of apogamy and apospory, which are merely abnormal digressions from the normal life-history.

In considering alternation of generations in the gymnosperms, it is to be regretted that our knowledge of the fossil record is so incomplete, especially knowledge of the gametophytic phase in the life-history. It is to be hoped that some new discoveries of material will show what the gametophytes were in the later heterosporous pteridophytes and early gymnosperms which came from them. Until facts are available, we can only imagine that the gametophyte generation will become more and more extensive the farther back the record goes, and that the sporophyte—in spite of Devonian trees—will not be quite so far removed from a pteridophyte ancestry.

BIBLIOGRAPHY

1. AASE, HANNAH, Vascular anatomy of the megasporophylls of conifers. Bot. Gazette **60**:277–313. *figs. 196.* 1915.

2. AFFOURTIT, MISS M. F. A., and LA RIVIÈRE, MISS H. C. C., On the ribbing of the seeds of *Ginkgo*. Ann. Botany **29**:591–95. *fig. 1.* 1915.

3. ALLEN, C. E., The early stages of spindle formation in the pollen mother-cells of *Larix*. Ann. Botany **17**:281–312. *pls. 14, 15.* 1903.

4. ARBER, AGNES, On the structure of the paleozoic seed *Mitrospermum compressum*. Ann. Botany **24**:491–509. *pls. 37–39. figs. 2.* 1910.

5. ———, A note on *Trigonocarpus*. Ann. Botany **28**:195, 196. *fig. 1.* 1914.

6. ARBER, E. A. NEWELL, On some new species of *Lagenostoma*, a type of pteridospermous seed from the Coal-measures. Ann. Botany **19**:326–28. 1905 (abstract).

7. ———, "The origin of gymnosperms"; a discussion at the Linnean Society. New Phytol. **5**:68–76, 141–48. 1906.

8. ———, On the past history of ferns. Ann. Botany **20**:215–32. 1906.

9. ———, On a new pteridosperm possessing the *Sphenopteris* type of foliage. Ann. Botany **22**:57–62. *pl. 6.* 1908.

10. ———, A revision of the seed impressions of the British Coal Measures. Ann. Botany **28**:81–108. *pls. 6–8. figs. 8.* 1914.

11. ———, On the fossil floras of the Wyre Forest, with special reference to the neighboring Coal Measure areas. Phil. Trans. Roy. Soc. London B **204**:363–445. *pls. 26–29.* 1914.

12. ARBER, E. A. NEWELL, AND PARKIN, JOHN, On the origin of angiosperms. Jour. Linn. Soc. London Bot. **38**:29–80. 1907.

13. ———, Studies in the evolution of angiosperms: the relationship of the angiosperms to the Gnetales. Ann. Botany **22**:489–515. 1908.

14. ———, Beiträge zur Morphologie einiger Gymnospermen. I. Die Entwickelung des Endosperms bei *Sequoia sempervirens*. Bull. Soc. Imp. Nat. Moscou. Pp. 13 *pls. 7, 8.* 1899.

15. ARNOLDI, W., Beiträge zur Morphologie und Entwickelungsgeschichte einiger Gymnospermen. II. Ueber die Corpuscula und Pollenschläuche bei *Sequoia sempervirens*. Bull. Soc. Imp. Nat. Moscou. Pp. 8. *pls. 10, 11.* 1899.

16. ———, Beiträge zur Morphologie der Gymnospermen. III. Embryogenie von *Cephalotaxus fortunei*. Flora **87**:46–63. *pls. 1–3.* 1900.

17. ———, Beiträge zur Morphologie der Gymnospermen. IV. Was sind die "Keimbläschen" oder "Hofmeister's-Körperchen" in der Eizelle der Abietineen? Flora **87**:194–204. *pls. 6, 7.* 1900.

18. ——, Beiträge zur Morphologie der Gymnospermen. VI. Ueber den Bau der Zellkerne im Embryo von *Ginkgo biloba*. VII. Die Embryobildung bei *Ginkgo biloba*. Ann. Inst. Agronomique et Forestière à Nowoe, Alexandria **16**:1–22. 1903.

19. ——, Beiträge zur Morphologie einiger Gymnospermen. V. Weitere Untersuchungen der Embryogenie in der Familie der *Sequoiaceen*. Bull. Soc. Imp. Nat. Moscou. pp. 28. *pls. 2.* 1910.

20. ARNOLD, C. A., Cordaitean wood from the Pennsylvanian of Michigan and Ohio. Bot. Gazette **91**:77–87. 1931.

21. BAILEY, F. M., Comprehensive catalogue of Queensland plants. Brisbane. 1909.

22. BAILEY, IRVING W., The structure of the wood in the Pineae. Bot. Gazette **48**:47–55. *pl. 5.* 1909.

23. ——, Anatomical characters in the evolution of *Pinus*. Amer. Nat. **44**: 284–93. 1910.

24. ——, A Cretaceous *Pityoxylon* with marginal tracheids. Ann. Botany **25**:315–25. *pl. 26.* 1911.

25. ——, The structure of the bordered pits of conifers and its bearing upon the tension hypothesis of the ascent of sap in plants. Bot. Gazette **62**: 133–42. *pl. 1.* 1916.

26. BAILEY, I. W., and SHEPHERD, H. B., Sanio's laws for the variation in size of coniferous tracheids. Bot. Gazette **60**:66–71. 1915.

27. BAILLON, H., Recherches organogéniques sur la fleur femelle des Coniferes. Ann. Sci. Nat. Bot. IV. **14**:186–99. *pls. 12, 13.* 1860.

28. BANCROFT, EDITH S. W., Pteridosperm anatomy and its relation to that of cycads. New Phytol. **13**:41. 1919.

29. BANCROFT, NELLIE, *Rhexoxylon africanum*, a new Medullosean stem. Trans. Linn. Soc. London **8**:87–103. *pls. 10, 11.* 1913.

30. ——, Pteridosperm anatomy and its relation to that of cycads. New Phytol. **13**:41–68. *figs. 20.* 1914.

31. ——, On some Indian Jurassic gymnosperms. Trans. Roy. Soc. London B **8**:69–86. *pls. 7–9.* 1913.

32. BARKLEY, GRACE, Differentiation of vascular bundle of *Trichosanthes anguina*. Bot. Gazette **83**:173–85. 1927.

33. BARTHOLOMEW, MARY, Abnormal prothallia of *Pinus sylvestris*. Notes Roy. Bot. Gard. Edinburgh **4**:253–55. *pl. 49.* 1909.

34. BARTLETT, A. W., Note on the occurrence of an abnormal strobilus of *Larix europaea* DC. Ann. Botany **27**:575, 576. *figs. 2.* 1913.

35. BEAL, J. M., Chromosome behavior in *Pinus banksiana* following fertilization. Bot. Gazette **95**:660–66. *pls. 2.* 1934.

36. BECCARI, O., Dei organi dei fiori feminei del *Gnetum gnemon L.* Nuovo Giorn. Bot. Ital. **7**:91–99. 1877.

37. BELAJEFF, W., Zur Lehre von dem Pollenschlauche der Gymnospermen. Ber. Deutsch. Bot. Gesell. **9**:280–86. *pl. 18.* 1891.

38. BELAJEFF, W., Zur Lehre von dem Pollenschlauche der Gymnospermen (Zweite Mittheilung). Ber. Deutsch. Bot. Gesell. 11:196–201. *pl. 12.* 1893.

39. BENSON, MARGARET, On a new lycopodiaceous seedlike organ. New Phytol. 1:58–59. *fig. 3.* 1902.

40. ———, The fructification of *Lyginodendron oldhamium.* Ann. Botany 16: 575–76. *figs. 31.* 1902.

41. ———, *Telangium scottii,* a new species of *Telangium* (*Calymmatotheca*) showing structure. Ann. Botany 18:161–77. *pl. 11.* 1904.

42. ———, On the contents of the pollen chamber of a specimen of *Lagenostoma ovoides.* Bot. Gazette 45:409–12. *figs. 2.* 1908.

43. ———, Report of Proc. Roy. Soc. London in Nature 80:239. 1909.

44. ———, *Cordaites Felicis,* sp. nov., a Cordaitean leaf from the Lower Coal Measures of England. Ann. Botany 26:201–7. *pl. 22. fig. 1.* 1912.

45. ———, *Sphaerostoma ovale* (*Conostoma ovale et intermedium* Williamson), a Lower Carboniferous ovule from Pettycur, Fifeshire, Scotland. Trans. Roy. Soc. Edinburgh 50:1–15. *pls. 1, 2. figs. 3.* 1914.

46. BERRIDGE, EMILY M., Fertilization in *Ephedra altissima.* Ann. Botany 23:509–14. *pl. 1.* 1909.

47. ———, The structure of the female strobilus in *Gnetum gnemon.* Ann Botany 26:987–92. *figs. 4.* 1912.

48. BERRIDGE, EMILY M., and SANDAY, ELIZABETH, Oogenesis and embryogeny in *Ephedra distachya.* New Phytol. 6:128–34, 167–74. *pls. 3, 4.* 1907.

49. BERRY, E. W., Vascular flora of the Lower Cretaceous. Bot. Gazette 53: 256. 1912.

50. ———, Some araucarian remains from the Atlantic coastal plain. Bull. Torr. Bot. Club 35:249–60. *pls. 11–16.* 1908.

51. ———, A mid-cretaceous species of *Torreya.* Amer. Jour. Sci. 25:382–86. 1908.

52. BERTRAND, C. E., Remarques sur la structure des graines de pollen de Cordaites. Compt. Rend. Assoc. française pour l'avancement des sciences. 436–41. 1898.

53. BERTRAND, C. E., et RENAULT, B., Recherches sur les Poroxylons. Archiv. Bot. Nord. France 3:147. *figs. 79.* 1886.

54. BESSEY, E. A., Notes on the spermatozoids of *Ginkgo.* Science 13:255. 1901.

55. BESSEY, CHARLES E., The morphology of the pine cone. Bot. Gazette 33: 157–59. *pl. 8.* 1902.

56. BLACKMAN, V. H., On the cytological features of fertilization and related phenomena in *Pinus sylvestris* L. Phil. Trans. Roy. Soc. London B 190: 395–426. *pls. 12–14.* 1898.

57. BOODLE, L. A., Concrescent and solitary foliage leaves in *Pinus.* New Phytol. 14:19–22. *figs. 4.* 1915.

58. BROOKS, F. T., and STILES, W., The structure of *Podocarpus spinulosa* (Smith) R. Br. Ann. Botany 24:305–18. *pl. 21.* 1910.

59. BOWER, F. O., On the germination and histology of the seedlings of *Welwitschia mirabilis*. Quart. Jour. Mic. Sci. **21**:15–30. *pls. 3, 4.* 1881.

60. ———, On the further development of *Welwitschia mirabilis*. Quart. Jour. Mic. Sci. **21**:571–94. *pls. 22, 23.* 1881.

61. ———, The germination and embryology of *Gnetum Gnemon*. Quart. Jour. Mic. Sci. **22**:278–98. *pl. 25.* 1882.

62. BRAUN, A., Vortrag auf dem Congrès scientifique de France, 10 ième Session (Strassburg), pp. 171, 172. 1842. (Communicated in BRAUN's Leben von C. Mettenius, p. 335. Berlin. 1882).

63. ———, BRONGNIART, A., Recherches sur les graines fossiles silicifiés. Paris. 1881.

64. ———, Recherches sur l'organisation des tiges des Cycadées. Ann. Sci. Nat. I. **16**:389–402. *pls. 20–22.* 1829.

65. BROWN, ROBT., Character and description of *Kingia*, a new genus of plants found on the S.W. coast of New Holland, with observations on the structure of its unimpregnated ovulum and the female flower in Cycadeae and Coniferae. 1827. Included also in BROWN's Miscellaneous botanical works **1**:1866.

66. BROWNE, LADY ISABEL, The phylogeny and interrelationships of the Pteridophyta. V. Filicales. New Phytol. **7**:230–53. 1908.

67. BUCHHOLZ, JOHN T., Suspensor and early embryo of *Pinus*. Bot. Gazette **66**:185–228. *pls. 5. figs. 3.* 1918.

68. ———, The suspensor and early embryo of *Pinus*. Bot. Gazette **66**:185–228. *pls. 6–10.* 1918.

69. ———, Studies concerning the evolutionary status of polycotyledony. Amer. Jour. Bot. **6**:106–19. *figs. 25.* 1919.

70. ———, Polyembryony among Abietineae. Bot. Gazette **69**:153–67. *figs. 15.* 1920.

71. ———, Embryo development and polyembryony in relation to the phylogeny of conifers. Amer. Jour. Bot. **7**:125–45. *figs. 89.* 1920.

72. ———, Embryogeny of *Cephalotaxus Fortunei*. Bull. Torr. Bot. Club. **52**: 311–24. *pl. 10. figs. 11, 12.* 1925.

73. ———, Origin of cleavage polyembryony in conifers. Bot. Gazette **81**: 55–71. *pls. 3. figs. 2.* 1926.

74. ———, The embryogeny of conifers. Proc. Fourth Internat. Bot. Congress. **1**:259–92. 1929.

75. ———, The Ozark White Cedar (Description of *Juniperus ashei* n. sp.). Bot. Gazette **90**:326–32. 1930.

76. ———, The pine embryo and embryos of related genera. Trans. Ill. Acad. Sci. **23**:117–25. 1931.

77. ———, The suspensor of *Sciadopitys*. Bot. Gazette **92**:243–62. 1931.

78. ———, The suspensor of *Cryptomeria japonica*. Bot. Gazette **93**:221–26. 1932.

79. BUCHHOLZ, JOHN T., The embryogeny of *Chamaecyparis obtusa*. Amer. Jour. Bot. **19**:230–38. 1932.

80. ———, Determinate cleavage polyembryony, with special reference to *Dacrydium*. Bot. Gazette **94**:579–88. 1933.

81. ———, The classification of Coniferales. Trans. Ill. Acad. Sci. **21**:(in press). 1934.

82. BUCHHOLZ, J. T., and OLD, EDITH M., The anatomy of the embryo of *Cedrus*, in the dormant stage. Amer. Jour. Bot. **20**:35–44. 1933.

83. BURLINGAME, L. L., The staminate cone and male gametophyte of *Podocarpus*. Bot. Gazette **46**:161–78. *pls. 8, 9. figs. 9.* 1908.

84. ———, The morphology of *Araucaria brasiliensis*. Bot. Gazette **55**:97–114. *pls. 4, 5.* 1913.

85. ———, The morphology of *Araucaria brasiliensis*. II. The ovulate cone and the female gametophyte. Bot. Gazette **57**:490–508. *pls. 25–27.* 1914.

86. ———, The origin and relationships of the Araucarians. II. Bot. Gazette **60**:89–114. 1915.

87. BUTTERWORTH, J., Some further investigation of fossil seeds of the genus *Lagenostoma* (Williamson) from the Lower Coal-measures. Mem. and Proc. Manchester Lit. and Phil. Soc. **41**:1–4. 1897.

88. CALDWELL, OTIS W., *Microcycas calocoma*. Bot. Gazette **44**:118–41. *pls. 10–13. figs. 14.* 1907.

89. CAMPBELL, D. H., Mosses and Ferns. New York. 1895.

90. CAROTHERS, IDA ELEANOR, The development of the ovule and the female gametophyte of *Ginkgo biloba*. Bot. Gazette **43**:116–30. *pls. 5, 6.* 1907.

91. CARRUTHERS, W., On gymnospermatous fruits from the secondary rocks of Britain. Jour. Botany **5**:1–21. 1867.

92. ———, On fossil cycadean stems from the secondary rocks of Great Britain. Trans. Linn. Soc. Bot. **26**:675–708. *pls. 54–63.* 1870.

93. CASPARY, R., Abietinearum floris femini structura morphologica. Ann. Sci. Nat. Bot. IV. **14**:200–209. 1860.

94. CAVARA, F., and ROGASI, G., Ricerche sulla fecondazione ed embryogenia dell'*Ephedra campylopoda* Meyer (review in Bot. Centralbl. **92**:5–6. 1902).

95. ———, Sulla germinazione del polline nelle *Ephedra*. Boll. accad. Gioenia Sci. Nat. Catania **81**:3–9. 1904.

96. ČELAKOVSKÝ, L., Zur Gymnospermie der Coniferen. Flora. **62**:257–64, 272, 283. 1879.

97. ———, Zur Kritik der Ansichten von der Fruchtschuppe der Abietineen. Abhandl. Kgl. Böhm. Gesell. Wiss. VI. **11**:1882.

98. ———, Die Gymnospermen: eine morphologisch-phylogenetische Studie. Abhandl. Kgl. Böhm. Gesell. Wiss. VII. **4**:1–148. 1890.

99. ———, Nachtrag zu meiner Schrift über die Gymnospermen. Engler's Bot. Jahrb. **24**:202–31. 1898.

100. ——, Die Vermehrung der sporangia von *Ginkgo biloba* L. Oesterreich. Bot. Zeitschr. **50**:229–37, 276–83, 337–41. 1900.

101. CHAMBERLAIN, C. J., Contribution to the life-history of Salix. Bot. Gazette **23**:147–79. *pls. 12–18.* 1897.

102. ——, Winter characters of certain sporangia. Bot. Gazette **25**:125–28. *pl. 11.* 1898.

103. ——, The homology of the blepharoplast. Bot. Gazette **26**:431–35. 1898.

104. ——, Oogenesis in *Pinus Laricio*. Bot. Gazette **27**:268–80. *pls. 4–6.* 1899.

105. ——, Nuclear phenomena of sexual reproduction in gymnosperms. Amer. Naturalist **44**:595–603. 1910.

106. ——, The ovule and female gametophyte of *Dioon*. Bot. Gazette **42**: 321–58. *pls. 13–15. figs. 9.* 1906.

107. ——, Preliminary note on *Ceratozamia*. Bot. Gazette **43**:137. 1907.

108. ——, Spermatogenesis in *Dioon edule*. Bot. Gazette **47**:215–36. *pls. 15–18.* 1909.

109. ——, *Dioon spinulosum*. Bot. Gazette **48**:401–13. *figs. 7.* 1909.

110. ——, Fertilization and embryogeny of *Dioon edule*. Bot. Gazette **50**: 415–29. *pls. 14–17.* 1910.

111. ——, The adult cycad trunk. Bot. Gazette **52**:81–104. *figs. 20.* 1911.

112. ——, Morphology of *Ceratozamia*. Bot. Gazette **53**:1–19. *pl. 1. figs. 7.* 1912.

113. ——, Two species of *Bowenia*. Bot. Gazette **54**:119–23. 1912.

114. ——, Morphology of *Ceratozamia*. Bot. Gazette **53**:1–19. *pl. 1. figs. 7.* 1912.

115. ——, A round the world botanical expedition. Popular Science Monthly **81**:417–33. 1912.

116. ——, *Macrozamia Moorei*, a connecting link between the living and fossil cycads. Bot. Gazette **55**:141–54. 1913.

117. ——, The oriental cycads in the field. Science **38**:164–67. 1913.

118. ——, A phylogenetic study of cycads. Proc. Nat. Acad. Sci. **1**:86–90. 1915.

119. ——, *Stangeria paradoxa*. Bot. Gazette **61**:353–72. *pls. 2, 3.* 1916.

120. ——, The living cycads. University of Chicago Press. 1919.

121. ——, The living cycads and the phylogeny of seed plants. Amer. Jour. Bot. **7**:145–53. 1920.

122. ——, The origin of Cycads. Science **61**:73–77. 1925.

123. ——, Hybrids in cycads. Bot. Gazette **81**:401–18. 1926.

124. ——, An evaluation of the structural evidence for genetical relationship in plants. Proc. Internat. Congr. Plant Sci. Ithaca, N.Y. **1**:473–80. 1929.

125. ——, Elements of Plant Science. McGraw-Hill Book Co. 1930.

126. ——, The age and size of plants. Scientific Monthly **35**:481–91. *figs. 1–9.* 1932.

127. ——, Methods in Plant Histology. University of Chicago Press. 1932.

128. Chauveaud, G., Le liber précurseur dan le sapin pinsapo. Am. Sci. Nat. Bot. VIII. **19**:321–33. 1904.

129. ———, Originè secondaire du double faisceau foliaire chez les sapins (*Abies*) et les pins (*Pinus*). Ann. Sci. Nat. Bot. VIII. **19**:335–48. 1904.

130. ———, Passage de la disposition primitive à la disposition secondaire dans les cotylédons du Pin maritime. Extr. Bull. Mus. Hist. Nat. Paris. 1902.

131. Chick, Edith, The seedling of *Torreya myristica*. New Phytol. **2**:83–91. *pls. 7, 8.* 1903.

132. Church, A. H., On the floral mechanism of *Welwitschia mirabilis*. Phil. Trans. Roy. Soc. London B **205**:115–51. *pls. 9–13.* 1914.

133. ———, Thalassiophyta and the sub-aerial transmigration. Botanical memoirs, No. 3. Oxford. 1919.

134. Chrysler, M. A., Tyloses in tracheids of conifers. New Phytol. **7**:198–204. *pl. 5.* 1908.

135. ———, The origin of the erect cells in the phloem of the Abietineae. Bot. Gazette **56**:36–50. 1913.

136. ———, The medullary rays of *Cedrus*. Bot. Gazette **59**:387–96. *figs. 7.* 1915.

137. ———, Vascular tissues of *Microcycas calocoma*. Bot. Gazette **82**:233–52. 1926.

138. Clarke, T. Sh., and Johnstone, G. R., Polyembryony and germination of polyembryonic coniferous seeds. Amer. Jour. Bot. **18**:673–83. *pl. 46.* 1931.

139. Coker, W. C., Observations on the gametophyte and embryo of *Taxodium distichum*. Johns Hopkins Univ. Circ. **19**:45, 46. 1900.

140. ———, Notes on the gametophytes and embryo of *Podocarpus*. Bot. Gazette **33**:89–107. *pls. 5–7.* 1902.

141. ———, On the gametophytes and embryo of *Taxodium*. Bot. Gazette **36**:1–27, 114–40. *pls. 1–11.* 1903.

142. ———, On the spores of certain Coniferae. Bot. Gazette **38**:206–13. *figs. 24.* 1904.

143. ———, Fertilization and embryogeny in *Cephalotaxus Fortunei*. Bot. Gazette **43**:1–10. *pl. 1. figs. 5.* 1907.

144. Constatin, J., et Morot, L., Sur l'origine des faisceaux libéro-ligneux supernuméraires dans la tige des Cycadées. Bull. Soc. Bot. France **32**:173. 1885.

145. Cook, Mel T., Polyembryony in *Ginkgo*. Bot. Gazette **34**:64, 65. *fig. 1.* 1902.

146. ———, Polyembryony in *Ginkgo*. Bot. Gazette **36**:142. 1903.

147. Coulter, John M., Notes on the fertilization and embryogeny of conifers. Bot. Gazette **23**:40–43. *pl. 6.* 1897.

148. ———, The embryosac and embryo of *Gnetum Gnemon*. Bot. Gazette **46**:43–49. *pl. 7.* 1908.

149. ———, Evolutionary tendencies among gymnosperms. Bot. Gazette **48**: 81–97. 1909.

150. COULTER, JOHN M., and CHAMBERLAIN, C. J., The embryogeny of *Zamia*. Bot. Gazette **35**:184–94. *pls. 6–8*. 1903.

151. COULTER, JOHN M., and CHRYSLER, M. A., Regeneration in *Zamia*. Bot. Gazette **38**:452–58. *figs. 8*. 1904.

152. COULTER, JOHN M., and LAND, W. J. G., Gametophytes and embryo of *Torreya taxifolia*. Bot. Gazette **39**:161–78. *pls. A, 1–3*. 1905.

153. COULTER, J. M., BARNES, C. R., and COWLES, H. C., A textbook of botany. New York. 1910.

154. COULTER, J. M., and CHAMBERLAIN, C. J., Morphology of Gymnosperms. University of Chicago Press. 1917.

155. CUTTING, E. M., On the meaning of the various forms of the male gametes in the pines and allied conifers. New Phytol. **7**:171–76. 1908.

156. DALLIMORE, W., and JACKSON, A. B., A handbook of Coniferae. 2d. ed. 1931.

157. DANGEARD, P. A., La mode d'union de la tige et la racine chez les Gymnospermes. Compt. Rend. Acad. Sci. Paris. **110**:253, 254. 1890.

158. ———, Recherches sur les plantules des Conifères. Le Botaniste **3**:126–204. *pls. 13–17*. 1892.

159. DANNEHL, Ueber die Bildung schizolysigener Schleimbehälter bei *Ceratozamia*. Bot. Arch. **29**:92–122. 1930.

160. DE BARY, A., Comparative anatomy of the vegetative organs of the phanerogams and ferns. English translation. 1884.

161. DE FRAINE, E., On the structure and affinities of *Sutcliffia*, in the light of a newly discovered specimen. Ann. Botany **26**:1031–66. *pls. 91, 92*. 1912.

162. DÉVISÉ, P., La figure achromatique et la plaque cellulaire dans les microsporocytes du *Larix europea*. La Cellule **32**:249–307. 1922.

163. DICKSON, A., Observations on some bisexual cones occurring in the spruce fir (*Abies excelsa*). Trans. Edinburgh Bot. Soc. **6**:418–22. 1860.

164. DIELS, L., Pflanzengeographie. 3d. ed. 1929.

165. DIXON, H. N., Fertilization in *Pinus sylvestris*. Ann. Botany **8**:21–34. *pls. 3–5*. 1894.

166. DOAK, C. C., Multiple male cells in *Cupressus arizonica*. Bot. Gazette **94**:168–82. *figs. 15*. 1932.

167. DORETY, HELEN A. (SISTER HELEN ANGELA), The embryo of *Ceratozamia;* a physiological study. Bot. Gazette **45**:412–16. *figs. 7*. 1908.

168. ———, The seedling of *Ceratozamia*. Bot. Gazette **46**:203–20. *pls. 12–16*. 1908.

169. ———, Vascular anatomy of the seedling of *Microcycas calocoma*. Bot. Gazette **47**:139–47. *pls. 5, 6*. 1909.

170. ———The extrafascicular cambium of *Ceratozamia*. Bot. Gazette **47**: 150–52. *pl. 7*. 1909.

171. DORETY, HELEN A. (SISTER HELEN ANGELA), Diagrams in COULTER and CHAMBERLAIN's Morphology of Gymnosperms. 1917.

172. ———, Embryo and seedling of *Dioon spinulosum*. Bot. Gazette **67**:251–58. 1919.

173. DOWNIE, DOROTHY G., The male gametophyte of *Microcycas calocoma*. Bot. Gazette **85**:437–50. *pls. 19–21.* 1928.

174. DOYLE, J., Note on the structure of the ovule of *Larix leptolepis*. Ann. Botany **30**:193–95. 1916.

175. DUCHARTRE, P. E., Mémoire sur les embryons qui ont été decrits comme polycotyles. Ann. Sci. Nat. Bot. III. **10**:207–37. *pls. 7–10.* 1848.

176. DUPLER, A. W., The gametophytes of *Taxus canadensis* Marsh. Bot. Gazette **64**:115–36. *pls. 11–14.* 1917.

177. ———, The staminate strobilus of *Taxus canadensis*. Bot. Gazette **68**:345–66. *pls. 24–26.* 1919.

178. ———, Ovuliferous structures of *Taxus canadensis*. Bot. Gazette **69**:492–520. *pl. 23.* 1920.

179. DUTHIE, AUGUSTA V., Anatomy of *Gnetum africanum*. Ann. Botany **26**:593–602. *pls. 3.* 1912.

180. EAMES, A. J., The gametophytes of the Kauri. Science N. S. **35**:160. 1912.

181. ———, The morphology of *Agathis australis*. Ann. Botany **27**:1–38. *pls. 1–4.* 1913.

182. EAMES, A. J., and MACDANIELS, L. H., An introduction to Plant Anatomy. McGraw-Hill Book Co. 1925.

183. EICHLER, A. W., Ueber *Welwitschia mirabilis*, etc. Flora **47**:459–64, 473–79, 489–96, 508–10, 513–20. 1863.

184. ———, Sind die Coniferen Gymnospermen oder nicht? Flora **56**:241–47, 260–72. 1873.

185. ———, Coniferae in Engler und Prantl's Die Natürlichen Pflanzenfamilien **2**:108. 1889.

186. ELKINS, M. G., and WIELAND, G. R., Cordaitean wood from the Indiana black shale. Amer. Jour. Sci. **38**:65–78. *pls. 1, 2.* 1914.

187. ENGLEMANN, G., Morphology of the carpellary scales of Coniferae. Amer. Jour. Sci. III. **12**:469, 470. 1876.

188. ENGLER, A., Gymnospermae (Geographic distribution) in Engler and Prantl's Die natürlichen Pflanzenfamilien. 2d. ed. 1926.

189. ENGLER and PRANTL, Die natürlichen Pflanzenfamilien. 2d ed. **13**:1–447. *figs. 240.* 1926.

190. ENRICO, C. V., Contribuzione alla conoscenza della morphologia e dello sviluppo del fascio vascolare della foglie delle Cicadacee. Annales di Bot. **1**:109–21. *pls. 8, 9.* 1903.

191. FANKHAUSER, J., Entwickelung des Stengels und Blattes von *Ginkgo*. Bern. 1882.

192. FARMER, J. B., On the occurrence of two prothallia in the embryo sac of *Pinus*. Ann. Botany 6:213, 214. *fig. 5*. 1892.

193. FAULL, J. H., The anatomy of the Osmundaceae. Bot. Gazette 32:381–420. *pls. 14–17*. 1901.

194. FERGUSON, MARGARET C., The development of the pollen tube and the division of the generative nucleus in certain species of pines. Ann. Botany 15:193–223. *pls. 12–14*. 1901.

195. ——, The development of the egg and fertilization in *Pinus strobus*. Ann. Botany 15:435–79. *pls. 23–25*. 1901.

196. ——, Contributions to the life-history of *Pinus*, with special reference to sporogenesis, the development of the gametophytes, and fertilization. Proc. Wash. Acad. Sci. 6:1–202. *pls. 1–24*. 1904.

197. FLICHE, P., et ZEILLER, B., Note sur une florule portlandienne des environs de Boulogne-sur-Mer. Bull. Soc. Geol. France IV. 4:787–812. 1904.

198. FLORIN, RUDOLF, Untersuchungen zur Stammesgeschichte der Coniferales und Cordaitales. Erster Teil. pp. 1–588. *pls. 58. figs. 111*. Stockholm. Almquist & Wicksells. 1931.

199. FUJII, K., On the different views hitherto proposed regarding the morphology of the flowers of *Ginkgo biloba*. Bot. Mag. Tokyo 10:15–25, 104–10. *pl. 1*. 1896.

200. ——, (Has the spermatozoid a tail or not?). Bot. Mag. Tokyo 12:287–90. 1898. (Japanese.)

201. ——, (On the morphology of the spermatozoid of *Ginkgo*). Bot. Mag. Tokyo 13:260–66. *pl. 7*. 1899. (Japanese.)

202. ——, (Account of a sperm with two spiral bands). Bot. Mag. Tokyo 14:16, 17. 1900. (Japanese.)

203. FUJIOKA, M., Studien über den anatomischen Bau des Holzes japanischer Nadelbäume. Jour. Agric. 4:201–36. *pls. 18–24*. 1913.

204. FULLER, GEO. D., Reproduction by layering in the black spruce. Bot. Gazette 55:452–57. *figs. 6*. 1913.

205. GAGER, C. S., Rare cycads from Australia. Records Brooklyn Bot. Gard. 4:83–92. 1915.

206. GEITLER, L., Zur Zytologie von *Ephedra*. Oest. bot. Zeitsch. 78:242–50. 1929.

207. GERRY, ELOISE, The distribution of the "bars of Sanio" in the Coniferales. Ann. Botany 24:119–24. *pl. 13*. 1910.

208. ——, Tyloses: their occurrence and practical significance in some American woods. Jour. Agric. Research. 1:445–70. *pls. 52–59*. 1914.

209. GHOSE, S. L., A contribution to the morphology of *Agathis ovata* (Moore) Warb. Jour. Indian. Bot. Soc. 4:79–86. *pls. 2*. 1924.

210. GIBBS, L. S., On the development of the female strobilus in *Podocarpus*. Ann. Botany 26:515–71. *pls. 5*. 1912.

211. GOEBEL, K., Outlines of classification and special morphology. English translation, p. 316. 1887.

212. ———, Organography of plants. English translation. pp. 153–55. 1900.

213. ———, Morphologische und biologische Bemerkungen. 13. Ueber die Pollenentleerung bei einigen Gymnospermen. Flora 91:237–63. *figs. 19.* 1902.

214. GOODSPEED, T. H., Chromosome number in the *Sequoias.* Bot. Gazette 69:348–49. 1920.

215. GORDON, MARJORIE, Ray tracheids in *Sequoia sempervirens.* Bot. Gazette 54:256. 1912.

216. GOROSCHANKIN, J., Zur Kenntniss der Corpuscula bei den Gymnospermen. Bot. Zeit. 41:825–31. *pl. 7A.* 1883; Ueber den Befruchtungs-Process bei *Pinus Pumilio.* 1883.

217. GOTHAN, W., Zur Anatomie lebender und fossiler Gymnospermenhölzer. Abhandl. Preuss. Geol. Landesanstalt. Neue Folge. Heft 44. 1905.

218. ———, Die fossilen Hölzer von König Karls Land. Handl. Kgl. Svensk. Vetensk-Akad. 42:No. 10.

219. GRAND D'EURY, C., La flore carbonifère du Département de la Loire. Mém. Acad. Sci. 24: pp. 624. *pls. 38.* 1877.

220. ———, Sur les rhizomes et les racines des fougères fossiles et des Cycadofilices. Compt. Rend. Acad. Sci. Paris. 138:607–10. 1904.

221. ———, Sur les graines des Neuropteridées. Compt. Rend. Acad. Sci. Paris. 139:23–27, 782–86. 1904.

222. ———, Sur les *Rhabdocarpus*, les graines et l'évolution des Cordaitées. Compt. Rend. Acad. Sci. Paris 140:995–98. 1905.

223. ———, Sur les graines de Sphenopteris, sur l'attribution des *Codonospermum*, et sur l'extrême variété des grains des fougères. Compt. Rend. Acad. Sci. Paris 141:812–15. 1905.

224. ———, Sur les graines trouvées attachées au *Pecopteris pluckenetii* Schlot. Compt. Rend. Acad. Sci. Paris. 140:920–23. *figs. 2.* 1905.

225. ———, Sur les inflorescences des fougères avec graines, etc. Compt. Rend. Acad. Sci. Paris 143:764. 1906.

226. GROOM, PERCY, A preliminary inquiry into the significance of tracheid caliber in Coniferae. Bot. Gazette 57:287–307. 1914.

227. GROOM, PERCY, and RUSHTON, W., Structure of the wood of East Indian species of *Pinus.* Jour. Linn. Soc. Bot. 41:457–90. *pls. 24, 25.* 1913.

228. HAGERUP, O., Zur Organogenie und Phylogenie der Koniferen-Zapfen. Det. kgl. Danske. Videnskabernes Selokab. Biologiske Meddelelser 10:1–82. 1933.

229. HAINING, HULDA J., Development of embryo of *Gnetum.* Bot. Gazette 70:436–45. *pls. 39–41.* 1920.

230. HALE, J. D., The bars of Sanio. Bot. Gazette 76:241–56. 1923.

231. HANDA, M. R., The life-history of *Thuja occidentalis.* Jour. Burma Research Soc. 16:214–19. *pl. 1.* 1926.

232. HARRIS, T. M., A new member of the Caytoniales. New Phytol. **33**:97–114. No. 2. 97–114. 1933.

233. HARVEY, L. R. H., Intra-microsporangial development of the tube in the microspore of *Pinus sylvestris*. Rep. Michigan Acad. Sci. **19**:333–35. 1917.

234. HAWKER, L. E., Microsporogenesis in *Taxus*. Ann. Botany **44**:535–39. 1930.

235. HAYATA, B., *Taiwania*, a new genus of conifers. Jour. Linn. Soc. Bot. **32**: 330–32. *pl. 16*. 1906.

236. ———, On *Taiwania* and its affinity to other genera. Bot. Mag. Tokyo **21**:21–27. *pl. 1*. 1907.

237. HAYDON, WALTER T., The seed production of *Pinus sylvestris*. Proc. and Trans. Liverpool Biol. Soc. **22**:1–32. *figs. 16*. 1907.

238. ———Flora fossilis arctica. 1868–83.

239. HEER, O., Zur Geschichte der *Ginkgo*-artigen Bäume. Engler's Bot. Jahrb. **1**:1–13. 1880.

240. HEMENWAY, A. F., *Cryptomeria japonica*. Bot. Gazette **52**:153–54. *figs. 4*. 1911.

241. HEMSLEY, Hybrid cycads. Gardeners Chronicle. **19**:466–67. 1883.

242. HERZFELD, DR. STEPHANIE, Die Blüthen der Bennettitalen. Oesterr. Bot. Zeitsch. **62**:289–303. *figs. 14*. 1912.

243. ———, *Ephedra campylopoda*. Morphologie der weiblichen Blüthe und Befruchtungsvorgang. Denkschriften der Akademie der Wissenschaften in Wien. Mathematisch-Naturwissenschaftliche Klasse. **98**:243–68. *pls. 1, 2*. 1922.

244. ———, Beiträge zur Kenntniss von *Ginkgo*. Jahrb. Wiss. Bot. **66**:814–62. *pls. 14–17*. 1927.

245. ———, Ueber die Kernteilung im Proembryo von *Ginkgo biloba*. Jahrb. wiss. Bot. **69**:264–94. 1928.

246. HILL, T. G., On secondary thickening in recent Pteridophyta. New Phytol. **5**:208–14. 1906.

247. ———, The germination of *Gnetum Gnemon* L. Jour. Roy. Hort. Soc. **34**: 1, 2. 1908.

248. HILL, T. G., and DE FRAINE, E., On the seedling structure of gymnosperms. Ann. Botany **20**:471–73. 1906.

249. ———, On the seedling structure of gymnosperms. I. Ann. Botany **22**: 689–712. *pl. 8. figs. 35*. 1908.

250. ———, On the seedling structure of gymnosperms. II. Ann. Botany **23**: 189–227. *pl. 15. figs. 11*. 1909.

251. ———, On the seedling structure of gymnosperms. III. Ann. Botany **23**: 433–58. *pl. 30*. 1909.

252. ———, On the seedling structure of gymnosperms. IV. Gnetales. Ann. Botany **24**:319–33. *pls. 22, 23*. 1910.

253. HIRASÉ, S., Études sur la fécondation et l'embryogénie du *Ginkgo biloba*. Jour. Coll. Sci. Imp. Univ. Tokyo **8**:307–22. *pls. 31, 32.* 1895.

254. ———, (Announcement of the spermatozoid of *Ginkgo*). Bot. Mag. Tokyo **10**:171, 172. May 1896. (Japanese.)

255. ———, (Preliminary report on the spermatozoid of *Ginkgo*). Bot. Mag. Tokyo **10**:325–28. Oct. 1896. (Japanese.)

256. ———, Études sur la fécondation et l'embryogénie du *Ginkgo biloba*. Jour. Coll. Sci. Imp. Univ. Tokyo **12**:103–49. *pls. 7–9.* 1898.

257. ———, Nouvelles recherches sur la fécondation et l'embryogénie du *Ginkgo biloba*. Bot. Mag. Tokyo **32**:139–43. 1918.

258. HOFMEISTER, W., Embryobildung der Phanerogamen. Jahrb. W. Bot. **1**: 82–188. *pls. 7–10.* 1858.

259. ———, On the germination, development, and fructification of the higher Cryptogamia. English Translation. London. 1863.

260. ———, Lehre der Pflanzenzelle. 1867.

261. HOLDEN, RUTH, Ray tracheids in the Coniferales. Bot. Gazette **55**:56–66. *pls. 1, 2.* 1913.

262. ———, Some fossil plants from eastern Canada. Ann. Botany **27**:243–55. *pls. 22, 23.* 1913.

263. ———, Cretaceous *Pityoxyla* from Clifford, N.J. Proc. Amer. Acad. **48**: 609–23. *pls. 4.* 1913.

264. ———, Contributions to the anatomy of Mesozoic conifers. ·I. Jurassic coniferous woods from Yorkshire. Ann. Botany **27**:533–45. *pls. 39, 40.* 1913.

265. ———, On the relation between *Cycadites* and *Pseudocycas*. New Phytol. **13**:334–40. *pls. 3.* 1914.

266. ———, Contributions to the anatomy of Mesozoic conifers. II. Cretaceous lignites from Clifford, N.J. Bot. Gazette **58**:168–77. *pls. 12–15.* 1914.

267. ———, A Jurassic wood from Scotland. New Phytol. **14**:205–9. *pl. 3.* 1915.

268. ———, On the cuticles of some Indian conifers. Bot. Gazette **60**:215–27. *pl. 11.* 1915.

269. HOLLICK, A., Cycads, living and extinct. Jour. N.Y. Bot. Gard. **24**:135–40. 1926.

270. HOLLICK, A., and JEFFREY, E. C., Affinities of certain cretaceous plant remains commonly referred to the genera *Dammara* and *Brachyphyllum*. Amer. Nat. **40**:189–215. *pls. 1–5.* 1906.

271. ———, Studies of cretaceous coniferous remains from Kreischerville, New York. Mem. N.Y. Bot. Garden **3**:1–138. *pls. 1–29.* 1909.

272. HOOKER, J. D., On *Welwitschia*, a new genus of Gnetaceae. Trans. Linn. Soc. London **24**:1–48. *pls. 1–4.* 1863.

273. HUTCHINSON, A. H., The male gametophyte of *Abies*. Bot. Gazette **57**: 148–52. *figs. 15.* 1914.

274. ———, On the male gametophyte of *Picea canadensis*. Bot. Gazette **59**: 287–300. *pls. 15–19.* 1915.

275. ———, Fertilization in *Abies balsamea*. Bot. Gazette **60**:457–72. *pls. 16–20.* 1915.

276. ———, Morphology of *Keteleeria fortunei*. Bot. Gazette **63**:124–34. *pls. 7, 8.* 1917.

277. ———, Embryogeny of *Abies*. Bot. Gazette **77**:280–88. *pls. 4.* 1924.

278. IKENO, S., Das Spermatozoid von *Cycas revoluta*. Bot. Mag. Tokyo **10**: 367, 368. 1896.

279. ———, Vorläufige Mittheilung über die Spermatozoiden bei *Cycas revoluta*. Bot. Centralbl. **69**:1–3. 1897.

280. ———, Untersuchungen über die Entwickelung der Geschlechtsorgane und den Vorgang der Befruchtung bei *Cycas revoluta*. Jahrb. Wiss. Bot. **32**:557–602. *pls. 8–10.* 1898.

281. ———, Contribution à l'étude de la fécondation chez le *Ginkgo biloba*. Ann. Sci. Nat. Bot. VIII. **13**:305–18. *pls. 2, 3.* 1901.

282. ISHIKAWA, M., Ueber die Zahl der Chromosomen von *Ginkgo biloba*. Bot. Mag. Tokyo **24**:225, 226. *figs. 3.* 1910.

283. JACCARD, P., Le développement du pollen de l'*Ephedra helvetica*. Archiv. Sci. Phys. et Nat. III. **30**:280–82. 1893; rev. in Bot. Centralblatt. Beih. **4**:234. 1894.

284. ———, Recherches embryologiques sur l'*Ephedra helvetica*. Bull. Soc. Vaudoise Sci. Nat. **30**. *pls. 10.* 1894; rev. in Bot. Centralbl. **61**:111–13. 1895.

285. JÄGER, L., Beiträge zur Kenntniss der Endospermbildung und zur Embryologie von *Taxus baccata*. Flora **86**:241–88. *pls. 15–19.* 1899.

286. JEFFREY, E. C., The structure and development of the stem in the Pteridophyta and Gymnosperms. Phil. Trans. Roy. Soc. London B **195**:119–46. *pls. 1–6.* 1902.

287. ———, Comparative anatomy of gymnosperms in COULTER and CHAMBERLAIN's Morphology of Angiosperms. New York. Appleton. 1903.

288. ———, Vascular anatomy in COULTER and CHAMBERLAIN's Morphology of Angiosperms. New York. 1903.

289. ———, The origin and organization of coal. Mem. Amer. Acad. Sci. I, No. 1. 1924.

290. ———, The comparative anatomy of the Coniferales. I. The genus *Sequoia*. Mem. Boston Soc. Nat. Hist. **5**:441–59. *pls. 68–71.* 1903.

291. ———, A fossil *Sequoia* from the Sierra Nevada. Bot. Gazette **38**:321–32. *pls. 18, 19.* 1904.

292. ———, The comparative anatomy of the Coniferales. II. The Abietineae. Mem. Boston Soc. Nat. Hist. **6**:1–37. *pls. 1–7.* 1904.

293. ———, *Araucariopitys*, a new genus of araucarians. Bot. Gazette **44**: 435–44. *pls. 27–30.* 1907.

294. JEFFREY, E. C., On the structure of the leaf in cretaceous pines. Ann. Botany 22:207–20. *pls. 13, 14.* 1908.

295. ———, Traumatic ray tracheids in *Cunninghamia sinensis.* Ann. Botany 22:593–602. *pl. 31.* 1908.

296. ———, Are there foliar gaps in the Lycopsida? Bot. Gazette 46:241–58. *pls. 17, 18.* 1908.

297. ———, On the affinities of the genus *Yezonia.* Ann. Botany 24:767–73. *pl. 65.* 1910.

298. ———, A new araucarian genus from the Triassic. Proc. Boston Soc. Nat. Hist. 34:325–32. *pls. 31, 32.* 1910.

299. ———, A new *Prepinus* from Martha's Vineyard. Proc. Boston Soc. Nat. Hist. 34:333–38. *pl. 33.* 1910.

300. ———, The history, comparative anatomy, and evolution of the *Araucarioxylon* type. Proc. Amer. Acad. 48:531–71. *pl. 7.* 1912.

301. ———, The anatomy of woody plants. University of Chicago Press. 1917.

302. Technical Contribution I. Improved method of softening hard tissues. Bot. Gazette 86:456–57. 1928.

303. ———, Resin canals in the evolution of the conifers. Proc. Nat. Acad. Sci. 11:101–5. 1925.

304. JEFFREY, E. C., and CHRYSLER, M. A., On cretaceous Pityoxyla. Bot. Gazette 42:1–15. *pls. 1, 2.* 1906.

305. ———, The microgametophyte of the Podocarpineae. Amer. Nat. 41:355–64. *figs. 5.* 1907.

306. JUEL, H. O., Beiträge zur Kenntniss der Tetradenbildung. Jahrb. Wiss. Bot. 35:626–59. *pls. 15, 16.* 1900.

307. ———, Ueber den Pollenschlauch von *Cupressus.* Flora 93:56–62. *pl. 3.* 1904.

308. JURANYI, L., Bau und Entwickelung des Pollens bei *Ceratozamia longifolia* Miq. Jahrb. Wiss. Bot. 8:382–400. *pls. 31–34.* 1872.

309. KARSTEN, G., Beiträge zur Entwickelungsgeschichte der Gattung *Gnetum.* Bot. Zeit. 50:205–15, 221–31, 237–46. *pls. 5, 6.* 1892.

310. ———, Zur Entwickelungsgeschichte der Gattung *Gnetum.* Cohn's Beitr. Biol. Pflanz. 6:337–82. *pls. 8–11.* 1893.

311. ———, Untersuchungen über die Gattung *Gnetum.* Ann. Jard. Bot. Buitenzorg. 11:195–218. *pls. 17–19.* 1893.

312. KASHYAP, Abnormal sporophyll in the male cone of *Cycas circinalis.* Jour. Indian Bot. Soc. 4:312–14. 1924.

313. KERNER VON MARILAUN, Das Pflanzenleben. Leipzig & Vienna. 1896.

314. KERSHAW, E. M., Structure and development of the ovule of *Bowenia spectabilis.* Ann. Botany 26:625–46. *pl. 61. figs. 16.* 1912.

315. KIDSTON, R., On the fructifications of some ferns from the Carboniferous formation. Trans. Roy. Soc. Edinburgh 33:137–56. *pls. 8. figs. 7.* 1887.

316. ——, On the various divisions of British Carboniferous rocks, as determined by their fossil floras. Proc. Roy. Soc. Edinburgh **12**:183–257. 1893–94.

317. ——, On the fructification of *Neuropteris heterophylla* Brongniart. Proc. Roy. Soc. London **72**:487. 1904 (abstract); Phil. Trans. Roy. Soc. London B **197**:1–5. *pl. 1.* 1904.

318. ——, Preliminary note on the occurrence of microsporangia in organic connection with the foliage of *Lyginodendron*. Proc. Roy. Soc. London **76**: 358–60. *pl. 6.* 1905.

319. ——, The early history of seed bearing plants as recorded in the Carboniferous flora. Wilde Lecture. Mem. and Proc. Manchester Lit. and Phil. Soc. **49**:No. 12. pp. 32. *pls. 3.* 1905.

320. ——, On the microsporangia of the Pteridospermae, with remarks on their relationships to existing groups. Phil. Trans. Roy. Soc. London B 413–45. *pls. 25–28.* 1906.

321. ——, On the fossil flora of the Staffordshire coal fields. III. The fossil flora of the Westphalian series of the South Staffordshire coal fields. Trans. Roy. Soc. Edinburgh **50**:73–190. *pls. 5–16.* 1914.

322. KILDAHL, N. JOHANNA, Development of the walls in the proembryo of *Pinus Laricio*. Bot. Gazette **44**:102–7. *pls. 8, 9.* 1907.

323. ——, The morphology of *Phyllocladus alpina*. Bot. Gazette **46**:339–48. *pls. 20–22.* 1908.

324. ——, Affinities of *Phyllocladus*. Bot. Gazette **46**:464, 465. 1908.

325. KIRKWOOD, J. E., Bisporangiate cones of *Larix*. Bot. Gazette **61**:256, 257. *fig. 1.* 1916.

326. KOCH, F., Die Cycadeen im Lichte der Wegener'schen Kontinent- und Polarwanderungstheorie. Mitteil. Deutsch. Dendrol. Gesell. **35.** 1925.

327. KÖKETSU, R., Serodiagnostische Untersuchungen über die Verwandschaftsverhältnisse der Gymnospermen. Mitt. Mediz. Fakultät Univ. Kyushu. **4.** 1917.

328. KRÄUSEL, R., Die fossilen Koniferenhölzer. Palaeontographica. **62**:185–275. Stuttgart. 1919.

329. ——, Fossile Cycadaceae in ENGLER und PRANTL'S Die Nat. Pflanzenfamilien. 2d. ed. **13**:82–98. 1926.

330. ——, Wesen und phylogenetische Bedeutung der ältesten Gefässpflanzen. Ber. Deutsch. Bot. Gesell. **50**:5–12. 1932.

331. ——, Relation of *Pinoxylon dakotense* Knowlton to *Protopiceoxylon* Gothan. Bot. Gazette **94**:419–20. 1932.

332. KUBART, BRUNO, Die weibliche Blüthe von *Juniperus communis* L. Sitzungsber. Kais. Akad. Wiss. Wien **114**:29. *pls. 2.* 1905.

333. KURZ H. and DEMAREE, D., Cypress buttresses and knees in relation to water and air. Ecology, V **15**:36–41. 1934.

334. KUWADA, Y., On the staining reaction of the spermatozoids and egg protoplasm in *Cycas revoluta*. Bot. Mag. Tokyo **39**:128–32. 1925.

335. KUWADA and MAEDA, On the structure of the cytoplasm around the blepharoplast in *Cycas revoluta*. Mem. Coll. Sci. Kyoto Univ. 4:165–74. 1929.

336. LAMB, SISTER MARY ALICE, Leaflets of Cycadaceae. Bot. Gazette 76: 185–202. *pls. 15, 16.* 1923.

337. LAND, W. J. G., A morphological study of *Thuja*. Bot. Gazette 34:249–59. *pls. 6, 8.* 1902.

338. ——, Spermatogenesis and oogenesis in *Ephedra trifurca*. Bot. Gazette 38:1–18. *pls. 1–4.* 1904.

339. ——, Fertilization and embryogeny in *Ephedra trifurca*. Bot. Gazette 44:273–92. *pls. 20–22.* 1907.

340. ——, Vegetative reproduction in an *Ephedra*. Bot. Gazette 55:439–45. *figs. 5.* 1913.

341. LANG, W. H., Studies in the development and morphology of cycadean sporangia. I. The microsporangia of *Stangeria paradoxa*. Ann. Botany 11:421–38. *pl. 22.* 1897.

342. ——, Studies in the development and morphology of cycadean sporangia. II. The ovule of *Stangeria paradoxa*. Ann. Botany 14:281–306. *pls. 17, 18.* 1900.

343. LANGDON, DR. LA DEMA, Stem anatomy of *Dioon spinulosum*. Bot. Gazette 70:110–25. *pls. 15–17.* 1920.

344. LAWSON, A. A., The gametophyte, archegonia, fertilization, and embryo of *Sequoia sempervirens*. Ann. Botany 18:1–28. *pls. 1–4.* 1904.

345. ——, The gametophyte, archegonia, fertilization, and embryo of *Cryptomeria japonica*. Ann. Botany 18:417–44. *pls. 27–30.* 1904.

346. ——, The gametophytes, fertilization, and embryo of *Cephalotaxus drupacea*. Ann. Botany 21:1–23. *pls. 1–4.* 1907.

347. ——, The gametophytes and embryo of the Cupressineae, with special reference to *Libocedrus decurrens*. Ann. Botany 21:281–301. *pls. 24–26.* 1907.

348. ——, The gametophytes and embryo of *Pseudotsuga douglasii*. Ann. Botany 23:163–80. *pls. 12–14.* 1909.

349. ——, The gametophytes and embryo of *Sciadopitys verticillata*. Ann. Botany 24:403–21. *pls. 29–31.* 1910.

350. ——, The life history of *Microcachrys tetragona* (Hook.). Proc. Linn. Soc. New So. Wales 48:177–93. *pls. 15, 16.* 1923.

351. ——, The life history of *Pherosphaera*. Proc. Linn. Soc. New So. Wales 48:499–516. *pl. 1. figs. 31.* 1923.

352. ——, A contribution to the life history of *Bowenia*. Proc. Roy. Soc. Edinb. 54:357–94. 1926.

353. LE GOC, M. J., Observations on the centripetal and centrifugal xylems in the petioles of cycads. Ann. Botany 28:183–93. *pl. 11.* 1914.

354. LE GOC, M. G., Effect of foreign pollination in *Cycas Rumphii*. Ann. Roy. Bot. Gard. Paradenya 6:187–94. 1917.

355. LIFE, A. C., The tuber-like roots of *Cycas revoluta*. Bot. Gazette 31:265–71. *figs. 10.* 1901.

356. LIGNIER, O., Des *"Raducilites reticulatus* Lignier" sont probablement des radicelles de Cordaitales. Separate without citation.

357. ——, Structure et affinités du *Bennettites Morieri*. Mem. Soc. Linn. Normandie 18. 1894.

358. ——, La fleur des Gnétacées est-elle intermédiaire entre celle des gymnospermes et celle des angiospermes? Bull. Soc. Linn. Normandie V. 7: 55–71. 1903.

359. ——, Le fruit du *Williamsonia gigas* Carr. et les Bennettitales, documents nouveaux et notes critiques. Mém. Soc. Linn. Normandie 21:19–56. *figs. 9.* 1903.

360. ——, Notes complémentaires sur la structure du *Bennettites Morieri*. Bull. Soc. Linn. Normandie V. 8:3–7. *figs. 3.* 1905.

361. ——, Le fruit des Bennettitées et l'ascendance des angiospermes. Bull. Soc. Bot. France IV. 8:1–17. 1908.

362. ——, Le *Bennettites Morieri* Lignier se reproduisait probablement par parthénogénèse. Bull. Soc. Bot. France 58:224–27. 1911.

363. ——, Les Gnétales, leurs fleurs, et leur position systématique. Ann. Sci. Nat. Bot. IX. 16:55–185. *figs. 40.* 1912.

364. ——, Stomates des écailles interséminales chez le *Bennettites Morieri*. Bull. Soc. Bot. France 59:425–28. *figs. 2.* 1912.

365. ——, Différenciation des tissus dans le bourgeon végétatif du *Cordaites lingulatus* B. Ren. Ann. Sci. Nat. Bot. IX. 17:233–54. 1913.

366. LIGNIER, O., and TISON, A., Les Gnétales sont des angiospermes apétales. Compt. Rend. Acad. Sci. Paris 152:201–4. 1911.

367. LINDLEY, J., and HUTTON, J., Fossil flora of Great Britain. 1830.

368. LLOYD, FRANCIS E., Vivipary in *Podocarpus*. Torreya 2:113–17. *figs. 3.* 1902.

369. ——, Morphological instability, especially in *Pinus radiata*. Bot. Gazette 57:314–19. *pl. 14. figs. 2.* 1914.

370. LOMAX, J., Some new features in relation to *Lyginodendron oldhamium*. Ann. Bot. 16:601–2. 1902.

371. LOTSY, J. P., Contributions to the life history of the genus *Gnetum*. Ann. Jard. Botl. Buitenzorg. II. 1:46–114. *pls. 2–11.* 1899.

372. ——, Parthenogenesis bei *Gnetum ula* Brangn. Flora 92:397–404. *pls. 9, 10.* 1903.

373. LOPRIORE, G., Ueber die Vielkörnigkeit der Pollenkörner von *Araucaria Bidwillii*. Vorläufige Mitteilung. Ber. Deutsch. Bot. Gesell. 23:335–46. *pl. 15.* 1905.

374. LUTZ, H. J., A new species of *Cupressoxylon* (Goeppert) Gothan from the Jurassic of South Dakota. Bot. Gazette 90:92–107. *figs. 13.* 1930.

375. LYON, HAROLD L., The embryogeny of *Ginkgo*. Minn. Bot. Studies 3: 275–90. *pls. 29–43.* 1904.

376. MacMillan, Conway, Note on some British Columbian dwarf trees. Bot. Gazette **38**:379–81. *figs. 3.* 1904.

377. McNab, W. R., On the development of the flowers of *Welwitschia mirabilis.* Trans. Linn. Soc. London **28**:507–12. *pl. 40.* 1873.

378. Mägdefrau, K., Die Stammesgeschichte der Lycopodiales. Biol. Zentralbl. **52**:280–94. 1932.

379. Mann, E. A., and Wallas, T. J., Investigation of the disease in cattle known as "rickets" or "wobbles" and examination of the poisonous principle of the *Zamia* palm (*Macrozamia Fraseri*). Proc. Roy. Soc. N. S. Wales. 1906.

380. Mann, M. C., Microsporogenesis of *Ginkgo biloba* with especial reference to the distribution of the plastids and to cell wall formation. Univ. Calif. Publ. Agric. Sci. **2**:243–48. *pl. 44.* 1924.

381. Markgraf, Fr., Gnetales, in Engler-Prantl's Die Natürlichen Pflanzenfamilien. 1926.

382. Marloth, R., The flora of South Africa. **1**:92–100. 1913.

383. ———, Note on the entomophilous nature of *Encephalartos.* Trans. Roy. Soc. South Africa. **4**:69–71. 1914.

384. Maslen, A. J., The structure of *Mesoxylon Sutcliffii.* Ann. Botany **25**:381–414. *pls. 33–36.* 1911.

385. Masters, M. T., Comparative morphology, anatomy and life history of the Coniferae. Jour. Linn. Soc. London Bot. **27**:226–332. *figs. 29.* 1891.

386. Masters, Maxwell T., On the Conifers of China. Jour. Linn. Soc. London Bot. **37**:410–24. 1906.

387. ———, On the distribution of the species of conifers in the several districts of China, and the occurrence of the same species in neighboring countries. Jour. Linn. Soc. London Bot. **38**:198–205. 1908.

388. Matte, H., Une anomalie de structure dans l'écaille ovulifère de *Ceratozamia mexicana.* Bull. Soc. Linn. Normandie V. **7**:52–54. 1903.

389. ———, Recherches sur l'appareil libéro-ligneux des Cycadées. pp. 233. *pls. 16. figs. 246.* 1904.

390. ———, Compléments à la structure mériphytaire du *Bowenia spectabilis* Hord. Compt. Rend. Assoc. Fr. Adv. Sci. **1905**:409–16.

391. ———, Sur la structure de l'embryon et des germinations du genre *Zamia* L. Bull. Soc. Sci. et Méd. de l'Ouest **18**:Nos. 2 and 3. 1909.

392. Messeri, A., Sul valore sistematico dei caratteri anatomici delle folioline delle Cicadee. Nuovo Giorn. Bot. Ital. n. ser. **35**:319–27. 1927.

393. Mettenius, G. H., Beiträge zur Anatomie der Cycadeen. Abh. K. Sächs. Gesell. Wiss. **7**:565–608. *pls. 1–5.* 1861.

394. Miller, Ward L., Polyxylic stem of *Cycas media.* Bot. Gazette **68**:208–21. *figs. 11.* 1919.

395. Miquel, F. A. W., Monographia Cycadearum. 1841.

396. Miyake, K. (On the spermatozoid of *Ginkgo*). Bot. Mag. Tokyo **12**:23–39. 1898. (Japanese.)

397. ———, The spermatozoid of *Ginkgo*. Jour. Applied Micr. **5**:1773–80. *figs. 10*. 1902.

398. ———, Contribution to the fertilization and embryogeny of *Abies balsamea*. Beih. Bot. Centralbl. **14**:134–44. *pls. 6–8*. 1903.

399. ———, On the development of the sexual organs and fertilization in *Picea excelsa*. Ann. Botany **17**:351–72. *pls. 16, 17*. 1903.

400. ———, Ueber die Spermatozoiden von *Cycas revoluta*. Ber. Deutsch. Bot. Gesell. **24**:78–83. *pl. 6*. 1906.

401. ———, The development of the gametophytes and embryogeny of *Cunninghamia* (preliminary note). Bot. Mag. Tokyo **22**:45–50. *figs. 14*. 1908.

402. ———, The development of the gametophytes and embryogeny in *Cunninghamia sinensis*. Beih. Bot. Centralbl. **27**:1–25. *pls. 1–5. figs. 2*. 1910.

403. MIYAKE, K., and YASUI, KONO, On the gametophytes and embryo of *Pseudolarix*. Ann. Botany **25**:639–47. *pl. 48*. 1911.

404. MOTTIER, D. M., On the archegonium and apical growth of the stem in *Tsuga canadensis* and *Pinus sylvestris*. Bot. Gazette **17**:141–43. *pl. 8*. 1892.

405. MURRILL, W. A., The development of the archegonium and fertilization in the hemlock spruce (*Tsuga canadensis*). Ann. Botany **14**:583–607. *pls. 31, 32*. 1900.

406. NAKAMURA, T., The pollen mother-cells in *Cycas revoluta*. Mem. Coll. Sci. Kyoto Univ. **4**:353–70. 1929.

407. NATHORST, A. G., Beiträge zur Kenntniss einiger mesozoischen Cycadophyten. Handl. Kgl. Svensk. Vetensk.-Akad. **36**:1–28. *pls. 1–3*. 1902.

408. ———, Palaeobotanische Mitteilungen. İ. *Pseudocycas*, eine neue Cycadophytengattung aus den cenomanen Kreideablagerungen Grönlands. Handl. Kgl. Svensk. Vetensk.-Akad. **42**:1–11. *pls. 1–3*. 1907.

409. ———, Palaeobotanische Mitteilungen. III. *Lycostrobus Scotti*, eine grosse Sporophyllähre aus den rätischen Ablagerungen Schonens. Handl. Kgl. Svensk. Vetensk.-Akad. **43**:1–12. *pls. 1, 2*. 1908.

410. ———, Palaeobotanische Mitteilungen. IV. Ueber die Untersuchung kutinisierter fossiler Pflanzenteile. Handl. Kgl. Svensk. Vetensk.-Akad. **43**: 1–13. *pls. 1, 2*. 1908.

411. ———, Palaeontologische Mitteilungen. VI. *Antholithus Zeilleri*, n. sp., mit noch erhaltenen Pollenkörnern aus den rhätischen Ablagerungen Schonens. Handl. Kgl. Svensk. Vetensk.-Akad. **43**:20–24. *pls. 2, 4*. 1908.

412. ———, Palaeobotanische Mitteilungen. VIII. Handl. Kgl. Svensk. Vetensk.-Akad. **45**:No. 4. 1910.

413. ———, Ueber die Gattung *Cycadocarpidium* (Nath) nebst einigen Bemerkungen über *Podozamites*. Handl. Kgl. Svensk. Vetensk.-Akad. **41**: No. 8. pp. 11.

414. NICHOLS, GEORGE E., A morphological study of *Juniperus communis* var. depressa. Beih. Bot. Centralbl. **25**:201–41. *pls. 8–17. figs. 4*. 1910.

415. Noé, A. C., Pennsylvanian Flora of Northern Illinois. Ill. Geol. Survey Bull. 52. 1925.

416. Noelle, W., Studien zur vergleichenden Anatomie der Coniferenwurzeln mit Rücksicht auf die Systematik. Bot. Zeit. 68:169–266. 1910.

417. Norén, C. O., Ueber Befruchtung bei *Juniperus communis*. Vorläufige Mitteilung. Arkiv. Bot. Svensk. Vetensk.-Akad. 3:11. 1904.

418. ——, Zur Entwickelungsgeschichte des *Juniperus communis*. Uppsala Universitets Ärsskrift 1907:pp. 64. *pls. 4.*

419. ——, Zur Kenntniss der Entwickelung von *Saxogothea conspicua* Lindl. Svensk. Bot. Tidsskr. 2:101–22. *pls. 7–9.* 1908.

420. Oersted, A. S., Bidrag til Naaletroeernes Morphologi. Videns. Meddel. Nat. Foren. Copenhagen. 1864.

421. Oliver, F. W., On some points of apparent resemblance in certain fossil and recent gymnospermous seeds. New Phytol. 1:145–54. *figs. 4–6.* 1902.

422. ——, The ovules of the older gymnosperms. Ann. Botany 17:451–76. *pl. 24. figs. 20.* 1903.

423. ——, Notes on *Trigonocarpon* Brongn. and *Polylophospermum* Brongn., two genera of paleozoic seeds. New Phytol. 3:96–104. *pl. 2.* 1904.

424. ——, A new pteridosperm. New Phytol. 3:32. 1904.

425. ——, On the structure and affinities of *Stephanospermum* Brongn., a genus of fossil gymnosperm seeds. Trans. Linn. Soc. London Bot. II. 6: 361–400. *pls. 41–44.* 1904.

426. ——, Ueber die neuentdeckten Samen der Steinkohlenfarne. Biol. Centralbl. 25:401–18. *figs. 6.* 1905.

427. ——, "The origin of gymnosperms"; a discussion at the Linnaean Society. New Phytol. 5:68–76, 141–48. 1906.

428. ——, Pteridosperms and angiosperms. New Phytol. 5:232–42. 1906.

429. ——, On *Phystoma elegans* Williamson, an archaic type of seed from the paleozoic rocks.. Ann. Bot. 23:73–116. *pls. 5–7. figs. 10.* 1909.

430. Oliver, F. W., and Scott, D. H., On *Lagenostoma lomaxii*, the seed of *Lyginodendron*. Proc. Roy. Soc. London 71:477–81. 1903; reprint in Ann. Botany 17:625–29. 1903.

431. ——, On the structure of the paleozoic seed *Lagenostoma lomaxii*, with a statement of the evidence on which it is referred to *Lyginodendron*. Proc. Roy. Soc. London, Jan. 21. 1904 (abstract preprint); Phil. Trans. Roy. Soc. London B 197:193–247. *pls. 4–10.* 1904.

432. Osborn, T. G. B., The lateral roots of *Amyelon radicans* Will., and their mycorhiza. Ann. Botany 24:236–39. 1909.

433. Ottley, Alice M., The development of the gametophytes and fertilization in *Juniperus communis* and *Juniperus virginiana*. Bot. Gazette 48: 31–46. *pls. 1–4.* 1909.

434. Papadopoulos, Sophia, A morphological comparison of leaflets of a hybrid cycad and the two parents. Bot. Gazette 85:30–45. *figs. 21.* 1928.

435. PARLATORE, F., Studi organografici sui fiori e sui frutti delle conifere. Opuscula botanica. 1864.

436. PAVOLINI, A. F., La *Stangeria paradoxa* Th. Moore. Nuovo Giorn. Bot. Ital. **16**:335-51. 1909.

437. PAX, F., Allgemeine Morphologie der Pflanzen mit besonderer Berücksichtigung der Blüthenmorphologie. 1890.

438. PEARSON, H. H. W., Notes on the South African cycads. I. Trans. S. African Phil. Soc. **16**:341-54. *pls. 6-8.* 1906.

439. ———, Some observations on *Welwitschia mirabilis* Hooker. Phil. Trans. Roy. Soc. London B **198**:265-304. *pls. 18-22.* 1906.

440. ———, Further observations on *Welwitschia* Phil. Trans. Roy. Soc. London B **200**:331-402. *pls. 22-30.* 1909.

441. ———, On the embryo of *Welwitschia*. Ann. Botany **24**:759-66. *pl. 64.* 1910.

442. ———, On the microsporangium and microspore of *Gnetum*, with some notes on the structure of the inflorescence. Ann. Botany **26**:603-20. *pls. pls. 2. figs. 6.* 1912.

443. ———, Notes on the morphology of certain structures concerned in reproduction in the genus *Gnetum* (preliminary). Jour Linn. Soc. **43**:55, 56. 1915.

444. ———, A note on the inflorescence and flower of *Gnetum*. Ann. Bolus Herbarium **1**:152-72. *pls. 24-26.* 1915.

445. ———, Notes on the morphology of certain structures concerned in reproduction in the genus *Gnetum*. Trans. Linn. Soc. **8**:311-32. *pls. 31, 32.* 1915.

446. ———, Gnetales. Cambridge University Press. 1929.

447. ———, Notes on the morphology of the female flower of *Gnetum*. Trans. Roy. Soc. So. Africa **6**, Part I. 1917.

448. PENHALLOW, D. P., The anatomy of North American Coniferales, together with certain exotic species from Japan and Australia. Amer. Nat. **38**:243-73, 331-59, 523-54, 691-723. 1904.

449. ———, A manual of the North American gymnosperms, exclusive of the Cycadales but together with certain exotic species. Boston. 1907.

450. PETRIE, A. H. K., The chemist's examination of *Macrozamia spiralis*. Proc. Linn. Soc. N. S. Wales **45**:424-42. 1920.

451. PILGER, R., Taxaceae, in ENGLER's Das Pflanzenreich. 1903.

452. ———, Gymnospermae in ENGLER und PRANTL's Die Natürlichen Pflanzenfamilien. 2d. ed. 1926.

453. POLLOCK, JAMES B., Variations in the pollen grains of *Picea excelsa*. Amer. Nat. **49**:253-86. *pl. 1.* 1906.

454. POOLE, J. P., Comparative anatomy of leaves of cycads with reference to Cycadofilicales. Bot. Gazette **76**:203-14. *pls. 17-19.* 1923.

455. POTONIÉ, H., Lehrbuch der Pflanzenpalaeontologie. Berlin. 1899.

456. ———, Cycadofilicales, in ENGLER and PRANTL's Die Natürlichen Pflanzenfamilien **1**:780-98. 1902.

457. PRANKERD, THEODORA L., On the structure of the paleozoic seed *Lagenostoma ovoides*. Jour. Linn. Soc. London 40:461–90. *pls. 22–24.* 1912.

458. PRAT, HENRI, Note sur les pousses courtes du pin maritime. Bull. Biol. Arcachon 27:49–67. 1930.

459. PROSINA, M. N., Verhalten der Chondriosomen bei der Pollenentwickelung von *Larix dahurica*. Zeit. Zellforsch. u. Mic. Anat. 7:114–34. 1928.

460. RATTRAY, GEO., Notes on the pollination of some South African Cycads. Trans. Roy Soc. So. Africa. 3:259–71. 1913.

461. REED, FREDDA D., Flora of an Illinois coal ball. Bot. Gazette V. 81:460–69. 1926.

462. REINKE, J., Parasitische *Anabaena* in Wurzeln der Cycadeen. Gött. Nachr. 107. 1872.

463. RENAULT, B., Recherches sur la fructification de quelques végétaux provenant des gisements silicifiés d'Autun et de Saint Étienne. Ann. Sci. Nat. Bot. VI. 3:5–29. *pls. 1–4.* 1876.

464. ———, Structure comparée de quelques tiges de la flore carbonifère. Nouv. Arch. Mus. Hist. Nat. II. 2:213–48. *pls. 8.* 1879.

465. ———, Cours de botanique fossile. Paris. 1880–84.

466. ———, Note sur le genre *Atheotesta*. Mém. Soc. Hist. Nat. Saône-et-Loire. pp. 156, 158. 1887.

467. ———, Bassin houiller et Permien d'Autun et Épinac. IV. Flore fossile. pp. 557. 1896.

468. ———, Bassin houiller et Permien d'Antun et d'Épinae. IV. Flore fossile. Part II. pp. 578. *pls. 62.* Paris. 1896.

469. RENNER, OTTO, Ueber Zwitterblüthen bei *Juniperus communis*. Flora. 93:297–300. *figs. 3.* 1904.

470. REYNOLDS, LILLIAN G., The female gametophyte of *Microcycas*. Bot. Gazette 77:391–403. *pls. 28, 29.* 1924.

471. RHINE, J. B., Clogging of stomata in conifers in relation to smoke injury and distribution. Bot. Gazette 78:226–32. 1924.

472. ROBERTSON, AGNES, Spore formation in *Torreya californica*. New Phytol. 3:133–48. *pls. 3, 4.* 1904.

473. ———, Studies in the morphology of *Torreya californica*. II. The sexual organs and fertilization. New Phytol. 3:205–16. *pls. 7–9.* 1904.

474. ———, Some points in the morphology of *Phyllocladus alpina* Hook. Ann. Botany 20:259–65. *pls. 17, 18.* 1906.

475. ———, The Taxoideae; a phylogenetic study. New Phytol. 6:92–102. *pl. 1.* 1907.

476. ROSE, J. N., A new species of *Ephedra*. Contributions from the U.S. National Herbarium. 12:261. 1909.

477. SABLON, LECLERC DU, Recherches sur le tige des fougères. Ann. Sci. Nat. Bot. VII. 11:1–16. *pls. 1, 2.* 1890.

478. SACHS, J., Lehrbuch. 1868.

479. ———, Textbook of botany. Second English edition. 1882.

480. SAHNI, BIRBAL, Foreign pollen in the ovules of *Ginkgo* and of fossil plants. New Phytol. **14**:149–51. *pl. 2.* 1915.

481. ———, On the structure and affinities of *Acmopyle pancheri*, Pilger. Phil. Trans. Roy. Soc. London B **210**:253–310. *pls. 9–11.* 1920.

482. SAHNI, B., and MITRA, A. K., Notes on the anatomy of some New Zealand species of *Dacrydium*. Ann. Botany 75–89. *pl. 7.* 1927.

483. SAHNI, B., and SINGH, T. C. N., Notes on the vegetative anatomy and female cones of *Fitzroya patagonica*. Jour. Ind. Bot. Soc. **10**:1–20. 1931.

484. SALISBURY, E. J., On the relation between *Trigonocarpus* and *Ginkgo*. Ann. Botany **30**:356. 1916.

485. SANIO, K., Anatomie der gemeinen Kiefer. Jahrb. Wiss. Bot. **9**:50–120. 1873.

486. SAXTON, W. T., Development of the embryo in *Pinus Pinaster* Soland, with some notes on the life-history of the species in Cape Colony. S. African Jour. Sci. **6**:52–59. *pl. 2.* 1909.

487. ———, Preliminary account of the development of the ovule, gametophytes, and embryo of *Widdringtonia cupressoides* Endl. Bot. Gazette **48**:161–78. *pl. 11. figs. 3.* 1909.

488. ———, Parthenogenesis in *Pinus Pinaster*. Bot. Gazette **47**:406–9. *figs. 7.* 1909.

489. ———, The development of the embryo of *Encephalartos*. Bot. Gazette **49**:13–18. *pl. 2.* 1910.

490. ———, Contributions to the life-history of *Widdringtonia cupressoides*. Bot. Gazette **50**:30–48. *pls. 1–3.* 1910.

491. ———, Contributions to the life-history of *Callitris*. Ann. Botany **24**: July, 1910.

492. ———, Notes on the anatomy of *Widdringtonia* and *Callitris*. S. African Jour. Sci. **7**:282–86. *figs. 11.* 1910.

493. ———, Notes on an abnormal prothallus of *Pinus maritima* L. Ann.-Botany **26**:943–45. *fig. 1.* 1912.

494. ———, The classification of conifers. New Phytol. **12**:242–62. 1913.

495. ———, Contributions to the life-history of *Tetraclinis articulata* Masters with notes on the phylogeny of the Cupressoideae and Callitroideae. Ann. Botany **27**:577–605. 1913.

496. ———, Contributions to the life-history of *Actinostrobus pyramidalis* Miq. Ann. Botany **27**:321–45. *pls. 25–28.* 1913.

497. ———, Notes on conifers. I. The older fertile ovule of *Saxagothea*. Ann. Botany **43**:375–77. 1929.

498. ———, Notes on conifers. VIII. The morphology of *Austrotaxus spicata* Compton. Ann. Botany **48**:412–27. *figs. 25.* 1934.

499. ———, Notes on conifers. IX. The ovule and embryogeny of *Widdringtonia*. Ann. Botany **48**:429–31. 1934.

500. SAXTON, W. T., and DOYLE, J., The ovule and gametophyte of *Arthrotaxis selaginoides*. Ann. Botany **43**:833–40. 1929.

501. SCHIMPER, W. PH., and SCHENK, A., Handbuch der Palaeontologie. 1890.

502. SCHLEIDEN, M. J., Sur la signification morphologique du placentaire. Ann. Sci. Nat. Bot. II. 12:373–76. 1839.

503. SCHNARF, KARL, Embryologie der Gymnospermen. Handbuch der Pflanzenanatomie (K. LINSBAUER). II. Abteil. 2. Teil. Archegoniaten. 1933. Berlin. Gebrüder Bornträger.

504. SCHNEIDER, A., Mutualistic Symbiosis of algae and bacteria with *Cycas revoluta*. Bot. Gazette 10:25–32. *pl. 3*. 1894.

505. SCHUEPP, OTTO, Meristeme. Handbuch der Pflanzenanatomie. 1. Abteil. 2. Teil. Histologie. Band V. pp. 1–115. 1926.

506. SCHUSTER, JULIUS, Bemerkungen über Podozamites. Ber. Deutsch. Bot. Gesells. 29:450–56. *pl. 17*. 1911.

507. ———, Ueber die Fruktificanti von *Schuetzia anomala*. Sitzungsber. Kaiserl. Akad. Wiss. Wien 120:pp. 10. *pls. 2*. 1911.

508. ———, *Welwitschia* und Bennettitales. Bull. Soc. Linn. Normandie. 1912.

509. ———, Ueber das Verhältnis der systematischen Gliederung der geographischen Verbreitung und der paläontologischen Entwickelung der Cycadeen. ENGLER's Bot. Jahrb. 64:165–260. 1931.

510. ———, Cycadaceae. IV. Das Pflanzenreich. Vol. I. 1932.

511. SCOTT, D. H., The anatomical characters presented by the peduncles of Cycadaceae. Ann. Botany 11:399–419. *pls. 20, 21*. 1897.

512. ———, On the structure and affinities of fossil plants from the paleozoic rocks. III. *Medullosa anglica*, a new representative of the Cycadofilicales. Proc. Roy. Soc. London 64:249–53. 1889 (abstract). Phil. Trans. Roy. Soc. London B 191:81–126. *pls. 5–13*. 1899.

513. ———, On the primary wood of certain araucarioxylons. Ann. Botany 13:615–19. 1899.

514. ———, Studies in fossil botany. 1900.

515. ———, Note on the occurrence of a seedlike fructification in certain paleozoic lycopods. Proc. Roy. Soc. London 67:306–9. 1900.

516. ———, On the structure and affinities of fossil plants from the paleozoic rocks. IV. The seedlike fructification of *Lepidocarpon*, a genus of lycopodiaceous cones from the Carboniferous formation. Phil. Trans. Roy. Soc. London B 194:291–333. *pls. 38–43*. 1901.

517. ———, Primary structure of certain paleozoic stems. Trans. Roy. Soc. Edinburgh 40²:331–65. *pls. 1–6. figs. 5*. 1902.

518. ———, The old wood and the new. New Phytol. 1:25–30. 1902.

519. ———, The fernlike seed plants of the carboniferous flora. Sci. papers Internat. Bot. Congress. Vienna, 1905.

520. ———, What were the carboniferous ferns? Jour. Roy. Mic. Soc. 1905²:137–49. *pls. 1–3. figs. 32, 33*.

521. ———, The early history of seed bearing plants, as recorded in the carboniferous flora (The Wilde Lecture). Mem. and Proc. Manchester Lit. and Phil. Soc. 49³:32. *pls. 3*. 1905.

522. ———, The sporangia of *Stauropteris oldhamia* Binney. New Phytol. **4**: 114–20. *figs. 2*. 1905.

523. ———, On *Sutcliffia insignis*, a new type of Medulloseae from the lower Coal-measures. Trans. Linn. Soc. London II. **7**:45–68. *pl. 4*. 1906.

524. ———, The present position of paleozoic botany. Progressus rei botanicae (ed. J. P. LOTSY) I¹:139–217. *figs. 37*. 1906.

525. ———, The occurrence of germinating spores in *Stauropteris oldhamia*. New Phytol. **5**:170–72. 1906.

526. ———, "The origin of gymnosperms"; a discussion at the Linnaean Society. New Phytol. **5**:68–76, 141–48. 1906.

527. ———, Studies in fossil botany. Second ed. Vol. I. London. 1908.

528. ———, Studies in fossil botany. Second ed. Vol. II. London. 1909.

529. ———, The paleontological record. II. Plants. Darwin and modern science, pp. 200–222. Cambridge University Press, 1909.

530. ———, The structure of *Mesoxylon Lomaxii* and *M. poroxyloides*. Ann. Botany. **26**:1011–30. *pls. 87–90*. 1912.

531. ———, The evolution of plants. London and New York. 1912.

532. ———, On *Medullosa pusilla*. Proc. Roy. Soc. London B **87**:221–28. *pl. 13*. 1914.

533. ———, Studies in fossil botany. Third ed. Vol. II. 1923. Spermophyta. A. and C. Black. London.

534. ———, Extinct plants and problems of evolution. 1924. London. Macmillan & Co.

535. SCOTT, D. H., and MASLEN, ARTHUR, J., The structure of the paleozoic seeds *Trigonocarpus parkinsonii* Brongn. and *Trigonocarpus oliveri* sp. nov. I. Ann. Botany **21**:89–134. *pls. 11–14*. 1907.

536. ———, On *Mesoxylon*, a new genus of the Cordaitales (preliminary note). Ann. Botany **24**:236–39. 1910.

537. SEDGWICK, P. J., The life-history of *Encephalartos*. Bot. Gazette **77**:300–310. *pls. 2*. 1924.

538. SELLARDS, E. H., *Codonotheca*, a new type of spore-bearing organ from the Coal-measures. Amer. Jour. Sci. IV. **16**:87–95. *pl. 8*. 1903.

539. ———, Notes on the spore-bearing organ *Codonotheca* and its relationship with the Cycadofilicales. New Phytol. **6**:175–78. 1907.

540. SEWARD, A. C., On *Encephalartos Ghellinckii*, a rare cycad. Proc. Cambridge Phil. Soc. **9**:340–44. 1898.

541. ———, Notes on the Binney collection of Coal-measure plants. II. *Megaloxylon*, gen. nov. Proc. Cambridge Phil. Soc. **10**:158–74. *pls. 5–7*. 1899.

542. ———, Floras of the past; their composition and distribution. Rept. British Assoc. Adv. Sci. Section K. 1903. pp. 25.

543. ———, Notes on cycads. Proc. Cambridge Phil. Soc. **13**:293–302. 1906.

544. ———, "The origin of gymnosperms"; a discussion at the Linnean Society. New Phytol. **5**:68–76, 141–48. 1906.

545. SEWARD, A. C., A petrified *Williamsonia* from Scotland. Phil. Trans. Roy. Soc. London B **302**:101–26. *pls. 9–12.* 1912.

546. ———, Fossil plants. III. Pteridospermae to Cycadophyta. 1917.

547. ———, Fossil plants. IV. *Ginkgoales Coniferales Gnetales.* 1919.

548. ———, Plant life through the ages. Cambridge University Press. 1931.

549. SEWARD, A. C., and GOWAN, MISS J., The maidenhair tree (*Ginkgo biloba* L.). Ann. Botany **14**:109–54. *pls. 8–10.* 1900.

550. SEWARD, A. C., and FORD, SIBILLE, O., The Araucarieae, recent and extinct. Abstract read before Roy. Soc. London. December, 1905.

551. ———, The Araucarieae, recent and extinct. Phil. Trans. Roy. Soc. London B **198**:305–411. *pls. 23, 24. figs. 28,* 1906.

552. SHAW, W. R., Contribution to the life-history of *Sequoia.* Bot. Gazette **21**:332–39. *pl. 24.* 1896.

553. SHAW, F. J. F., A contribution to the anatomy of *Ginkgo biloba.* New Phytol. **7**:85–92. *figs. 16–18.* 1908.

554. ———, The seedling structure of *Araucaria bidwillii.* Ann. Botany **23**: 321–34. *pl. 21. figs. 6.* 1909.

555. SHIMAMURA, T., On the formation of proembryo of *Ginkgo biloba* L. Bot. Mag. Tokyo **42**:71–76. *pls. 2, 3.* 1928.

556. SIFTON, H. B., On the occurrence and significance of the "bars" or "rims" of Sanio in the cycads. Bot. Gazette **60**:400–405. *pl. 15.* 1915.

557. ———, Some characters of xylem tissue in cycads. Bot. Gazette **70**:425–35. 1920.

558. ———, The bars of Sanio and primordial pit in the gymnosperms. Trans. Roy. Soc. Canada **16**:83–99. 1922.

559. SIGRIANOKI, ALEXANDRE, Quelques observations sur l'*Ephedra helvetica* Mey. Thesis. pp. 62. *figs. 74.* Geneva. 1913.

560. SINNOTT, E. A. W., *Paracedroxylon,* a new type of araucarian wood. Rhodora **11**:165–73. *pls. 80, 81.* 1909.

561. ———, The gametophytes of Australasian podocarps. Science. N.S. **35**: 160. 1912.

562. ———, The morphology of the reproductive structures in the Podocarpineae. Ann. Botany **27**:39–82. *pls. 5–9.* 1913.

563. SLUDSKY, N., Ueber die Entwickelungsgeschichte des *Juniperus communis.* Vorläufige Mitteilung. Ber. Deutsch. Bot. Gesell. **23**:212–16. *pl. 7.* 1905.

564. SMALL, J. K., Seminole bread, the history of the genus *Zamia* in Florida. Jour. N.Y. Bot. Garden **22**:121–37. 1921.

565. SMITH, FRANCES GRACE, Morphology of the trunk and development of the microsporangium of cycads. Bot. Gazette **43**:187–204. *pl. 10.* 1907.

566. ———, Development of the ovulate strobilus and young ovule of *Zamia floridana.* Bot. Gazette **50**:128–41. *figs. 22.* 1910.

567. ———, Multiple cones in *Zamia floridana.* Bot. Gazette **88**:204–18. 1929.

568. SMITH, ISABEL S., The nutrition of the egg in *Zamia*. Bot. Gazette **37**: 346–52. *figs. 6.* 1904.

569. SMITH, R. W., The life-history of *Cedrus atlantica*. Bot. Gazette **75**:203–8. *pl. 11.* 1923.

570. SOKOLOWA, C., Naissance de l'endosperme dans le sac embryonnaire de quelques gymnospermes. Moscou. 1880.

571. SOLMES-LAUBACH, H., Ueber die Fructification von *Bennettites gibsonianus* Carr. Bot. Zeit. **48**:789–98, 805–15, 821–33, 843–47. *pls. 9, 10.* 1890.

572. ———, Die Sprossfolge der *Stangeria* und der übrigen Cycadeen. Bot. Zeit. **48**:177–87, 193–99, 209–15, 225–30. 1890.

573. ———, Fossil Botany. English translation. Oxford. 1891.

574. SOUTH, F. W., and COMPTON, R. H., On the anatomy of *Dioon edule* Lindl. New Phytol. **7**:222–29. 1908.

575. SPRATT, ETHEL R., The formation and physiological significance of root nodules in the Podocarpineae. Ann. Botany **26**:801–14. *pls. 77–80.* 1912.

576. SPRECHER, ANDREAS, Le *Ginkgo biloba* L. pp. 208. *figs. 225.* Genève. 1907.

577. STANDLEY, P. C., Cycadaceae in trees and shrubs of Mexico. Contrib. U.S. Nat. Herb. **18**:47–50. 1920.

578. STARR, ANNA M., The microsporophylls of *Ginkgo*. Bot. Gazette **49**: 51–55. *pl. 7.* 1910.

579. ———, Poisoning by *Ginkgo*. Bot. Gazette **55**:251. 1913.

580. STENZEL, G., Beobachtungen an durchwachsenen Fichtenzapfen. Ein Beitrag zur Morphologie der Nadelhölzer. Nov. Act. Nat. Cur. **38**:289–350. *pls. 12–15.* 1876.

581. STILES, W., The anatomy of *Saxagothea conspicua* Lindl. New Phytol. **7**: 209–22. *figs. 28–34.* 1908.

582. ———, A note on the gametophytes of *Dacrydium*. New Phytol. **10**:342–47. *figs. 4.* 1911.

583. ———, The Podocarpeae. Ann. Botany **26**:443–514. *pls. 3. figs. 8.* 1912.

584. STOPES, MARIE C., On the leaf structure of *Cordaites*. New Phytol. **2**: 91–98. *pl. 9.* 1903.

585. ———, Beiträge zur Kenntniss der Fortpflanzungsorgane der Cycadeen. Flora **93**:435–82. *figs. 37.* 1904.

586. ———, On the double nature of the cycadean integument. Ann. Botany **19**:561–66. 1905.

587. ———, A new fern from the Coal-measures: *Tubicaulis sutcliffii*, spec. nov. Mem. and Proc. Manchester Lit. and Phil. Soc. **50**:1–30. *pls. 1–3.* 1906.

588. ———, Adventitious budding and branching in *Cycas revoluta*. New Phytol. **9**:234–41. *fig. 7.* 1910.

589. ———, A new *Araucarioxylon* from New Zealand. Ann. Botany **28**:341–50. *pl. 20.* 1914.

590. ———, An early type of the Abietineae(?) from the Cretaceous of New Zealand. Ann. Botany **30**:111–25. *pl. 4. figs. 5.* 1916.

591. STOPES, MARIE C., and FUJII, K., The nutritive relations of the surrounding tissues to the archegonia of gymnosperms. Beih. Bot. Centralbl. **20:** 1–24. *pl. 1.* 1906.

592. ———, Studies on the structure and affinities of cretaceous plants. Phil. Trans. Roy. Soc. London B **201:**1–90. *pls. 1–9.* 1910. Abstract in Ann. Botany **24:**231, 232. 1910.

593. STOPES, MARIE C., and KERSHAW, E. M., The anatomy of Cretaceous pine leaves. Ann. Botany **24:**395–402. *pls. 27, 28.* 1910.

594. STRASBURGER, E., Die Befruchtung bei den Coniferen. 1869.

595. ———, Die Angiospermen und die Gymnospermen. 1870.

596. ———, Die Coniferen und die Genetaceen. 1872.

597. ———, Ueber Zellbildung und Zelltheilung. 1876.

598. ———, Die Befruchtung und Zelltheilung. Jen. Zeitsch. **2:**435–536. *pls. 27–35.* 1877.

599. ———, Befruchtung und Zelltheilung. 1878.

600. ———, Die Angiospermen und die Gymnospermen. 1879.

601. ———, Neue Untersuchungen, etc. 1884.

602. ———, Histologische Beiträge **3:**151. 1891.

603. ———, Ueber das Verhalten des Pollens und die Befruchtungsvorgänge bei den Gymnospermen. Hist. Beiträge. **4:**1–158. *pls. 1–3.* 1892.

604. ———, Anlage des Embryosackes und Prothalliumbildung bei der Eibe nebst anschliessenden Erörterungen. Festschr. zum siebzigsten Geburtstage von ERNST HAECKEL. pp. 18. *pls. 2.* Jena. 1904.

605. STUR, D., Zur Morphologie und Systematik der Kulm- und Karbonfarne. Sitzungsb. Akad. Wiss. Wien **88.** pp. 214. *figs. 4.* 1883.

606. SUDWORTH, GEO. B., Forest trees of the Pacific slope. U.S. Dept. Agric. Forest Service. 1908. *(Dover reprint, in prep.)*

607. SUZUKI, Y., On the structure and affinities of two new conifers and a new fungus from the Upper Cretaceous of Hokkaido (Yezo). Bot. Mag. Tokyo. **24:**181–96. *pl. 7.* 1910.

608. SYKES, M. G., The anatomy of *Welwitschia mirabilis* in the seedling and adult states. Trans. Linn. Soc. London II. Bot. **7:**327–54. *pls. 34, 35. figs. 5.* 1910.

609. TAKEDA, H., A theory of "transfusion tissue." Ann. Botany **27:**359–63. 1913.

610. ———, Some points in the anatomy of the leaf of *Welwitschia mirabilis.* Ann. Botany **27:**345–57. *pl. 29.* 1913.

611. Development of the stoma in *Gnetum gnemon.* Ann. Botany **27:**365–66. 1913.

612. TANSLEY, A. G., Lectures on the evolution of the filicinean vascular system. II. The Botryopterideae. New Phytol. **6:**53–68. *figs. 22.* 1907.

613. THIBOUT, E., Recherches sur l'appareil mâle des gymnospermes. pp. 265. *pls. 16.* Lille. 1896.

614. THIESSEN, REINHARDT, The vascular anatomy of the seedling of *Dioon edule*. Bot. Gazette 46:357–80. *pls. 23–29*. 1908.

615. THODAY (SYKES), MARY G., The female inflorescence and ovules of *Gnetum africanum*, with notes on *G. scandens*. Ann. Botany 25:1101–35. *pls. 86, 87. figs. 16*. 1911.

616. THODAY (SYKES), MARY G. and BERRIDGE, EMILY M., The anatomy and morphology of the inflorescences of and flowers of *Ephedra*. Ann. Botany 26:953–85. *pl. 1. figs. 21*. 1912.

617. THOMAS, ETHEL N., "The origin of gymnosperms"; a discussion at the Linnean Society. New Phytol. 5:68–76, 141–48. 1906.

618. ———, A theory of the double leaf trace founded on seedling structure. New Phytol. 6:77–91. *figs. 4*. 1907.

619. ———, A theory of the double leaf trace founded on seedling structure. New Phytol. 6:77–91. *figs. 4*. 1907.

620. THOMAS, H. H., The fossil flora of the Cleveland district of Yorkshire. I. The flora of the Marske-Quarry. Quart. Jour. Geol. Soc. 69:223–51. *pls. 23–26*. 1913.

621. ———, On Williamsoniella, a new type of Bennettitalean flower. Phil. Trans. Roy. Soc. London B 207:113–48. *pls. 12–14*. 1915.

622. ———, On some new and rare Jurassic plants from Yorkshire: the male flower of *Williamsonia gigas*. Proc. Cambridge Phil. Soc. 18:105–10. *pl. 6. figs. 2*. 1915.

623. ———, The Caytoniales, a new group of angiospermous plants from the Jurassic rocks of Yorkshire. Phil. Trans. Roy. Soc. London. Series B 213:299–363. 1925.

624. THOMAS, H. H., and BANCROFT, NELLIE, On the cuticles of some recent and fossil cycadean fronds. Trans. Linn. Soc. London Bot. 8:155–204. *pls. 17–20. figs. 32*. 1913.

625. THOMPSON, W. P., On the origin of ray tracheids in the Coniferae. Bot. Gazette 50:101–16. *figs. 6*. 1910.

626. ———, Ray tracheids in *Abies*. Bot. Gazette 53:331–38. *pls. 24, 25*. 1912.

627. ———, The structure of the stomata of certain Cretaceous conifers. Bot. Gazette 54:63–67. *pls. 5, 6*. 1912.

628. ———, The anatomy and relationships of the Gnetales. Ann. Botany 26:1077–1104. *pls. 4. figs. 2*. 1912.

629. ———, Preliminary note on the morphology of *Gnetum*. Amer. Jour. Bot. 2:161. 1915.

630. ———, The morphology and affinities of *Gnetum*. Amer. Jour. Bot. 3:135–84. *pls. 2–7*. 1916.

631. ———, Independent evolution of vessels in Gnetales and angiosperms. Bot. Gazette 65:83–90. *figs. 11*. 1918.

632. THOMSON, R. B., Preliminary note on the Araucarineae. Science N.S. **22**: 88. 1905.

633. ———, The megaspore membrane of the gymnosperms. Univ. Toronto Studies, Biol. Series No. 4:pp. 64. *pls. 5.* 1905.

634. ———, "The origin of gymnosperms"; a discussion at the Linnean Society. New Phytol. **5**:68–76, 141–48. 1906.

635. ———, Note on the pollen of *Microcachrys*. Bot. Gazette **46**:465, 466. 1908.

636. ———, On the pollen of *Microcachrys tetragona*. Bot. Gazette **47**:26–29. *pls. 1, 2.* 1909.

637. ———, The megasporophyll of *Saxagothea* and *Microcachrys*. Bot. Gazette **47**:345–54. *pls. 21–25.* 1909.

638. ———, On the comparative anatomy and affinities of the Araucarineae. Phil. Trans. Roy. Soc. London B **204**:1–50. *pls. 1–7.* 1913.

639. ———, The spur shoot of the pines. Bot. Gazette **57**:362–85. *pls. 20–23.* 1914.

640. THOMSON, R. B., and ALLIN, A. E., Do the Abietineae extend to the Carboniferous? Bot. Gazette **53**:339–64. *pl. 26. figs. 2.* 1912.

641. TISON, A., La nucelle stigmatifère chez la *Saxagothea conspicua*. Compt. Rend. Acad. Sci. Paris **147**:137–39. 1908.

642. ———, Sur le *Saxagothea* Lindl. Mém. Soc. Linn. Normandie **23**:139–60. *pls. 9, 10.* 1909.

643. ———, Remarques sur les goulettes collectrices des ovules des Conifères. Mém. Soc. Linn. Normandie **24**:51–66. *pls. 3, 4.* 1910.

644. TORREY, R. E., The comparative anatomy and phylogeny of the Coniferales, Part 3. Mesozoic and Tertiary Coniferous woods. Mem. Boston Soc. Nat. Hist. V. **6**:No. 2. 1923.

645. TREUB, M., Recherches sur les Cycadées. Ann. Jard. Bot. Buitenzorg **2**: 32–53. *pls. 1–7.* 1881 (date of reprint, volume date being 1885).

646. ———, Recherches sur les Cycadées. 3. Embryogénie du *Cycas circinalis*. Ann. Jard. Bot. Buitenzorg **4**:1–11. *pls. 1–3.* 1884.

647. TUPPER, WALTER, Notes on *Ginkgo biloba*. Bot. Gazette **51**:374–77. 1911.

648. UNGER, R., *Cycas revoluta* in ihrer Heimat. Möller's deutsche Gärtner-zeitung **20**:222–25. 1905.

649. VAN TIEGHEM, PH., Anatomie comparée de la fleur femelle et du fruit des Cycadées, des Conifères, et des Gnétacées. Ann. Sci. Nat. Bot. V. **10**: 269–304. *pls. 13–16.* 1869.

650. ———, Recherches sur la symétrie de structure des plants vasculaires. Ann. Sci. Nat. Bot. V. **13**:1–314. *pls. 3–8.* 1870.

651. ———, Traité de botanique. Paris. 1891.

652. VAN TIEGHEM, PH., et DOULIOT, H., Sur la polystelie. Ann. Sci. Nat. Bot. VII. **3**:275–322. *pls. 13, 14.* 1886.

653. VIERHAPPER, F., Entwurf eines neuen Systemes der Coniferen. Abhandl. K. K. Zool.-Bot. Gesell. Wien **5**:1–56. 1910.

654. VON MOHL, HUGO, Ueber die männlichen Blüthen der Coniferen. Verm. Bot. Schriften, pp. 45–61. 1845. (Published as a dissertation, 1837.)

655. ——, Ueber den Bau des Cycadeen-Stammes. Abh. K. Acad. München 1:397–442. 1832; republished and revised in Vermischte Schriften, pp. 195–211. 1845.

656. ——, Morphologische Betrachtung der Blätter von *Sciadopitys*. Bot. Zeit. **29**:17–23. 1871.

657. WARD, LESTER F., The Cretaceous formation of the Black Hills, as indicated by the fossil plants. Nineteenth Annual Report, U.S. Geol. Survey. 1900.

658. ——, Description of a new genus and twenty new species of fossil cycadean trunks from the Jurassic of Wyoming. Proc. Wash. Acad. Sci. 1: 253–300. *pls. 14–21.* 1900.

659. ——, Elaboration of the fossil cycads of the Yale Museum. Amer. Jour. Sci. IV. **10**:327–45. *pls. 2–4.* 1900.

660. WARMING, E., Recherches et remarques sur les Cycadées. Oversigter Vidensk. Selsk. Forh. 1877.

661. ——, Contributions à l'histoire naturelle des Cycadées. Oversigter Vidensk. Selsk. Forh. 1879.

662. WATSON, SERENO, Botany of King's Expedition. 1871.

663. WEBER, O., und STERZEL, J. T., Beiträge zur Kenntniss der Medulloseae. XIII. Ber. Naturwiss. Gesell. Chemnitz. pp. 102. *pls. 9. figs. 33.* 1896.

664. WEBBER, H. J., Notes on the fecundation of *Zamia* and the pollen tube apparatus of *Ginkgo*. Bot. Gazette **24**:225–35. *pl. 10.* 1897.

665. ——, The development of the antherozoids of *Zamia*. Bot. Gazette **24**: 16–22. 1897.

666. ——, Peculiar structures occurring in the pollen tube of *Zamia*. Bot. Gazette **23**:453–59. *pl. 40.* 1897.

667. ——, Spermatogenesis and fecundation of *Zamia*. U.S. Dept. Agric., Bur. Pl. Ind. Bull. 2. pp. 100. *pls. 7.* 1901.

668. WEISS, F. E., "The origin of gymnosperms"; a discussion at the Linnean Society. New Phytol. **5**:68–76, 141–48. 1906.

669. ——, A *Tylodendron*-like fossil. Mem. Proc. Manchester Phil. Soc. **57**: 14. *pls. 2.* 1913.

670. WETTSTEIN, R. VON, Der Ursprung des Pollenschlauches. Naturw. Rundschau **21**:12. 1906.

671. WHITE, DAVID, Fossil plants of the group Cycadofilices. Smithson. Misc. Coll. **47**:377–90. *pls. 53–55.* 1904.

672. ——, The seeds of *Aneimites*. Smithson. Misc. Coll. **47**:322–31. *pls. 47, 48.* 1904.

673. WIGGLESWORTH, GRACE, The cotyledons of *Ginkgo biloba* and *Cycas revoluta*. Ann. Botany **17**:789–91. 1903.

674. WIELAND, G. R., A study of some American fossil cycads. I. The male flower of *Cycadeoidea*. Amer. Jour. Sci. IV. **7**:223–26. *pls. 2–4.* 1899.

675. ———, A study of some American fossil cycads. III. The female fructification of *Cycadeoidea*. Amer. Jour. Sci. IV. **7**:383–91. *pls. 8–10.* 1899.

676. ———, The Yale collection of fossil cycads. Yale Sci. Monthly **6**:1–11. *pl. 1.* 1900.

677. ———, A study of some American fossil cycads. IV. On the microsporangiate fructification of *Cycadeoidea*. Amer. Jour. Sci. IV. **11**:423–36. 1901.

678. ———, Notes on living Cycads. On the *Zamias* of Florida. Amer. Jour. Sci. **13**:331–38. 1902.

679. ———, The proembryo of the Bennettiteae. Amer. Jour. Sci. IV. **18**:445–47. *pl. 20.* 1904.

680. ———, American fossil cycads. Publ. No. 34. Carnegie Institution of Washington. pp. 296. *pls. 50. figs. 138.* 1906.

681. ———, Historic fossil Cycads. Amer. Jour. Sci. IV. **25**:93–101. 1908.

682. ———, The Williamsonias of the "Mixteca Alta." Bot. Gazette **48**:427–41. *figs. 10.* 1909.

683. ———, A study of some American fossil cycads. V. Further notes on seed structures. Amer. Jour. Sci. IV. **32**:133–55. *figs. 9.* 1911.

684. ———, On the Williamsonian tribe. Amer. Jour. Sci. **32**:433–66. *figs. 18.* 1911.

685. ———, A study of some American fossil cycads. VI. On the smaller flower buds of *Cycadeoidea*. Amer. Jour. Sci. **33**:73–91. *figs. 11.* 1912.

686. ———, La Flora Liassica de la Mixteca Alta. Bol. Inst. Geol. Mexico. No. 31. 1916.

687. ———, American fossil cycads. Vol. II. Taxonomy. Carnegie Inst. Washington, Publ. 34. 1916.

688. ———, On the classification of the Cycadophyta. Am. Jour. Sci. **47**:391–406. 1919.

689. ———, Certain fossil plants erroneously referred to Cycadales. Bot. Gazette **86**:32–50. 1928.

690. WIGGLESWORTH, GRACE, The cotyledons of *Ginkgo biloba* and *Cycas revoluta*. Ann. Botany **17**:789–91. 1903.

691. WILD, G., On *Trigonocarpon olivaeforme*. Trans. Manchester Geol. Soc. **26**:pp. 16. *pls. 2.* 1900.

692. WILLIAMSON, W. C., On the structure and affinities of the plants hitherto known as Sternbergiae. Mem. Manchester Lit. and Phil. Soc. **14**:340–56. *pl. 10.* 1851.

693. ———, Contributions toward the history of *Zamia gigas*. Trans. Linn. Soc. Bot. **26**:663–74. *pls. 52, 53.* 1870.

694. ———, On the organization of the fossil plants of the Coal measures. IV. *Dictyoxylon, Lyginodendron,* and *Heterangium.* Phil. Trans. Roy. Soc. London B **168**:377–408. *pls. 22–31.* 1873.

695. ———, On some fossil seeds from the Lower Carboniferous beds of Lancashire. Rep. 45th Meeting British Assoc. (1875):159–60. 1876.

696. ———, On the organization, etc. VIII. Ferns (continued) and gymnospermous stems and seeds. Ann. Mag. Nat. Hist. **18**:268–73. 1876 (preliminary notice); Proc. Roy. Soc. London. **25**:68–73. 1877 (abstract). Phil. Trans. Roy. Soc. London B **167**:213–70. *pls. 5–16.* 1878 (full paper).

697. ———, On the organization etc. X. Phil. Trans. Roy. Soc. London B **171**:493–539. *pls. 14–21.* 1880.

698. ———, On the organization, etc. XII. Phil. Trans. Roy. Soc. London B **174**:459–75. *pls. 27–34.* 1883.

699. ———, On the organization, etc. XIII. Phil. Trans. Roy. Soc. London B **178**:289–304. *pls. 21–24.* 1887.

700. ———, On the organization, etc. XVII. Phil. Trans. Roy. Soc. London C **181**:89–106. *pls. 12–15.* 1890.

701. WILLIAMSON, W. C., and SCOTT, D. H., Further observations on the organization of the fossil plants from the Coal-measures. III. *Lyginodendron* and *Heterangium*. Phil. Trans. Roy. Soc. London B **186**:703–79. *pls. 18–21.* 1896.

702. WORSDELL, W. C., Anatomy of the stem of *Macrozamia* compared with that of other genera of Cycadeae. Ann. Botany **10**:601–20. *pls. 27, 28.* 1896.

703. ———, On transfusion tissue; its origin and function in the leaves of gymnospermous plants. Trans. Linn. Soc. London Bot. II **5**:301–19. *pls. 23–26.* 1897.

704. ———, The vascular structure of the sporophylls of the Cycadaceae. Ann. Botany **12**:203–41. *pls. 17, 18.* 1898.

705. ———, The anatomical structure of *Bowenia spectabilis*. Ann. Botany **14**:159, 160. 1900.

706. ———, The affinities of the Mesozoic fossil Bennettites *Gibsonianus*. Ann. Botany **14**:717–21. 1900.

707. ———, The structure of the female "flower" in Coniferae. Ann. Botany **14**:39–82. 1900.

708. ———, The vascular structure of the ovule of *Cephalotaxus*. Ann. Botany **14**:317, 318. 1900.

709. ———, The evolution of the vascular tissue of plants. Bot. Gazette **34**:216–23. 1902.

710. ———, "The origin of gymnosperms"; a discussion at the Linnean Society. New Phytol. **5**:68–76, 141–48. 1906.

711. ———, The structure and origin of the Cycadaceae. Ann. Botany **20**:129–59. *figs. 17.* 1906.

712. ———, An abnormal shoot of *Pinus thunbergii* Parl. New Phytol. **14**:23–26. *figs. 5.* 1915.

713. WOYCICKI, Z. (On fertilization in Coniferae.) pp. 57. *pls. 2.* 1899. (Russian.)

714. YOUNG, MARY S., The male gametophyte of *Dacrydium.* Bot. Gazette **44**:189–96. *pl. 19.* 1907.

715. ———, The morphology of the Podocarpineae. Bot. Gazette **50**:81–100. *pls. 4–6.* 1910.

716. ZACH, FRANZ. Studie über Phagocytose in den Wurzelknöllchen der Cycadeen. Oesterreich. Bot. Zeitschr. **60**:49–55. *pl. 2.* 1910.

717. ZEILLER, R., Eléments de paléobotanique. 1900.

718. ———, Une nouvelle classe de Gymnospermes: les Ptéridospermées. Rev. Gen. Sci. **16**:718–27. *figs. 7.* 1905.

719. ZEILLER, R., et FLICHE, P., Découverte des strobiles de *Sequoia* et de Pin dans le Portlandien des environs de Boulogne-sur-Mer. Compt. Rend. Acad. Sci. Paris. **137**:1020–22. 1903.

INDEX

CATALOGUE OF DOVER BOOKS

Nature

AN INTRODUCTION TO BIRD LIFE FOR BIRD WATCHERS, Aretas A. Saunders. Fine, readable introduction to birdwatching. Includes a great deal of basic information on about 160 different varieties of wild birds—elementary facts not easily found elsewhere. Complete guide to identification procedures, methods of observation, important habits of birds, finding nests, food, etc. "Could make bird watchers of readers who never suspected they were vulnerable to that particular virus," CHICAGO SUNDAY TRIBUNE. Unabridged, corrected edition. Bibliography. Index. 22 line drawings by D. D'Ostilio. Formerly "The Lives of Wild Birds." 256pp. 5⅜ x 8½.
T1139 Paperbound **$1.00**

LIFE HISTORIES OF NORTH AMERICAN BIRDS, Arthur Cleveland Bent. Bent's historic, all-encompassing series on North American birds, originally produced under the auspices of the Smithsonian Institution, now being republished in its entirety by Dover Publications. The twenty-volume collection forms the most comprehensive, most complete, most-used source of information in existence. Each study describes in detail the characteristics, range, distribution, habits, migratory patterns, courtship procedures, plumage, eggs, voice, enemies, etc. of the different species and subspecies of the birds that inhabit our continent, utilizing reports of hundreds of contemporary observers as well as the writings of the great naturalists of the past. Invaluable to the ornithologist, conservationist, amateur naturalist, and birdwatcher. All books in the series contain numerous photographs to provide handy guides for identification and study.

LIFE HISTORIES OF NORTH AMERICAN BIRDS OF PREY. Including hawks, eagles, falcons, buzzards, condors, owls, etc. Index. Bibliographies of 923 items. 197 full-page plates containing close to 400 photographs. Total of 907pp. 5⅜ x 8½.
Vol. I: T931 Paperbound **$2.50**
Vol. II: T932 Paperbound **$2.50**
The set Paperbound **$5.00**

LIFE HISTORIES OF NORTH AMERICAN SHORE BIRDS. Including 81 varieties of such birds as sandpipers, woodcocks, snipes, phalaropes, oyster catchers, and many others. Index for each volume. Bibliographies of 449 entries. 121 full-page plates including over 200 photographs. Total of 860 pp. 5⅜ x 8½.
Vol. I: T933 Paperbound **$2.35**
Vol. II: T934 Paperbound **$2.35**
The set Paperbound **$4.70**

LIFE HISTORIES OF NORTH AMERICAN WILD FOWL. Including 73 varieties of ducks, geese, mergansers, swans, etc. Index for each volume. Bibliographies of 268 items. 106 full-page plates containing close to 200 photographs. Total of 685pp. 5⅜ x 8½.
Vol. I: T285 Paperbound **$2.50**
Vol. II: T286 Paperbound **$2.50**
The set Paperbound **$5.00**

LIFE HISTORIES OF NORTH AMERICAN GULLS AND TERNS. 50 different varieties of gulls and terns. Index. Bibliography. 93 plates including 149 photographs. xii + 337pp. 5⅜ x 8½.
T1029 Paperbound **$2.75**

LIFE HISTORIES OF NORTH AMERICAN GALLINACEOUS BIRDS. Including partridge, quail, grouse, pheasant, pigeons, doves, and others. Index. Bibliography. 93 full-page plates including 170 photographs. xiii + 490pp. 5⅜ x 8½.
T1028 Paperbound **$2.75**

THE MALAY ARCHIPELAGO, Alfred Russel Wallace. The record of the explorations (8 years, 14,000 miles) of the Malay Archipelago by a great scientific observer. A contemporary of Darwin, Wallace independently arrived at the concept of evolution by natural selection, applied the new theories of evolution to later genetic discoveries, and made significant contributions to biology, zoology, and botany. This work is still one of the classics of natural history and travel. It contains the author's reports of the different native peoples of the islands, descriptions of the island groupings, his accounts of the animals, birds, and insects that flourished in this area. The reader is carried through strange lands, alien cultures, and new theories, and will share in an exciting, unrivalled travel experience. Unabridged reprint of the 1922 edition, with 62 drawings and maps. 3 appendices, one on cranial measurements. xvii + 515pp. 5⅜ x 8.
T187 Paperbound **$2.00**

THE TRAVELS OF WILLIAM BARTRAM, edited by Mark Van Doren. This famous source-book of American anthropology, natural history, geography is the record kept by Bartram in the 1770's, on travels through the wilderness of Florida, Georgia, the Carolinas. Containing accurate and beautiful descriptions of Indians, settlers, fauna, flora, it is one of the finest pieces of Americana ever written. Introduction by Mark Van Doren. 13 original illustrations. Index. 448pp. 5⅜ x 8.
T13 Paperbound **$2.00**

COMMON SPIDERS OF THE UNITED STATES, J. H. Emerton. Only non-technical, but thorough, reliable guide to spiders for the layman. Over 200 spiders from all parts of the country, arranged by scientific classification, are identified by shape and color, number of eyes, habitat and range, habits, etc. Full text, 501 line drawings and photographs, and valuable introduction explain webs, poisons, threads, capturing and preserving spiders, etc. Index. New synoptic key by S. W. Frost. xxiv + 225pp. 5⅜ x 8.
T223 Paperbound **$1.45**

LIFE HISTORIES OF NORTH AMERICAN MARSH BIRDS. A wealth of data on 54 different kinds of marsh bird (flamingo, ibis, bittern, heron, egret, crane, crake, rail, coot, etc.). Index. Bibliography. 98 full-page plates containing 179 black-and-white photographs. xiv + 392pp. 5⅜ x 8½.
T1082 Paperbound **$2.75**

LIFE HISTORIES OF NORTH AMERICAN DIVING BIRDS. Thirty-six different diving birds including grebe, loon, auk, murre, puffin, and the like. Index. Bibliography. 55 full-page plates (92 photographs). xiv + 239pp. 5⅜ x 8½.
T1091 Paperbound **$2.75**

LIFE HISTORIES OF NORTH AMERICAN WOOD WARBLERS. Covers about 58 types. Index. Bibliography. 83 full-page plates containing 125 black-and-white photographs. xi + 734pp. of text. 5⅜ x 8½.
Vol. I: T1153 Paperbound **$2.50**
Vol. II: T1154 Paperbound **$2.50**
The set Paperbound **$5.00**

LIFE HISTORIES OF NORTH AMERICAN FLYCATCHERS, LARKS, SWALLOWS, AND THEIR ALLIES. Complete information on about 78 different varieties. Index. Bibliography. 70 full-page plates (117 photographs). xi + 555pp. of text. 5⅜ x 8½.
T1090 Paperbound **$2.75**

AMERICAN WILDLIFE, AND PLANTS: A GUIDE TO WILDLIFE FOOD HABITS, A. C. Martin, H. S. Zim, A. L. Nelson. Result of 75 years of research by U. S. Fish and Wildlife Service into food and feeding habits of more than 1,000 species of birds and mammals, their distribution in America, migratory habits, and the most important plant-animal relationships. Treats over 300 common species of birds, fur and game animals, small mammals, hoofed browsers, fish, amphibians, reptiles by group, giving data on their food, ranges, habits and economies. Also focuses on the different genera of plants that furnish food for our wildlife, animals that use them, and their value. Only thorough study of its kind in existence. "Of immense value to sportsmen, naturalists, bird students, foresters, landscape architects, botanists," NATURE. "Undoubtedly an essential handbook," SCIENTIFIC MONTHLY. Unabridged republication of 1951 edition. Over 600 illustrations, maps, etc. Classified bibliography. Index. x + 500pp. 5⅜ x 8.
T793 Paperbound **$2.50**

HOW TO KNOW THE WILD FLOWERS, Mrs. Wm. Starr Dana. A Guide to the names, haunts, and habits of wild flowers. Well-known classic of nature lore. Informative and delightful. Plants classified by color and season of their typical flowers for easy identification. Thorough coverage of more than 1,000 important flowering, berry-bearing and foliage plants of Eastern and Central United States and Canada. Complete botanical information about each important plant. Also history, uses, folklore, habitat, etc. Nomenclature modernized by C. J. Hylander. 174 full-page illustrations by Marion Satterlee. xii + 481pp. 5⅜ x 8½.
T332 Paperbound **$2.00**

HOW PLANTS GET THEIR NAMES, L. H. Bailey. Introduction to botanical nomenclature for the horticulturist and garden-lover. Discussions of Carl Linnaeus, "father of botany," and analysis of his definitions of genus and species, a brief history of the science before Linnaean systematization, a chapter on plant identification, a mine of information on the rules of nomenclature and Latin stems and word-endings used in botanical nomenclature, with pronunciation guides. An important section contains a full list of generic terms of horticultural literature and common Latin words and their English botanical applications and meanings. "Written with knowledge and authority, charm and eloquence and poetic imagination on the varied aspects of the author's specialty," New York Times. 11 illustrations. vi + 181pp. 5⅜ x 8½.
T796 Paperbound **$1.25**

THE CACTACEAE: DESCRIPTIONS AND ILLUSTRATIONS OF PLANTS OF THE CACTUS FAMILY, N. L. Britton and J. N. Rose. Definitive study of plants of the Cactus Family. The authors devoted more than 15 years of research to this monumental task and produced an exhaustive, rigorously scientific account never likely to be superseded. 3 major classifications, or tribes, are recognized, under which they arrange and describe in full detail 124 genera and 1,235 species of cactus from all over the world. Complete data on each species: leaves, flowers, seeds, fruit, distribution, growth, spines, stem structure, economic uses, etc. In addition, 125 keys facilitate identification of genera and species. For teachers and students of botany and forestry, naturalists, conservationists, and nature lovers, this is an indispensable work. Unabridged republication of second (1937) edition. First edition originally published under the auspices of the Carnegie Institution, Washington, D.C. 4 vols. bound as 2. 1279 illustrations, photographs, sketches, etc. 137 plates. Total of xxvii + 1039pp. 8 x 10¼.
T771 Clothbound, 2-volume set **$20.00**

GUIDE TO SOUTHERN TREES, Elwood S. and J. George Harrar. A handy, comprehensive 700-page manual with numerous illustrations and information on more than 350 different kinds of trees, covering the entire area south of the Mason-Dixon line from the Atlantic Ocean to the Florida Keys and western Texas. Descriptions range from the common pine, cypress, walnut, beech, and elm to such rare species as Franklinia, etc. A mine of information on leaves, flowers, twigs, bark, fruit, distribution etc. of each kind of tree. Eminently readable, written in non-technical language, it is an indispensable handbook for all lovers of the outdoors. Revised edition. Index. 81-item bibliography. Glossary. 200 full-page illustrations. ix + 709pp. 4⅝ x 6⅜.
T945 Paperbound **$2.35**

WESTERN FOREST TREES, James B. Berry. For years a standard guide to the trees of the Western United States. Covers over 70 different subspecies, ranging from the Pacific shores to western South Dakota, New Mexico, etc. Much information on range and distribution, growth habits, appearance, leaves, bark, fruit, twigs, etc. for each tree discussed, plus material on wood of the trees and its uses. Basic division (Trees with needle-like leaves, scale-like leaves, and compound, lobed or divided, and simple broadleaf trees), along with almost 100 illustrations (mostly full-size) of buds, leaves, etc., aids in easy identification of just about any tree of the area. Many subsidiary keys. Revised edition. Introduction. 12 photos. 85 illustrations by Mary E. Eaton. Index. xii + 212pp. 5⅜ x 8.
T1138 Paperbound **$1.35**

MANUAL OF THE TREES OF NORTH AMERICA (EXCLUSIVE OF MEXICO), Charles Sprague Sargent. The magnum opus of the greatest American dendrologist. Based on 44 years of original research, this monumental work is still the most comprehensive and reliable sourcebook on the subject. Includes 185 genera and 717 species of trees (and many shrubs) found in the U.S., Canada, and Alaska. 783 illustrative drawings by C. E. Faxon and Mary W. Gill. An all-encompassing lifetime reference book for students, teachers of botany and forestry, naturalists, conservationists, and all nature lovers. Includes an 11-page analytical key to genera to help the beginner locate any tree by its leaf characteristics. Within the text over 100 further keys aid in easy identification. Synopsis of families. Glossary. Index. 783 illustrations, 1 map. Total of 1 + 891pp. 5⅜ x 8.
T277 Vol. I Paperbound **$2.25**
T278 Vol. II Paperbound **$2.25**
The set **$4.50**

TREES OF THE EASTERN AND CENTRAL UNITED STATES AND CANADA, W. M. Harlow, Professor of Wood Technology, College of Forestry, State University of N. Y., Syracuse, N. Y. This middle-level text is a serious work covering more than 140 native trees and important escapes, with information on general appearance, growth habit, leaf forms, flowers, fruit, bark, and other features. Commercial use, distribution, habitat, and woodlore are also given. Keys within the text enable you to locate various species with ease. With this book you can identify at sight almost any tree you are likely to encounter; you will know which trees have edible fruit, which are suitable for house planting, and much other useful and interesting information. More than 600 photographs and figures. xiii + 288pp. 4⅝ x 6½.
T395 Paperbound **$1.35**

FRUIT KEY AND TWIG KEY TO TREES AND SHRUBS (FRUIT KEY TO NORTHEASTERN TREES, TWIG TREE TO DECIDUOUS WOODY PLANTS OF EASTERN NORTH AMERICA), W. M. Harlow. The only guides with photographs of every twig and fruit described—especially valuable to the novice. The fruit key (both deciduous trees and evergreens) has an introduction explaining seeding, organs involved, fruit types and habits. The twig key introduction treats growth and morphology. In the keys proper, identification is easy and almost automatic. This exceptional work, widely used in university courses, is especially useful for identification in winter, or from the fruit or seed only. Over 350 photos, up to 3 times natural size. Bibliography, glossary, index of common and scientific names, in each key. xvii + 125pp. 5⅝ x 8⅜.
T511 Paperbound **$1.25**

HOW TO KNOW THE FERNS, F. T. Parsons. Ferns, among our most lovely native plants, are all too little known. This modern classic of nature lore will enable the layman to identify any American fern he is likely to come across. After an introduction on the structure and life of ferns, the 57 most important ferns are fully pictured and described (arranged upon a simple identification key). Index of Latin and English names. 61 illustrations and 42 full-page plates. xiv + 215pp. 5⅜ x 8.
T740 Paperbound **$1.35**

OUR SMALL NATIVE ANIMALS: THEIR HABITS AND CARE, R. Snedigar, Curator of Reptiles, Chicago Zoological Park. An unusual nature handbook containing all the vital facts of habitat, distribution, foods, and special habits in brief life histories of 114 different species of squirrels, chipmunks, rodents, larger mammals, birds, amphibians, lizards and snakes. Liberally sprinkled with first-hand anecdotes. A wealth of information on capturing and caring for these animals: proper pens and cages, correct diet, curing diseases, special equipment required, etc. Addressed to the teacher interested in classroom demonstrations, the camp director, and to anyone who ever wanted a small animal for a pet. Revised edition, New preface. Index. 62 halftones. 14 line drawings. xviii + 296pp. 5⅜ x 8⅛.
T1022 Paperbound **$1.75**

INSECT LIFE AND INSECT NATURAL HISTORY, S. W. Frost. Unusual for emphasizing habits, social life, and ecological relations of insects, rather than more academic aspects of classification and morphology. Prof. Frost's enthusiasm and knowledge are everywhere evident as he discusses insect associations, and specialized habits like leaf-mining, leaf-rolling, and case-making, the gall insects, the boring insects, aquatic insects, etc. He examines all sorts of matters not usually covered in general works, such as: insects as human food; insect music and musicians; insect response to electric and radio waves; use of insects in art and literature. The admirably executed purpose of this book, which covers the middle ground between elementary treatment and scholarly monographs, is to excite the reader to observe for himself. Over 700 illustrations. Extensive bibliography. x + 524pp. 5⅜ x 8.
T517 Paperbound **$2.45**

Biological Sciences

AN INTRODUCTION TO GENETICS, A. H. Sturtevant and G. W. Beadle. A very thorough exposition of genetic analysis and the chromosome mechanics of higher organisms by two of the world's most renowned biologists, A. H. Sturtevant, one of the founders of modern genetics, and George Beadle, Nobel laureate in 1958. Does not concentrate on the biochemical approach, but rather more on observed data from experimental evidence and results . . . from Drosophila and other life forms. Some chapter titles: Sex chromosomes; Sex-Linkage; Autosomal Inheritance;; Chromosome Maps; Intra-Chromosomal Rearrangements; Inversions—and Incomplete Chromosomes; Translocations; Lethals; Mutations; Heterogeneous Populations; Genes and Phenotypes; The Determination and Differentiation of Sex; etc. Slightly corrected reprint of 1939 edition. New preface by Drs. Sturtevant and Beadle. 1 color plate. 126 figures. Bibliographies. Index. 391pp. 5⅜ x 8½. S306 Paperbound **$2.00**

THE GENETICAL THEORY OF NATURAL SELECTION, R. A. Fisher. 2nd revised edition of a vital reviewing of Darwin's Selection Theory in terms of particulate inheritance, by one of the great authorities on experimental and theoretical genetics. Theory is stated in mathematical form. Special features of particulate inheritance are examined: evolution of dominance, maintenance of specific variability, mimicry and sexual selection, etc. 5 chapters on man and his special circumstances as a social animal. 16 photographs. Bibliography. Index. x + 310pp. 5⅜ x 8. S466 Paperbound **$2.00**

THE ORIENTATION OF ANIMALS: KINESES, TAXES AND COMPASS REACTIONS, Gottfried S. Fraenkel and Donald L. Gunn. A basic work in the field of animal orientations. Complete, detailed survey of everything known in the subject up to 1940s, enlarged and revised to cover major developments to 1960. Analyses of simpler types of orientation are presented in Part I: kinesis, klinotaxis, tropotaxis, telotaxis, etc. Part II covers more complex reactions originating from temperature changes, gravity, chemical stimulation, etc. The two-light experiment and unilateral blinding are dealt with, as is the problem of determinism or volition in lower animals. The book has become the universally-accepted guide to all who deal with the subject—zoologists, biologists, psychologists, and the like. Second, enlarged edition, revised to 1960. Bibliography of over 500 items. 135 illustrations. Indices. xiii + 376pp. 5⅜ x 8½. T786 Paperbound **$2.25**

THE BEHAVIOUR AND SOCIAL LIFE OF HONEYBEES, C. R. Ribbands. Definitive survey of all aspects of honeybee life and behavior; completely scientific in approach, but written in interesting, everyday language that both professionals and laymen will appreciate. Basic coverage of physiology, anatomy, sensory equipment; thorough account of honeybee behavior in the field (foraging activities, nectar and pollen gathering, how individuals find their way home and back to food areas, mating habits, etc.); details of communication in various field and hive situations. An extensive treatment of activities within the hive community—food sharing, wax production, comb building, swarming, the queen, her life and relationship with the workers, etc. A must for the beekeeper, natural historian, biologist, entomologist, social scientist, et al. "An indispensable reference," J. Hambleton, BEES. "Recommended in the strongest of terms," AMERICAN SCIENTIST. 9 plates. 66 figures. Indices. 693-item bibliography. 252pp. 5⅜ x 8½. T1137 Paperbound **$2.00**

BIRD DISPLAY: AN INTRODUCTION TO THE STUDY OF BIRD PSYCHOLOGY, E. A. Armstrong. The standard work on bird display, based on extensive observation by the author and reports of other observers. This important contribution to comparative psychology covers the behavior and ceremonial rituals of hundreds of birds from gannet and heron to birds of paradise and king penguins. Chapters discuss such topics as the ceremonial of the gannet, ceremonial gaping, disablement reactions, the expression of emotions, the evolution and function of social ceremonies, social hierarchy in bird life, dances of birds and men, songs, etc. Free of technical terminology, this work will be equally interesting to psychologists and zoologists as well as bird lovers of all backgrounds. 32 photographic plates. New introduction by the author. List of scientific names of birds. Bibliography. 3-part index. 431pp. 5⅜ x 8½. T1128 Paperbound **$2.00**

THE SPECIFICITY OF SEROLOGICAL REACTIONS, Karl Landsteiner. With a Chapter on Molecular Structure and Intermolecular Forces by Linus Pauling. Dr. Landsteiner, winner of the Nobel Prize in 1930 for the discovery of the human blood groups, devoted his life to fundamental research and played a leading role in the development of immunology. This authoritative study is an account of the experiments he and his colleagues carried out on antigens and serological reactions with simple compounds. Comprehensive coverage of the basic concepts of immunolgy includes such topics as: The Serological Specificity of Proteins, Antigens, Antibodies, Artificially Conjugated Antigens, Non-Protein Cell Substances such as polysaccharides, etc., Antigen-Antibody Reactions (Toxin Neutralization, Precipitin Reactions, Agglutination, etc.). Discussions of toxins, bacterial proteins, viruses, hormones, enzymes, etc. in the context of immunological phenomena. New introduction by Dr. Merrill Chase of the Rockefeller Institute. Extensive bibliography and bibliography of author's writings. Index. xviii + 330pp. 5⅜ x 8½. S299 Paperbound **$2.00**

CULTURE METHODS FOR INVERTEBRATE ANIMALS, P. S. Galtsoff, F. E. Lutz, P. S. Welch, J. G. Needham, eds. A compendium of practical experience of hundreds of scientists and technicians, covering invertebrates from protozoa to chordata, in 313 articles on 17 phyla. Explains in great detail food, protection, environment, reproduction conditions, rearing methods, embryology, breeding seasons, schedule of development, much more. Includes at least one species of each considerable group. Half the articles are on class insecta. Introduction. 97 illustrations. Bibliography. Index. xxix + 590pp. 5⅜ x 8. **S526 Paperbound $3.00**

THE BIOLOGY OF THE LABORATORY MOUSE, edited by G. D. Snell. 1st prepared in 1941 by the staff of the Roscoe B. Jackson Memorial Laboratory, this is still the standard treatise on the mouse, assembling an enormous amount of material for which otherwise you spend hours of research. Embryology, reproduction, histology, spontaneous tumor formation, genetics of tumor transplantation, endocrine secretion & tumor formation, milk, influence & tumor formation, inbred, hybrid animals, parasites, infectious diseases, care & recording. Classified bibliography of 1122 items. 172 figures, including 128 photos. ix + 497pp. 6⅛ x 9¼. **S248 Clothbound $6.00**

MATHEMATICAL BIOPHYSICS: PHYSICO-MATHEMATICAL FOUNDATIONS OF BIOLOGY, N. Rashevsky. One of most important books in modern biology, now revised, expanded with new chapters, to include most significant recent contributions. Vol. 1: Diffusion phenomena, particularly diffusion drag forces, their effects. Old theory of cell division based on diffusion drag forces, other theoretical approaches, more exhaustively treated than ever. Theories of excitation, conduction in nerves, with formal theories plus physico-chemical theory. Vol. 2: Mathematical theories of various phenomena in central nervous system. New chapters on theory of color vision, of random nets. Principle of optimal design, extended from earlier edition. Principle of relational mapping of organisms, numerous applications. Introduces into mathematical biology such branches of math as topology, theory of sets. Index. 236 illustrations. Total of 988pp. 5⅜ x 8. **S574 Vol. 1 (Books 1, 2) Paperbound $2.50**
S575 Vol. 2 (Books 3, 4) Paperbound $2.50
2 vol. set $5.00

ELEMENTS OF MATHEMATICAL BIOLOGY, A. J. Lotka. A pioneer classic, the first major attempt to apply modern mathematical techniques on a large scale to phenomena of biology, biochemistry, psychology, ecology, similar life sciences. Partial Contents: Statistical meaning of irreversibility; Evolution as redistribution; Equations of kinetics of evolving systems; Chemical, inter-species equilibrium; parameters of state; Energy transformers of nature, etc. Can be read with profit even by those having no advanced math; unsurpassed as study-reference. Formerly titled ELEMENTS OF PHYSICAL BIOLOGY. 72 figures. xxx + 460pp. 5⅜ x 8. **S346 Paperbound $2.45**

THE BIOLOGY OF THE AMPHIBIA, G. K. Noble, Late Curator of Herpetology at the Am. Mus. of Nat. Hist. Probably the most used text on amphibia, unmatched in comprehensiveness, clarity, detail. 19 chapters plus 85-page supplement cover development; heredity; life history; speciation; adaptation; sex, integument, respiratory, circulatory, digestive, muscular, nervous systems; instinct, intelligence, habits, environment, economic value, relationships, classification, etc. "Nothing comparable to it," C. H. Pope, Curator of Amphibia, Chicago Mus. of Nat. Hist. 1047 bibliographic references. 174 illustrations. 600pp. 5⅜ x 8. **S206 Paperbound $2.98**

STUDIES ON THE STRUCTURE AND DEVELOPMENT OF VERTEBRATES, E. S. Goodrich. A definitive study by the greatest modern comparative anatomist. Exceptional in its accounts of the ossicles of the ear, the separate divisions of the coelom and mammalian diaphragm, and the 5 chapters devoted to the head region. Also exhaustive morphological and phylogenetic expositions of skeleton, fins and limbs, skeletal visceral arches and labial cartilages, visceral clefts and gills, vacular, respiratory, excretory, and peripheral nervous systems, etc., from fish to the higher mammals. 754 illustrations. 69 page biographical study by C. C. Hardy. Bibliography of 1186 references. "What an undertaking . . . to write a textbook which will summarize adequately and succinctly all that has been done in the realm of Vertebrate Morphology these recent years," Journal of Anatomy. Index. Two volumes. Total 906pp. 5⅜ x 8. **Two vol. set S449-50 Paperbound $5.00**

A TREATISE ON PHYSIOLOGICAL OPTICS, H. von Helmholtz, Ed. by J. P. C. Southall. Unmatched for thoroughness, soundness, and comprehensiveness, this is still the most important work ever produced in the field of physiological optics. Revised and annotated, it contains everything known about the subject up to 1925. Beginning with a careful anatomical description of the eye, the main body of the text is divided into three general categories: The Dioptrics of the Eye (covering optical imagery, blur circles on the retina, the mechanism of accommodation, chromatic aberration, etc.); The Sensations of Vision (including stimulation of the organ of vision, simple and compound colors, the intensity and duration of light, variations of sensitivity, contrast, etc.); and The Perceptions of Vision (containing movements of the eyes, the monocular field of vision, direction, perception of depth, binocular double vision, etc.). Appendices cover later findings on optical imagery, refraction, ophthalmoscopy, and many other matters. Unabridged, corrected republication of the original English translation of the third German edition. 3 volumes bound as 2. Complete bibliography, 1911-1925. Indices. 312 illustrations. 6 full-page plates, 3 in color. Total of 1,749pp. 5⅜ x 8. **Two-volume set S15, 16 Clothbound $15.00**

CATALOGUE OF DOVER BOOKS

INTRODUCTION TO PHYSIOLOGICAL OPTICS, James P. C. Southall, former Professor of Physics in Columbia University. Readable, top-flight introduction, not only for beginning students of optics, but also for other readers—physicists, biochemists, illuminating engineers, optometrists, psychologists, etc. Comprehensive coverage of such matters as the Organ of Vision (structure of the eyeball, the retina, the dioptric system, monocular and binocular vision, adaptation, etc.); The Optical System of the Eye (reflex images in the cornea and crystalline lens, Emmetropia and Ametropia, accommodation, blur circles on retina); Eye-Glasses; Eye Defects; Movements of the Eyeball in its Socket; Rod and Cone Vision; Color Vision; and other similar topics. Index. 134 figures. x +426pp. 5⅜ x 8.   S924 Paperbound **$2.25**

LIGHT, COLOUR AND VISION, Yves LeGrand. A thorough examination of the eye as a receptor of radiant energy and as a mechanism (the retina) consisting of light-sensitive cells which absorb light of various wave lengths—probably the most complete and authoritative treatment of this subject in print. Originally prepared as a series of lectures given at the Institute of Optics in Paris, subsequently enlarged for book publication. Partial contents: Radiant Energy—concept, nature, theories, etc., Sources of Radiation—artificial and natural, the Visual Receptor, Photometric Quantities, Units, Calculations, Retinal Illumination, Trivariance of Vision, Colorimetry, Luminance Difference Thresholds, Anatomy of the Retina, Theories of Vision, Photochemistry and Electro-physiology of the Retina, etc. Appendices, Exercises, with solutions. 500-item bibliography. Authorized translation by R. Hunt, J. Walsh, F. Hunt. Index. 173 illustrations. xiii + 512pp. 5⅜ x 8½.   S979 Clothbound **$10.00**

FINGER PRINTS, PALMS AND SOLES: AN INTRODUCTION TO DERMATOGLYPHICS, Harold Cummins and Charles Midlo. An introduction in non-technical language designed to acquaint the reader with a long-neglected aspect of human biology. Although a chapter dealing with fingerprint identification and the systems of classification used by the FBI, etc. has been added especially for this edition, the main concern of the book is to show how the intricate pattern of ridges and wrinkles on our fingers have a broader significance, applicable in many areas of science and life. Some topics are: the identification of two types of twins; the resolution of doubtful cases of paternity; racial variation; inheritance; the relation of fingerprints to body measurements, blood groups, criminality, character, etc. Classification and recognition of fundamental patterns and pattern types discussed fully. 149 figures. 49 tables. 361-item bibliography. Index. xii + 319pp. 5⅝ x 8⅜.   T778 Paperbound **$1.95**

Classics and histories

ANTONY VAN LEEUWENHOEK AND HIS "LITTLE ANIMALS," edited by Clifford Dobell. First book to treat extensively, accurately, life and works (relating to protozoology, bacteriology) of first microbiologist, bacteriologist, micrologist. Includes founding papers of protozoology, bacteriology; history of Leeuwenhoek's life; discussions of his microscopes, methods, language. His writing conveys sense of an enthusiastic, naive genius, as he looks at rainwater, pepper water, vinegar, frog's skin, rotifers, etc. Extremely readable, even for non-specialists. "One of the most interesting and enlightening books I have ever read," Dr. C. C. Bass, former Dean, Tulane U. School of Medicine. Only authorized edition. 400-item bibliography. Index. 32 illust. 442pp. 5⅜ x 8.   S594 Paperbound **$2.25**

THE GROWTH OF SCIENTIFIC PHYSIOLOGY, G. J. Goodfield. A compact, superbly written account of how certain scientific investigations brought about the emergence of the distinct science of physiology. Centers principally around the mechanist-vitalist controversy prior to the development of physiology as an independent science, using the arguments which raged around the problem of animal heat as its chief illustration. Covers thoroughly the efforts of clinicians and naturalists and workers in chemistry and physics to solve these problems—from which the new discipline arose. Includes the theories and contributions of: Aristotle, Galen, Harvey, Boyle, Bernard, Benjamin Franklin, Palmer, Gay-Lussac, Priestley, Spallanzani, and many others. 1960 publication. Biographical bibliography. 174pp. 5 x 7½.   T1066 Clothbound **$3.00**

MICROGRAPHIA, Robert Hooke. Hooke, 17th century British universal scientific genius, was a major pioneer in celestial mechanics, optics, gravity, and many other fields, but his greatest contribution was this book, now reprinted entirely from the original 1665 edition, which gave microscopy its first great impetus. With all the freshness of discovery, he describes fully his microscope, and his observations of cork, the edge of a razor, insects' eyes, fabrics, and dozens of other different objects. 38 plates, full-size or larger, contain all the original illustrations. This book is also a fundamental classic in the fields of combustion and heat theory, light and color theory, botany and zoology, hygrometry, and many other fields. It contains such farsighted predictions as the famous anticipation of artificial silk. The final section is concerned with Hooke's telescopic observations of the moon and stars. 323pp. 5⅜ x 8.   T8 Paperbound **$2.00**

Medicine

CLASSICS OF MEDICINE AND SURGERY, edited by C. N. B. Camac. 12 greatest papers in medical history, 11 in full: Lister's "Antiseptic Principle;" Harvey's "Motion in the Heart and Blood;" Auenbrugger's "Percussion of the Chest;" Laënnec's "Auscultation and the Stethoscope;" Jenner's "Inquiry into Smallpox Vaccine," 2 related papers; Morton's "Administering Sulphuric Ether," letters to Warren, "Physiology of Ether;" Simpson's "A New Anaesthetic Agent;" Holmes' "Puerperal Fever." Biographies, portraits of authors, bibliographies. Formerly "Epoch-making Contributions to Medicine, Surgery, and the Allied Sciences." Introduction. 14 illus. 445pp. 5⅜ x 8. S539 Paperbound **$2.25**

A WAY OF LIFE, Sir William Osler. The complete essay, stating his philosophy of life, as given at Yale University by this great physician and teacher. 30 pages. Copies limited, no more than 1 to a customer. Free.

SOURCE BOOK OF MEDICAL HISTORY, compiled, annotated by Logan Clendening, M.D. Unequalled collection of 139 greatest papers in medical history, by 120 authors, covers almost every area: pathology, asepsis, preventive medicine, bacteriology, physiology, etc. Hippocrates, Gain, Vesalius, Malpighi, Morgagni, Boerhave, Pasteur, Walter Reed, Florence Nightingale, Lavoisier, Claude Bernard, 109 others, give view of medicine unequalled for immediacy. Careful selections give heart of each paper save you reading time. Selections from non-medical literature show lay-views of medicine: Aristophanes, Plato, Arabian Nights, Chaucer, Molière, Dickens, Thackeray, others. "Notable . . . useful to teacher and student alike," Amer. Historical Review. Bibliography. Index. 699pp. 5⅜ x 8. T621 Paperbound **$2.75**

EXPERIMENTS AND OBSERVATIONS ON THE GASTRIC JUICE AND THE PHYSIOLOGY OF DIGESTION, William Beaumont. A gunshot wound which left a man with a 2½ inch hole through his abdomen into his stomach (1822) enabled Beaumont to perform the remarkable experiments set down here. The first comprehensive, thorough study of motions and processes of the stomach, "his work remains a model of patient, persevering investigation. . . . Beaumont is the pioneer physiologist of this country." (Sir William Osler, in his introduction.) 4 illustrations. xi + 280pp. 5⅜ x 8. S527 Paperbound **$1.50**

AN INTRODUCTION TO THE STUDY OF EXPERIMENTAL MEDICINE, Claude Bernard. 90-year-old classic of medical science, only major work of Bernard available in English, records his efforts to transform physiology into exact science. Principles of scientific research illustrated by specific case histories from his work; roles of chance, error, preliminary false conclusions, in leading eventually to scientific truth; use of hypothesis. Much of modern application of mathematics to biology rests on the foundation set down here. New foreword by Professor I. B. Cohen, Harvard Univ. xxv + 266pp. 5⅜ x 8. T400 Paperbound **$1.50**

A WAY OF LIFE, AND OTHER SELECTED WRITINGS, Sir William Osler, Physician and humanist, Osler discourses brilliantly in thought provoking essays and on the history of medicine. He discusses Thomas Browne, Gui Patin, Robert Burton, Michael Servetus, William Beaumont, Laënnec. Includes such favorite writings as the title essay, "The Old Humanities and the New Science," "Creators, Transmitters, and Transmuters," "Books and Men," "The Student Life," and five more of his best discussions of philosophy, religion and literature. 5 photographs. Introduction by G. L. Keynes, M.D., F.R.C.S. Index. xx + 278pp. 5⅜ x 8. T488 Paperbound **$1.50**

THE HISTORY OF SURGICAL ANESTHESIA, Thomas E. Keys. Concise, but thorough and always engrossing account of the long struggle to find effective methods of eliminating pain during surgery, tracing the remarkable story through the centuries to the eventual successes by dedicated researchers, the acceptance of ether, the work of men such as Priestley, Morton, Lundy, and many, many others. Discussions of the developments in local, regional, and spinal anesthesia, etc. "The general reader as well as the medical historian will find material to interest him in this fascinating story," U.S. QUARTERLY BOOKLIST. Revised, enlarged publication of original edition. Introductory essay by C. D. Leake. Concluding chapter by N. A. Gillespie. Appendix by J. F. Fulton. 46 illustrations. New preface by the author. Chronology of events. Extensive bibliographies. Index. xxx + 193pp. 5⅜ x 8½. T1122 Paperbound **$2.00**

A SHORT HISTORY OF ANATOMY AND PHYSIOLOGY FROM THE GREEKS TO HARVEY, Charles Singer. Corrected edition of THE EVOLUTION OF ANATOMY, classic work tracing evolution of anatomy and physiology from prescientific times through Greek & Roman periods, Dark Ages, Renaissance, to age of Harvey and beginning of modern concepts. Centered on individuals, movements, periods that definitely advanced anatomical knowledge: Plato, Diocles, Aristotle, Theophrastus, Herophilus, Erasistratus, the Alexandrians, Galen, Mondino, da Vinci, Linacre, Sylvius, others. Special section on Vesalius; Vesalian atlas of nudes, skeletons, muscle tabulae. Index of names, 20 plates. 270 extremely interesting illustrations of ancient, medieval, Renaissance, Oriental origin. xii + 209pp. 5⅜ x 8. T389 Paperbound **$1.75**

Psychology

YOGA: A SCIENTIFIC EVALUATION, Kovoor T. Behanan. A complete reprinting of the book that for the first time gave Western readers a sane, scientific explanation and analysis of yoga. The author draws on controlled laboratory experiments and personal records of a year as a disciple of a yoga, to investigate yoga psychology, concepts of knowledge, physiology, "supernatural" phenomena, and the ability to tap the deepest human powers. In this study under the auspices of Yale University Institute of Human Relations, the strictest principles of physiological and psychological inquiry are followed throughout. Foreword by W. A. Miles, Yale University. 17 photographs. Glossary. Index. xx + 270pp. 5⅜ x 8. T505 Paperbound **$2.00**

CONDITIONED REFLEXES: AN INVESTIGATION OF THE PHYSIOLOGICAL ACTIVITIES OF THE CEREBRAL CORTEX, I. P. Pavlov. Full, authorized translation of Pavlov's own survey of his work in experimental psychology reviews entire course of experiments, summarizes conclusions, outlines psychological system based on famous "conditioned reflex" concept. Details of technical means used in experiments, observations on formation of conditioned reflexes, function of cerebral hemispheres, results of damage, nature of sleep, typology of nervous system, significance of experiments for human psychology. Trans. by Dr. G. V. Anrep,. Cambridge Univ. 235-item bibliography. 18 figures. 445pp. 5⅜ x 8.   S614 Paperbound **$2.35**

EXPLANATION OF HUMAN BEHAVIOUR, F. V. Smith. A major intermediate-level introduction to and criticism of 8 complete systems of the psychology of human behavior, with unusual emphasis on theory of investigation and methodology. Part I is an illuminating analysis of the problems involved in the explanation of observed phenomena, and the differing viewpoints on the nature of causality. Parts II and III are a closely detailed survey of the systems of McDougall, Gordon Allport, Lewin, the Gestalt group, Freud, Watson, Hull, and Tolman. Biographical notes. Bibliography of over 800 items. 2 indexes. 38 figures. xii + 460pp. 5½ x 8¾.
T253 Clothbound **$6.00**

SEX IN PSYCHO-ANALYSIS (formerly CONTRIBUTIONS TO PSYCHO-ANALYSIS), S. Ferenczi. Written by an associate of Freud, this volume presents countless insights on such topics as impotence, transference, analysis and children, dreams, symbols, obscene words, masturbation and male homosexuality, paranoia and psycho-analysis, the sense of reality, hypnotism and therapy, and many others. Also includes full text of THE DEVELOPMENT OF PSYCHO-ANALYSIS by Ferenczi and Otto Rank. Two books bound as one. Total of 406pp. 5⅜ x 8.
T324 Paperbound **$1.85**

BEYOND PSYCHOLOGY, Otto Rank. One of Rank's most mature contributions, focussing on the irrational basis of human behavior as a basic fact of our lives. The psychoanalytic techniques of myth analysis trace to their source the ultimates of human existence: fear of death, personality, the social organization, the need for love and creativity, etc. Dr. Rank finds them stemming from a common irrational source, man's fear of final destruction. A seminal work in modern psychology, this work sheds light on areas ranging from the concept of immortal soul to the sources of state power. 291pp. 5⅜ x 8.   T485 Paperbound **$2.00**

ILLUSIONS AND DELUSIONS OF THE SUPERNATURAL AND THE OCCULT, D. H. Rawcliffe. Holds up to rational examination hundreds of persistent delusions including crystal gazing, automatic writing, table turning, mediumistic trances, mental healing, stigmata, lycanthropy, live burial, the Indian Rope Trick, spiritualism, dowsing, telepathy, clairvoyance, ghosts, ESP, etc. The author explains and exposes the mental and physical deceptions involved, making this not only an exposé of supernatural phenomena, but a valuable exposition of characteristic types of abnormal psychology. Originally titled "The Psychology of the Occult." 14 illustrations. Index. 551pp. 5⅜ x 8.   T503 Paperbound **$2.00**

THE PRINCIPLES OF PSYCHOLOGY, William James. The full long-course, unabridged, of one of the great classics of Western literature and science. Wonderfully lucid descriptions of human mental activity, the stream of thought, consciousness, time perception, memory, imagination, emotions, reason, abnormal phenomena, and similar topics. Original contributions are integrated with the work of such men as Berkeley, Binet, Mills, Darwin, Hume, Kant, Royce, Schopenhauer, Spinoza, Locke, Descartes, Galton, Wundt, Lotze, Herbart, Fechner, and scores of others. All contrasting interpretations of mental phenomena are examined in detail — introspective analysis, philosophical interpretation, and experimental research. "A classic," JOURNAL OF CONSULTING PSYCHOLOGY. "The main lines are as valid as ever," PSYCHO-ANALYTICAL QUARTERLY. "Standard reading . . . a classic of interpretation," PSYCHIATRIC QUARTERLY. 94 illustrations. 1408pp. 2 volumes. 5⅜ x 8.   Vol. 1, T381 Paperbound **$2.50**
                                                                         Vol. 2, T382 Paperbound **$2.50**

THE DYNAMICS OF THERAPY IN A CONTROLLED RELATIONSHIP, Jessie Taft. One of the most important works in literature of child psychology, out of print for 25 years. Outstanding disciple of Rank describes all aspects of relationship or Rankian therapy through concise, simple elucidation of theory underlying her actual contacts with two seven-year olds. Therapists, social caseworkers, psychologists, counselors, and laymen who work with children will all find this important work an invaluable summation of method, theory of child psychology. xix + 296pp. 5⅜ x 8.   T325 Paperbound **$1.75**

Books Explaining Science and Mathematics

WHAT IS SCIENCE?, N. Campbell. The role of experiment and measurement, the function of mathematics, the nature of scientific laws, the difference between laws and theories, the limitations of science, and many similarly provocative topics are treated clearly and without technicalities by an eminent scientist. "Still an excellent introduction to scientific philosophy," H. Margenau in PHYSICS TODAY. "A first-rate primer . . . deserves a wide audience," SCIENTIFIC AMERICAN. 192pp. 5⅜ x 8.   S43 Paperbound **$1.25**

THE NATURE OF PHYSICAL THEORY, P. W. Bridgman. A Nobel Laureate's clear, non-technical lectures on difficulties and paradoxes connected with frontier research on the physical sciences. Concerned with such central concepts as thought, logic, mathematics, relativity, probability, wave mechanics, etc. he analyzes the contributions of such men as Newton, Einstein, Bohr, Heisenberg, and many others. "Lucid and entertaining . . . recommended to anyone who wants to get some insight into current philosophies of science," THE NEW PHILOSOPHY. Index. xi + 138pp. 5⅜ x 8.   S33 Paperbound **$1.25**

EXPERIMENT AND THEORY IN PHYSICS, Max Born. A Nobel Laureate examines the nature of experiment and theory in theoretical physics and analyzes the advances made by the great physicists of our day: Heisenberg, Einstein, Bohr, Planck, Dirac, and others. The actual process of creation is detailed step-by-step by one who participated. A fine examination of the scientific method at work. 44pp. 5⅜ x 8.   S308 Paperbound **75¢**

THE PSYCHOLOGY OF INVENTION IN THE MATHEMATICAL FIELD, J. Hadamard. The reports of such men as Descartes, Pascal, Einstein, Poincaré, and others are considered in this investigation of the method of idea-creation in mathematics and other sciences and the thinking process in general. How do ideas originate? What is the role of the unconscious? What is Poincaré's forgetting hypothesis? are some of the fascinating questions treated. A penetrating analysis of Einstein's thought processes concludes the book. xiii + 145pp. 5⅜ x 8.   T107 Paperbound **$1.25**

THE NATURE OF LIGHT AND COLOUR IN THE OPEN AIR, M. Minnaert. Why are shadows sometimes blue, sometimes green, or other colors depending on the light and surroundings? What causes mirages? Why do multiple suns and moons appear in the sky? Professor Minnaert explains these unusual phenomena and hundreds of others in simple, easy-to-understand terms based on optical laws and the properties of light and color. No mathematics is required but artists, scientists, students, and everyone fascinated by these "tricks" of nature will find thousands of useful and amazing pieces of information. Hundreds of observational experiments are suggested which require no special equipment. 200 illustrations; 42 photos. xvi + 362pp. 5⅜ x 8.   T196 Paperbound **$2.00**

*MATHEMATICS IN ACTION, O. G. Sutton. Everyone with a command of high school algebra will find this book one of the finest possible introductions to the application of mathematics to physical theory. Ballistics, numerical analysis, waves and wavelike phenomena, Fourier series, group concepts, fluid flow and aerodynamics, statistical measures, and meteorology are discussed with unusual clarity. Some calculus and differential equations theory is developed by the author for the reader's help in the more difficult sections. 88 figures. Index. viii + 236pp. 5⅜ x 8.   T440 Clothbound **$3.50**

SOAP-BUBBLES: THEIR COLOURS AND THE FORCES THAT MOULD THEM, C. V. Boys. For continuing popularity and validity as scientific primer, few books can match this volume of easily-followed experiments, explanations. Lucid exposition of complexities of liquid films, surface tension and related phenomena, bubbles' reaction to heat, motion, music, magnetic fields. Experiments with capillary attraction, soap bubbles on frames, composite bubbles, liquid cylinders and jets, bubbles other than soap, etc. Wonderful introduction to scientific method, natural laws that have many ramifications in areas of modern physics. Only complete edition in print. New Introduction by S. Z. Lewin, New York University. 83 illustrations; 1 full-page color plate. xii + 190pp. 5⅜ x 8½.   T542 Paperbound **95¢**

CATALOGUE OF DOVER BOOKS

THE FOURTH DIMENSION SIMPLY EXPLAINED, edited by Henry P. Manning. Originally written as entries in contest sponsored by "Scientific American," then published in book form, these 22 essays present easily understood explanations of how the fourth dimension may be studied, the relationship of non-Euclidean geometry to the fourth dimension, analogies to three-dimensional space, some fourth-dimensional absurdities and curiosities, possible measurements and forms in the fourth dimension. In general, a thorough coverage of many of the simpler properties of fourth-dimensional space. Multi-points of view on many of the most important aspects are valuable aid to comprehension. Introduction by Dr. Henry P. Manning gives proper emphasis to points in essays, more advanced account of fourth-dimensional geometry. 82 figures. 251pp. 5⅜ x 8.   T711 Paperbound **$1.35**

TRIGONOMETRY REFRESHER FOR TECHNICAL MEN, A. A. Klaf. A modern question and answer text on plane and spherical trigonometry. Part I covers plane trigonometry: angles, quadrants, trigonometrical functions, graphical representation, interpolation, equations, logarithms, solution of triangles, slide rules, etc. Part II discusses applications to navigation, surveying, elasticity, architecture, and engineering. Small angles, periodic functions, vectors, polar coordinates, De Moivre's theorem, fully covered. Part III is devoted to spherical trigonometry and the solution of spherical triangles, with applications to terrestrial and astronomical problems. Special time-savers for numerical calculation. 913 questions answered for you! 1738 problems; answers to odd numbers. 494 figures. 14 pages of functions, formulae. Index. x + 629pp. 5⅜ x 8.   T371 Paperbound **$2.00**

CALCULUS REFRESHER FOR TECHNICAL MEN. A. A. Klaf. Not an ordinary textbook but a unique refresher for engineers, technicians, and students. An examination of the most important aspects of differential and integral calculus by means of 756 key questions. Part I covers simple differential calculus: constants, variables, functions, increments, derivatives, logarithms, curvature, etc. Part II treats fundamental concepts of integration: inspection, substitution, transformation, reduction, areas and volumes, mean value, successive and partial integration, double and triple integration. Stresses practical aspects! A 50 page section gives applications to civil and nautical engineering, electricity, stress and strain, elasticity, industrial engineering, and similar fields. 756 questions answered. 556 problems; solutions to odd numbers. 36 pages of constants, formulae. Index. v + 431pp. 5⅜ x 8.
T370 Paperbound **$2.00**

PROBABILITIES AND LIFE, Emile Borel. One of the leading French mathematicians of the last 100 years makes use of certain results of mathematics of probabilities and explains a number of problems that for the most part, are related to everyday living or to illness and death: computation of life expectancy tables, chances of recovery from various diseases, probabilities of job accidents, weather predictions, games of chance, and so on. Emphasis on results not processes, though some indication is made of mathematical proofs. Simple in style, free of technical terminology, limited in scope to everyday situations, it is comprehensible to laymen, fine reading for beginning students of probability. New English translation. Index. Appendix. vi + 87pp. 5⅜ x 8½.   T121 Paperbound **$1.00**

POPULAR SCIENTIFIC LECTURES, Hermann von Helmholtz. 7 lucid expositions by a pre-eminent scientific mind: "The Physiological Causes of Harmony in Music," "On the Relation of Optics to Painting," "On the Conservation of Force," "On the Interaction of Natural Forces," "On Goethe's Scientific Researches" into theory of color, "On the Origin and Significance of Geometric Axioms," "On Recent Progress in the Theory of Vision." Written with simplicity of expression, stripped of technicalities, these are easy to understand and delightful reading for anyone interested in science or looking for an introduction to serious study of acoustics or optics. Introduction by Professor Morris Kline, Director, Division of Electromagnetic Research, New York University, contains astute, impartial evaluations. Selected from "Popular Lectures on Scientific Subjects," 1st and 2nd series. xii + 286pp. 5⅜ x 8½.   T799 Paperbound **$1.45**

SCIENCE AND METHOD, Henri Poincaré. Procedure of scientific discovery, methodology, experiment, idea-germination—the intellectual processes by which discoveries come into being. Most significant and most interesting aspects of development, application of ideas. Chapters cover selection of facts, chance, mathematical reasoning, mathematics, and logic; Whitehead. Russell, Cantor; the new mechanics, etc. 288pp. 5⅜ x 8.   S222 Paperbound **$1.50**

HEAT AND ITS WORKINGS, Morton Mott-Smith, Ph.D. An unusual book; to our knowledge the only middle-level survey of this important area of science. Explains clearly such important concepts as physiological sensation of heat and Weber's law, measurement of heat, evolution of thermometer, nature of heat, expansion and contraction of solids, Boyle's law, specific heat. BTU's and calories, evaporation, Andrews's isothermals, radiation, the relation of heat to light, many more topics inseparable from other aspects of physics. A wide, non-mathematical yet thorough explanation of basic ideas, theories, phenomena for laymen and beginning scientists illustrated by experiences of daily life. Bibliography. 50 illustrations. x + 165pp. 5⅜ x 8½.   T978 Paperbound **$1.00**

History of Science and Mathematics

THE STUDY OF THE HISTORY OF MATHEMATICS, THE STUDY OF THE HISTORY OF SCIENCE, G. Sarton. Two books bound as one. Each volume contains a long introduction to the methods and philosophy of each of these historical fields, covering the skills and sympathies of the historian, concepts of history of science, psychology of idea-creation, and the purpose of history of science. Prof. Sarton also provides more than 80 pages of classified bibliography. Complete and unabridged. Indexed. 10 illustrations. 188pp. 5⅜ x 8.   T240 Paperbound **$1.25**

A HISTORY OF PHYSICS, Florian Cajori, Ph.D. First written in 1899, thoroughly revised in 1929, this is still best entry into antecedents of modern theories. Precise non-mathematical discussion of ideas, theories, techniques, apparatus of each period from Greeks to 1920's, analyzing within each period basic topics of matter, mechanics, light, electricity and magnetism, sound, atomic theory, etc. Stress on modern developments, from early 19th century to present. Written with critical eye on historical development, significance. Provides most of needed historical background for student of physics. Reprint of second (1929) edition. Index. Bibliography in footnotes. 16 figures. xv + 424pp. 5⅜ x 8.   T970 Paperbound **$2.00**

A HISTORY OF ASTRONOMY FROM THALES TO KEPLER, J. L. E. Dreyer. Formerly titled A HISTORY OF PLANETARY SYSTEMS FROM THALES TO KEPLER. This is the only work in English which provides a detailed history of man's cosmological views from prehistoric times up through the Renaissance. It covers Egypt, Babylonia, early Greece, Alexandria, the Middle Ages, Copernicus, Tycho Brahe, Kepler, and many others. Epicycles and other complex theories of positional astronomy are explained in terms nearly everyone will find clear and easy to understand. "Standard reference on Greek astronomy and the Copernican revolution," SKY AND TELESCOPE. Bibliography. 21 diagrams. Index. xvii + 430pp. 5⅜ x 8.   S79 Paperbound **$2.25**

A SHORT HISTORY OF ASTRONOMY, A. Berry. A popular standard work for over 50 years, this thorough and accurate volume covers the science from primitive times to the end of the 19th century. After the Greeks and Middle Ages, individual chapters analyze Copernicus, Brahe, Galileo, Kepler, and Newton, and the mixed reception of their startling discoveries. Post-Newtonian achievements are then discussed in unusual detail: Halley, Bradley, Lagrange, Laplace, Herschel, Bessel, etc. 2 indexes. 104 illustrations, 9 portraits. xxxi + 440pp. 5⅜ x 8.   T210 Paperbound **$2.00**

PIONEERS OF SCIENCE, Sir Oliver Lodge. An authoritative, yet elementary history of science by a leading scientist and expositor. Concentrating on individuals—Copernicus, Brahe, Kepler, Galileo, Descartes, Newton, Laplace, Herschel, Lord Kelvin, and other scientists—the author presents their discoveries in historical order, adding biographical material on each man and full, specific explanations of their achievements. The full, clear discussions of the accomplishments of post-Newtonian astronomers are features seldom found in other books on the subject. Index. 120 illustrations. xv + 404pp. 5⅜ x 8.   T716 Paperbound **$1.65**

THE BIRTH AND DEVELOPMENT OF THE GEOLOGICAL SCIENCES, F. D. Adams. The most complete and thorough history of the earth sciences in print. Geological thought from earliest recorded times to the end of the 19th century—covers over 300 early thinkers and systems: fossils and hypothetical explanations of them, vulcanists vs. neptunists, figured stones and paleontology, generation of stones, and similar topics. 91 illustrations, including medieval, renaissance woodcuts, etc. 632 footnotes and bibliographic notes. Index. 511pp. 5⅜ x 8.   T5 Paperbound **$2.25**

THE STORY OF ALCHEMY AND EARLY CHEMISTRY, J. M. Stillman. "Add the blood of a red-haired man"—a recipe typical of the many quoted in this authoritative and readable history of the strange beliefs and practices of the alchemists. Concise studies of every leading figure in alchemy and early chemistry through Lavoisier, in this curious epic of superstition and true science, constructed from scores of rare and difficult Greek, Latin, German, and French texts. Foreword by S. W. Young. 246-item bibliography. Index. xiii + 566pp. 5⅜ x 8.   S628 Paperbound **$2.45**

HISTORY OF MATHEMATICS, D. E. Smith. Most comprehensive non-technical history of math in English. Discusses the lives and works of over a thousand major and minor figures, from Euclid to Descartes, Gauss, and Riemann. Vol. I: A chronological examination, from primitive concepts through Egypt, Babylonia, Greece, the Orient, Rome, the Middle Ages, the Renaissance, and up to 1900. Vol. 2: The development of ideas in specific fields and problems, up through elementary calculus. Two volumes, total of 510 illustrations, 1355pp. 5⅜ x 8. Set boxed in attractive container.   T429,430 Paperbound the set **$5.00**

CATALOGUE OF DOVER BOOKS

A CONCISE HISTORY OF MATHEMATICS, D. Struik. A lucid, easily followed history of mathematical ideas and techniques from the Ancient Near East up to modern times. Requires no mathematics but will serve as an excellent introduction to mathematical concepts and great mathematicians through the method of historical development. 60 illustrations including Egyptian papyri, Greek mss., portraits of 31 eminent mathematicians. Bibliography. xix + 299pp. 5⅜ x 8. T255 Paperbound **$1.75**

A SHORT ACCOUNT OF THE HISTORY OF MATHEMATICS, W. W. Rouse Ball. Last previous edition (1908) hailed by mathematicians and laymen for lucid overview of math as living science, for understandable presentation of individual contributions of great mathematicians. Treats lives, discoveries of every important school and figure from Egypt, Phoenicia to late nineteenth century. Greek schools of Ionia, Cyzicus, Alexandria, Byzantium, Pythagoras; primitive arithmetic; Middle Ages and Renaissance, including European and Asiatic contributions; modern math of Descartes, Pascal, Wallis, Huygens, Newton, Euler, Lambert, Laplace, scores more. More emphasis on historical development, exposition of ideas than other books on subject. Non-technical, readable text can be followed with no more preparation than high-school algebra. Index. 544pp. 5⅜ x 8. S630 Paperbound **$2.00**

ON MATHEMATICS AND MATHEMATICIANS, R. E. Moritz. A ten year labor of love by the discerning and discriminating Prof. Moritz, this collection has rarely been equalled in its ability to convey the full sense of mathematics and the personalities of great mathematicians. A collection of anecdotes, aphorisms, reminiscences, philosophies, definitions, speculations, biographical insights, etc., by great mathematicians and writers: Descartes, Mill, De Morgan, Locke, Berkeley, Kant, Coleridge, Whitehead, Sylvester, Klein, and many others. Also, glimpses into the lives of mathematical giants from Archimedes to Euler, Gauss, and Weierstrass. To mathematicians; a superb book for browsing; to writers and teachers, an unequalled source of quotation; to the layman, an exciting revelation of the fullness of mathematics. Extensive cross index. 410pp. 5⅜ x 8. T489 Paperbound **$1.95**

SIR ISAAC NEWTON: A BIOGRAPHY, Louis Trenchard More. Standard, definitive biography of Newton, covering every phase of his life and career in its presentation of the renowned scientific genius as a living man. Objective, critical analysis of his character as well as a careful survey of his manifold accomplishments in many areas of science, and in theology, history, politics, finance. Text includes letters by Newton and acquaintances, many other papers, some translated from Latin to English by the author. Scientists, teachers of science will especially be interested in this book, which will appeal to all readers concerned with history of ideas, development of science. Republication of original (1934) edition. 1 full-page plate. Index. xii + 675pp. 5⅜ x 8½. S79 Paperbound **$2.50**

GUIDE TO THE LITERATURE OF MATHEMATICS AND PHYSICS, N. G. Parke III. Over 5000 entries included under approximately 120 major subject headings, of selected most important books, monographs, periodicals, articles in English, plus important works in German, French, Italian, Spanish, Russian (many recently available works). Covers every branch of physics, math, related engineering. Includes author, title, edition, publisher, place, date, number of volumes, number of pages. A 40-page introduction on the basic problems of research and study provides useful information on the organization and use of libraries, the psychology of learning, etc. This reference work will save you hours of time. 2nd revised edition. Indices of authors, subjects. 464pp. 5⅜ x 8. S447 Paperbound **$2.49**

Prices subject to change without notice.

Dover publishes books on art, music, philosophy, literature, languages, history, social sciences, psychology, handcrafts, orientalia, puzzles and entertainments, chess, pets and gardens, books explaining science, intermediate and higher mathematics, mathematical physics, engineering, biological sciences, earth sciences, classics of science, etc. Write to:

Dept. catrr.
Dover Publications, Inc.
180 Varick Street, N. Y. 14, N. Y.